Chemical Applications of Group Theory

Chemical Applications of Group Theory

F. Albert Cotton

Department of Chemistry, Massachusetts Institute of Technology

INTERSCIENCE PUBLISHERS

A division of John Wiley and Sons, Inc.

New York and London

To Diane

Preface

This book is the outgrowth of a one-semester course which has been taught for several years at the Massachusetts Institute of Technology to seniors and graduate students in chemistry. The treatment of the subject matter is unpretentious in that I have not hesitated to be mathematically unsophisticated, occasionally unrigorous, or somewhat prolix, where I felt that this really helps to make the subject more meaningful and comprehensible for the average student. By the average student, I mean one who does not aspire to be a theoretician but who wants to have a feel for the strategy used by theoreticians in treating problems in which symmetry properties are important and to have a working knowledge of the more common and well-established techniques. I feel that the great power and beauty of symmetry methods, not to mention the prime importance in all fields of chemistry of the results they give, make it very worthwhile for all chemists to be acquainted with the basic principles and main applications of group theoretical methods.

Despite the fact that there seems to be a growing desire among chemists at large to acquire this knowledge, it is still true that only a very few, other than professional theoreticians, have done so. The reason is not hard to discover. There is, so far as I know, no book available which is not likely to strike some terror into the hearts of all but those with an innate love of apparently esoteric theory. It seemed to me that ideas of the sort developed in this book would not soon be assimilated by a wide community of chemists until they were presented in as unpretentious and down-to-earth a manner as possible. That is what I have tried to do here. I have attempted to make this the kind of book which "one can read in bed without a pencil," as my colleague, John Waugh, once aptly described another textbook which has found wide favor because of its down-to-earth character.*

* This statement is actually (and intentionally) not applicable to parts of Chapter 3 where I have made no concessions to the reader who refuses to inspect steric models in conjunction with study of the text.

Perhaps the book may also serve as a first introduction for students intending to do theoretical work, giving them some overall perspective before they aim for depth.

I am most grateful for help I have received from many quarters in writing this book. Over the years students in the course have offered much valuable criticism and advice. In checking the final draft and the proofs I have had very welcome and efficient assistance from Dr. A. B. Blake and Messrs. R. C. Elder, T. E. Haas, and J. T. Mague. I, of course, assume sole responsibility for all remaining errors. Finally, I wish to thank Mrs. Nancy Blake for expert secretarial assistance.

F. ALBERT COTTON

Cambridge, Massachusetts
January, 1963

Contents

Part I

Principles

Introduction

The experimental chemist in his daily work and thought is concerned with observing and, to as great an extent as possible, understanding and interpreting his observations on the nature of chemical compounds. Today, chemistry is a vast subject. In order to do thorough and productive experimental work, one must know so much descriptive chemistry and so much about experimental techniques that there is not time to be also a master of chemical theory. Theoretical work of profound and creative nature requires a vast training in mathematics and physics which it is now the business of specialists to deal with. And yet, if one is to do more than merely *perform* experiments, one must have some theoretical framework for thought. In order to formulate experiments imaginatively and interpret them correctly, an understanding of the ideas provided by theory as to the behavior of molecules and other arrays of atoms is essential.

The problem in educating student chemists—and in educating ourselves—is to decide what kind of theory and how much of it is desirable. In other words, to what extent can the experimentalist afford to spend time on theoretical studies and at what point should he say, "beyond this I have not the time or inclination to go"? The answer to this question must of course vary with the special field of experimental work and with the individual. In some areas fairly advanced theory is indispensable. In others relatively little is really useful. For the most part, however, it seems fair to say that molecular quantum mechanics, that is, the theory of chemical bonding and molecular dynamics, is of general importance.

As we shall see in Chapter 5, the number and kinds of energy levels which an atom or molecule may have are rigorously and precisely determined by the symmetry of the molecule or of the environment of the atom. Thus, from symmetry considerations alone, we can always tell what the qualitative features of a problem must be. We shall know, without any quantitative calculations whatever, how many energy states there are and what interactions and transitions between them *may* occur. To put it another way, symmetry considerations *alone* can give us a complete and rigorous answer to the question "What is possible and what is completely impossible?" Symmetry considerations alone *cannot*, however, tell us how likely it is that the possible things will actually take place. Symmetry can tell us that, *in principle*, two states of the system *must* differ in their energy, but only by computation or measurement can we determine how great the difference will be. Again, symmetry can tell us that only certain absorption bands in the electronic or vibrational spectrum of a molecule may occur. But to learn where they will occur and with what intensity, calculations must be made.

Some illustrations of these statements may be helpful. Let us choose one illustration from each of the four major fields of application which are covered in Part II. In Chapter 6 the method of constructing hybrid orbitals will be explained. It will be shown, *inter alia*, that a set of sp^3d hybrid orbitals will form bonds directed to the apices of a trigonal bipyramid if the d orbital used is d_{z^2} whereas the set will form good bonds to atoms at the apices of a square pyramid if the d orbital used is $d_{x^2-y^2}$ or d_{xy}. The connection between the symmetry of the resulting set of hybrids and the d orbital used is absolutely rigorous on the basis of symmetry alone, but only by calculations (which are not practicable at present) could we determine which set of hybrids and hence which symmetry would be favored in a particular molecule. In Chapter 7 the symmetry and some other properties of molecular orbitals will be discussed. It will be shown, for example, that in symmetrical molecules the calculation of the energies of pi molecular orbitals can be accomplished by solving several sets of very small equations rather than one large equation, but the numerical accuracy of the results will still depend on how much labor we wish to put into computations. In Chapter 8, using symmetry arguments and only the most elementary quantitative considerations, we will learn how to construct energy level diagrams, which tell us a great deal about the order of the levels and the qualitative features of the spectra of the ions, for metal ions in ligand fields. Finally, in Chapter 9 it will be shown that using symmetry considerations alone we may predict the number of vibrational fundamentals, their activities in the infrared and Raman, and the way in which the various bonds and interbond angles contribute to them for any molecule possessing some symmetry. The actual magnitudes of the frequencies depend on the interatomic forces in the molecule, and these cannot be predicted from symmetry properties.

The main purpose of this book is to describe the methods by which we can extract the information which symmetry alone will provide. An understanding of this requires only a superficial knowledge of quantum mechanics. In several of the applications of symmetry methods, however, it would be artificial and stultifying to exclude religiously *all* quantitative considerations. Thus, in the chapter on molecular orbitals, it is natural to go a few steps beyond the procedure for determining the symmetries of the possible MO's and explain how the requisite linear combinations of atomic orbitals may be written down and how their energies may be estimated. It also appeared desirable to introduce some quantitative ideas into the treatment of ligand field theory.

It has been, necessarily, assumed that the reader has some prior familiarity with the basic notions of quantum theory. He is expected to know in a general way what the wave equation is, the significance of the Hamiltonian operator, the physical meaning of a wave function, and so forth, but no detailed knowledge of mathematical intricacies is presumed. Even the contents of a rather qualitative book such as Coulson's *Valence* should be sufficient, although, of course, further background knowledge will not be amiss.

The following comments on the organization of the book may prove useful to the prospective reader. It is divided into two parts. Part I, which includes Chapters 1 through 5, covers the principles which are basic to all of the applications. The applications are described in Part II, embracing Chapters 6 through 9. The material in Part I has been written to be read sequentially. That is, each chapter builds on the material developed in all preceding chapters. Part II, however, is written so that each chapter is independent of all other chapters in Part II, although each one, of course, depends on all of the material in Part I. The only exceptions to this statement are a few instances in which quantum principles are equally necessary in two places. They are given only once and in the second instance a reference is made to the first. This arrangement is advantageous to a reader whose immediate goal is to study only one particular area of application, since he can proceed directly to it, whichever it may be; it also allows the teacher freedom in selecting which applications to cover in a course too short to cover all of them, or to take them all but in an order different from that chosen here.

Basic Definitions and Theorems

of Group Theory

2.1 The Defining Properties of a Group

A *group* is a collection of *elements* which are interrelated according to certain rules. We need not specify what the elements are or attribute any physical significance to them in order to discuss the group which they constitute. In this book, of course, we shall be concerned entirely with the groups formed by the sets of symmetry operations which may be carried out on molecules, but the basic definitions and theorems of group theory are far more general.

In order for any set of elements to form a mathematical group, the following conditions or rules must be satisfied.

1. *The product of any two elements in the group and the square of each element must be an element in the group.* In order for this condition to have meaning, we must, of course, have agreed on what we mean by the terms "multiply" and "product." They need not mean what they do in ordinary algebra and arithmetic. Perhaps we might say "combine" instead of "multiply" and "combination" instead of "product" in order to avoid unnecessary and perhaps incorrect connotations. Let us not yet commit ourselves to any particular law of combination, but merely say that if A and B are two elements of a group, we indicate that we are combining them by simply writing AB or BA. Now immediately the question arises if it makes any difference whether we write AB or BA. In ordinary algebra it does not, and we say that multiplication is commutative, that is, $xy = yx$, or $3 \times 6 = 6 \times 3$. In group theory, the commutative law does not in general hold. Thus AB may give C while BA may give D where C and D are two more elements in the group. There are some groups in which combination is commutative, and such

groups are called *Abelian* groups. Because of the fact that multiplication is not in general commutative, it is sometimes convenient in speaking to have a means of stating whether an element B is to be multiplied by A in the sense AB or BA. In the first case we can say that B is *left-multiplied* by A and in the second case that B is *right-multiplied* by A.

2. *One element in the group must commute with all the others and leave them unchanged.* It is customary to designate this element with the letter E and it is usually called the *identity element*. Symbolically we define it by writing $EX = XE = X$.

3. *The associative law of multiplication must hold.* This we may write as

$$A(BC) = (AB)C$$

In plain words, we may combine B with C in the order BC and then combine this product, S, with A in the order AS, or, we may combine A with B in the order AB, getting a product, say R, which we then combine with C in the order RC and get the same final product either way. In general, of course, this must hold for the continued product of any number of elements, viz.,

$$(AB)(CD)(EF)(GH) = A(BC)(DE)(FG)H = (AB)C(DE)(FG)H \cdots$$

4. *Every element must have a reciprocal, which is also an element of the group.* The element R is the reciprocal of the element S if $RS = SR = E$, where E is the identity. Obviously, if R is the reciprocal of S, then S is the reciprocal of R. Also, E is its own reciprocal.

At this point we shall prove a small theorem concerning reciprocals which will be of use later. The rule is:

The reciprocal of a product of two or more elements is equal to the product of the reciprocals, in reverse order. This means that

$$(ABC \cdots XY)^{-1} = Y^{-1}X^{-1} \cdots C^{-1}B^{-1}A^{-1}$$

PROOF. For simplicity we shall prove this for a ternary product, but it will be obvious that it is true generally. If A, B, and C are group elements, their product, say D, must also be a group element, viz.,

$$ABC = D$$

If now we right-multiply each side of this equation by $C^{-1}B^{-1}A^{-1}$, we obtain

$$ABCC^{-1}B^{-1}A^{-1} = DC^{-1}B^{-1}A^{-1}$$

$$ABEB^{-1}A^{-1} = DC^{-1}B^{-1}A^{-1}$$

$$\cdot$$
$$\cdot$$
$$\cdot$$

$$E \qquad\qquad = DC^{-1}B^{-1}A^{-1}$$

Since D times $C^{-1}B^{-1}A^{-1}$ equals E, $C^{-1}B^{-1}A^{-1}$ is the reciprocal of D, and since D equals ABC, we have

$$D^{-1} = (ABC)^{-1} = C^{-1}B^{-1}A^{-1}$$

which proves the above rule.

2.2   Some Examples of Groups

Groups may be either finite or infinite, that is, they may contain a limited or unlimited number of elements. The symmetry groups with which we shall be concerned are mostly finite, but two, namely those to which linear molecules may belong, are infinite. The number of elements in a finite group is called its *order*, and the conventional symbol for the order is h. To illustrate the above defining rules, we may consider both an infinite and a finite group.

As an infinite group we may take all of the integers, both positive, negative and zero. If we take as our law of combination the ordinary algebraic process of addition, then rule 1 is satisfied. Clearly, any integer may be obtained by adding two others. Note that we have an Abelian group since the order of addition is immaterial. The identity of our group is 0, since $0 + n = n + 0 = n$. Also, the associative law of combination holds, since, for example, $[(+3) + (-7)] + (+1043) = (+3) + [(-7) + (+1043)]$. The reciprocal of any element, n, is $(-n)$ since $(+n) + (-n) = 0$.

As another example of a group, this a finite one of order six, let us take the set of elements E (the identity), A, B, C, D, F. A consideration of the defining rules will show that every group has what we may call a multiplication table, that is, a tabular array of all the one-against-one or binary combinations of group elements. The multiplication table for the above group of six elements we shall take to be the following one, with the convention that each entry is the combination of the element at the top of its column with that at the left of its row in the order (column) (row).

Since inspection of the table shows that this group is not Abelian, it is obviously necessary that the above order of combination be specified and that it be remembered in using the multiplication table subsequently.

	E	A	B	C	D	F
E	E	A	B	C	D	F
A	A	E	D	F	B	C
B	B	F	E	D	C	A
C	C	D	F	E	A	B
D	D	C	A	B	F	E
F	F	B	C	A	E	D

Let us observe that this table has certain features which are necessary consequences of the defining rules. If it did not have them, we should be forced to conclude either that the set of elements did not actually constitute a group or, if the set does actually constitute a group, that a mistake had been made in working out the table.

(i) Note that each column and each row is a shuffled list of the elements, each occurring once and only once. That this must be so is easily seen if we consider, for instance, a column. The six entries in this column, say the column under C, are CE, CA, CB, CC, CD, CF. If any two products were the same, say the product of CA and CF, then we could write $CA = CF$, which would necessarily mean $A = F$. Thus two elements in the group would be identical, and thus two entire columns and two entire rows would have to be identical. This is not true, so we have shown that the initial assumption must be an impossibility.

(ii) Note that the products E are either on the diagonal or placed symmetrically with respect to it. This is because either an element is its own reciprocal (as for E, A, B, and C), or, in this case, since D is reciprocal to F, F is reciprocal to D.

(iii) The identity occurs only once in each column or row, because each element can have only one reciprocal. This is merely a special case of (i) above.

There are other features of this particular table which are not general, but specific to this group, such as the nonexistence of any commutative multiplications other than those involving E or producing E.

One special kind of group, of which there are many representatives among the symmetry groups, is the *cyclic group*. This is a set of elements X, X^2, X^3, X^4 ... X^n such that $X^n = E$. It may be noted that a cyclic group must be Abelian. The set of elements X, X^2 ... X^{n-1}, X^n, where n is a number such that $X^{n+1} = X$, is called the *period* of the element X, and this entire set of n elements may be symbolized by $\{X\}$.

2.3   Subgroups

Inspection of the multiplication table for the group $EABCDF$, given above, will show that within this group of order 6 there are smaller groups. E in itself is a group of order 1. This will, of course, be true in any group and is trivial. Of a nontrivial nature are the groups of order 2, viz., E, A; E, B; E, C; and the group of order 3, viz., E, D, F. The last should be recognized also as a cyclic group since $D^2 = F$, $D^3 = DF = FD = E$; it is thus a cycle of D, namely D, D^2 and $D^3 = E$. But to return to the main point, these smaller groups which may be found within a larger group are called subgroups. There are, of course, groups which have no subgroups other than the trivial one of E itself.

Let us now consider whether there are any restrictions on the nature of subgroups, restrictions which are logical consequences of the definition and not of any additional or special characteristics of a particular group. Indeed there are. We may note that the orders of the group above and its subgroups are 6 and 1, 2, 3; in short, the orders are all factors of the order of the main group. We shall now prove the theorem that:

The order of any subgroup, g, of a group of order h must be a divisor of h.
In other words, $h/g = k$ with k some integer.

PROOF. Suppose the set of g elements, $A_1, A_2, A_3 \ldots A_g$, form a subgroup. Now let us take another element B in the group which is not a member of this subgroup and form all of the g products: $BA_1, BA_2 \ldots BA_g$. No one of these products can be in the subgroup. If, for example,

$$BA_2 = A_4$$

then if we take the reciprocal of A_2, perhaps A_5, and right-multiply the above equality we obtain

$$BA_2A_5 = A_4A_5$$

$$BE = A_4A_5$$

$$B = A_4A_5$$

But this contradicts our assumption that B is not a member of the subgroup $A_1, A_2 \ldots A_g$, since A_4A_5 can only be one of the A_i. Hence, if all the products BA_i are in the large group in addition to the A_i themselves, there are at least $2g$ members of the group. If $h > 2g$, we can choose still another element of the group, namely C, which is not one of the A_i or one of the BA_i, and on multiplying the A_i by C we will obtain g

more elements, all members of the main group, but none members of the A_i or of the BA_i sets. Thus we now know that h must be at least equal to $3g$. Eventually, however, we must reach the point where there are no more elements by which we can multiply the A_i which are not among the sets A_i, BA_i, CA_i, and so forth, already obtained. Suppose after having found k such elements, we reach this point where there are no more. Then $h = kg$, where k is, of course, an integer. Then $h/g = k$, which is what we set out to prove. While we have shown that the order of any subgroup, g, must be a divisor of h, we have not proved the converse, namely that there are subgroups of all orders which are divisors of h, and, indeed, this is not in general true. Moreover, as our illustrative group proves, there can be more than one subgroup of a given order.

2.4   Classes

We have seen that in a given group it may be possible to select various smaller sets of elements, each such set including E, however, which are in themselves groups. There is another way in which the elements of a group may be separated into smaller sets, and such sets are called *classes*. Before defining a class we must consider an operation known as *similarity transformation*.

If A and X are two elements of a group, then $X^{-1}AX$ will be equal to some element of the group, say B. We have

$$B = X^{-1}AX$$

We express this relation in words by saying that B is the *similarity transform* of A by X. We also say that A and B are *conjugate*. The following properties of conjugate elements are important.

(i) *Every element is conjugate with itself.* This means that if we choose any particular element, A, it must be possible to find at least one element, X, such that

$$A = X^{-1}AX$$

If we left-multiply by A^{-1} we get

$$A^{-1}A = E = A^{-1}X^{-1}AX = (XA)^{-1}(AX)$$

which can only hold if A and X commute. Thus the element X may always be E, and it may be any other element which commutes with the chosen element, A.

(ii) *If A is conjugate with B, then B is conjugate with A.* This means that if

$$A = X^{-1}BX$$

then there must be some element, Y, in the group such that

$$B = Y^{-1}AY$$

That this must be so is easily proved by carrying out appropriate multiplications, viz.,

$$XAX^{-1} = XX^{-1}BXX^{-1} = B$$

Thus, if $Y = X^{-1}$ (and thus also $Y^{-1} = X$), we have

$$B = Y^{-1}AY$$

and this must be possible since any element, say X, must have an inverse, say Y.

(iii) *If A is conjugate with B and C, then B and C are conjugate with each other.* The proof of this should be easy to work out from the foregoing discussion and is left as an exercise.

We may now define a class of elements.

A complete set of elements which are conjugate to one another is called a class of the group. In order to determine the classes within any particular group we can begin with one element and work out all of its transforms using all the elements in the group, including itself, then take a second element, which is not one of those found to be conjugate to the first, and determine all its transforms, and so on until all elements in the group have been placed in one class or another.

Let us illustrate this with the group we have been considering so far. All of the results given below may be verified using the multiplication table. Let us start with E.

$$E^{-1}EE = EEE = E$$

$$A^{-1}EA = A^{-1}AE = E$$

$$B^{-1}EB = B^{-1}BE = E$$

. . .

Thus E must constitute by itself a class, of order 1, since it is not conjugate with any other element. This will, of course, be true in any group.

To continue,

$$E^{-1}AE = A$$
$$A^{-1}AA = A$$
$$B^{-1}AB = C$$
$$C^{-1}AC = B$$
$$D^{-1}AD = B$$
$$F^{-1}AF = C$$

Thus the elements A, B, and C are all conjugate and are therefore members of the same class. It is left for the reader to show that all of the transforms of B and C are either A, B, or C. Thus A, B, and C are in fact the only members of the class.

Continuing,

$$E^{-1}DE = D$$
$$A^{-1}DA = F$$
$$B^{-1}DB = F$$
$$C^{-1}DC = F$$
$$D^{-1}DD = D$$
$$F^{-1}DF = D$$

It will also be found that all the transforms of F are either D or F. Hence, D and F constitute a class of order 2.

It will be noted that the classes have orders 1, 2, and 3 which are all factors of the group order, 6. It can be proved, by a method similar to that used in connection with the orders of subgroups, that the following theorem is true.

The orders of all classes must be integral factors of the order of the group.

We shall later see that in a symmetry group the classes have useful geometrical significance.

Molecular Symmetry
and the Symmetry Groups

3.1 General Remarks

It is perhaps appropriate to begin this chapter by sketching what we intend to do here. It is certainly intuitively obvious what we mean when we say that some molecules are more symmetrical than others, or that some molecules have high symmetry while others have low symmetry or no symmetry. But in order to make the idea of molecular symmetry as useful as possible, we must develop some rigid mathematical criteria of symmetry. To do this we shall first consider the kinds of *symmetry elements* a molecule may have and the *symmetry operations* generated by the symmetry elements. We shall then show that a complete but nonredundant set of symmetry *operations* (not elements) constitutes a mathematical group. Last, we shall use the general properties of groups, developed in the previous chapter, to aid in correctly and systematically determining the symmetry operations of any molecule we may care to consider. We shall also describe a system of notation for the various symmetry groups.

It may also be worthwhile to offer the following advice to the student of this chapter. The use of three-dimensional models is extremely helpful in learning to recognize and visualize symmetry elements. Indeed, it is most unlikely that any but a person of the most exceptional gifts in this direction can fail to profit significantly from the examination of models. At the same time, it may also be said that anyone with the intelligence to master other aspects of modern chemical knowledge should, by the use of models, surely succeed in acquiring a good working knowledge of molecular symmetry.

3.2   Symmetry Elements and Operations

The two things, symmetry elements and symmetry operations, are inextricably related, and therefore are often confused. They are, however, different *kinds* of things, and it is important to grasp and retain, from the outset, a clear understanding of the difference between them.

Definition of a Symmetry Operation

A symmetry operation is a movement of a body such that, after the movement has been carried out, every point of the body is coincident with an equivalent point (or perhaps the same point) of the body in its original orientation. In other words, if we note the position and orientation of a body before and after a movement is carried out, that movement is a symmetry operation if these two positions and orientations are indistinguishable. This would mean that if we were to look at the body, turn away long enough for someone to carry out a symmetry operation and then look again, we would be completely unable to tell whether the operation had actually been performed or not, because in either case, the position and orientation would be indistinguishable from the original. One final way in which we can define a symmetry operation is to say that its effect is to take the body into an *equivalent configuration*. By equivalent configuration we mean one which is indistinguishable from though not necessarily identical with the original.

Definition of a Symmetry Element

A symmetry element is a geometrical entity such as a line, a plane, or a point, with respect to which one or more symmetry operations may be carried out.

Symmetry elements and symmetry operations are so closely interrelated because the operation can only be defined with respect to the element, and at the same time, the existence of a symmetry element can be demonstrated only by showing that the appropriate symmetry operations exist. Thus, since the existence of the element is contingent on the existence of the operation(s) and vice versa, we shall discuss related types of elements and operations together.

Table 3.1   The Four Kinds of Symmetry Elements and Operations Required in Specifying Molecular Symmetry

SYMMETRY ELEMENT	SYMMETRY OPERATION(S)
1. Plane	Reflection in the plane
2. Center of symmetry or center of inversion	Inversion of all atoms through the center
3. Proper axis	One or more rotations about the axis
4. Improper axis	One or more repetitions of the sequence: rotation followed by reflection in a plane $\perp$ to the rotation axis

In treating molecular symmetry, only four types of symmetry elements and operations need be considered. These, in the order in which they will be discussed, are listed in Table 3.1.

3.3   Symmetry Planes and Reflections

A symmetry plane must pass through a body, that is, the plane cannot be completely outside of the body. The conditions which must be fulfilled in order that a given plane be a symmetry plane can be stated as follows. Let us apply a Cartesian coordinate system to the molecule in such a way that the plane includes two of the axes (say x and y) and is therefore perpendicular to the third (that is, z). The position of every atom in the molecule may also be specified in this same coordinate system. Suppose now, for each and every atom, we leave the x and y coordinates fixed and change the sign of the z coordinate: thus the ith atom, originally at (x_i, y_i, z_i), is moved to the point $(x_i, y_i, -z_i)$. Another way of expressing the above operation is to say, let us drop a perpendicular from each atom to the plane, extend that line an equal distance on the opposite side of the plane, and move the atom to this other end of the line. If, when such an operation is carried out on every atom in a molecule, an equivalent configuration is obtained, the plane used is a symmetry plane.

Clearly, atoms lying in the plane constitute special cases since the operation of reflecting through the plane does not move them at all. Consequently, any planar molecule is bound to have at least one plane of symmetry, namely, its molecular plane. Another significant and immediate consequence of the definition is a restriction on the numbers of various kinds of atoms in a molecule having a plane of symmetry. All atoms of a given species which do not lie in the plane must occur in even numbers, since each one must have a twin on the other side of the plane. Of course, any number of atoms of a given species may be in the plane. Further, if there is only one atom of a given species in a molecule, it must be in each and every symmetry plane the molecule may have. This means that it must be on the line of intersection between two or more planes or at the point of intersection of three or more planes (if there is such a point) since this atom must lie in all of the symmetry planes simultaneously.

The standard symbol for a plane of symmetry is σ; this is also the symbol for the operation of reflecting through the plane.

It should be explicitly noted that the existence of *one* symmetry plane gives rise to, requires, or, as it is usually stated, *generates*, *one* symmetry operation. We may also note here, for future use, that the effect of applying the same reflection operation twice is to bring all atoms into their original positions. Thus, while the operation σ produces a configuration *equivalent* to the original, the application of the same σ twice produces a configuration *identical* with the original. Now we can conveniently denote the successive application of the operation σ n times by writing σ^n. We can then also write, $\sigma^2 = E$ where we use the symbol E to represent *any* combination of operations which takes the molecule to a configuration identical with the original one. We call E, or any combination of operations equal to E, the *identity operation*. It should be obvious that $\sigma^n = E$ when n is even and $\sigma^n = \sigma$ when n is odd.

Let us now consider some illustrative examples of symmetry planes in molecules. At one extreme are molecules which have no symmetry planes at all. One such general class are those which are not planar and which have odd numbers of all atoms. For instance, FClSO:

At the other extreme are molecules possessing an infinite number of symmetry planes; that is, linear molecules. For these any plane containing the molecular axis is a symmetry plane, and there are obviously an infinite number of these. Most small molecules fall between these extremes; that is, they have one or a few symmetry planes. If, instead of FClSO, we take F_2SO or Cl_2SO, we have molecules with one symmetry plane, which passes through S and O and is perpendicular to the Cl, Cl, O, or F, F, O plane. The H_2O molecule has two symmetry planes. One is, of course, coextensive with the molecular plane. The other includes the oxygen atom (it must since there is only one) and is perpendicular to the molecular plane. The effect of reflection through this second plane is to leave the oxygen atom fixed but to exchange the hydrogen atoms, while reflection through the first plane leaves all atoms unshifted. A tetrahedral molecule of the type AB_2C_2 (for example, CH_2Cl_2) also has two mutually perpendicular planes of symmetry. One contains AB_2 and reflection through it leaves these three atoms unshifted while interchanging the C atoms, while the other contains AC_2 and reflection through it interchanges only the B atoms.

The molecules NH_3 and $CHCl_3$ are representative of a type containing three planes of symmetry. For NH_3, any plane of symmetry would have to include the N atom and either one or all three of the H atoms. Since NH_3 is not planar, there can be no symmetry plane including N and all three H's; hence we look for planes including N and one H and bisecting the line between the remaining two H's. There are clearly three such planes. For $CHCl_3$, the situation is quite analogous except that the H atom must also lie in the symmetry planes.

The NH_3 molecule is only one example of the general class of pyramidal AB_3 molecules. Let us see what happens as we begin flattening such a molecule by pushing the A atom down toward the plane of the three B atoms. It should be easily seen that this does not disturb the three symmetry planes, even in the limit of coplanarity. Nor does it introduce any new planes of symmetry *except* in the limit of coplanarity. Once AB_3 becomes planar there is then a fourth symmetry plane which is the molecular plane. Molecules and ions of the planar AB_3 type possessing four symmetry planes, three perpendicular to the molecular plane, are fairly numerous and important, for example, the boron halides, CO_3^{2-}, NO_3^-, SO_3.

A planar species of the type $[PtCl_4]^{2-}$ or $[AuCl_4]^-$ possesses five symmetry planes. One is the molecular plane. There are also two which are perpendicular to the molecular plane and perpendicular to one another which pass through three atoms. Finally, there are two more, also perpendicular to the molecular plane and perpendicular to one another which bisect Cl—Pt—Cl or Cl—Au—Cl angles.

A regular tetrahedral molecule possesses six planes of symmetry. Using the numbering system illustrated, we may specify them by stating the atoms they contain.

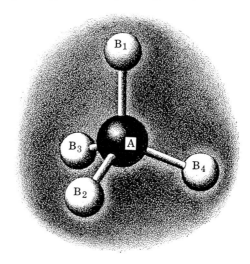

Symmetry planes contain the atoms:

AB_1B_2, AB_1B_3, AB_1B_4

AB_2B_3, AB_2B_4, AB_3B_4

A regular octahedron possesses altogether nine symmetry planes. Reference will be made to the accompanying numbered figure in specifying these. There are first three of the same type, viz., those including the following sets of atoms: $AB_1B_2B_3B_4$, $AB_2B_4B_5B_6$, and $AB_1B_3B_5B_6$. There are then six more of a second type, one of which includes AB_5B_6 and bisects the B_1—B_2 and B_3—B_4 lines, a second which includes AB_1B_3 and bisects the B_2—B_5 and B_4—B_6 lines, and so forth.

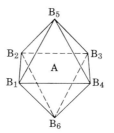

3.4   The Inversion Center

If a molecule can be brought into an equivalent configuration by changing the coordinates (x, y, z) of every atom, where the origin of coordinates lies at some point within the molecule, into $(-x, -y, -z)$, then the point at which the origin lies is said to be a center of symmetry or center of inversion. The symbol for the inversion center and for the operation of inversion is an italic i. Like a plane, the center is an element which generates only one operation.

It may be noted that when a center of inversion exists, restrictions are placed on the numbers of all, or all but one atom in the molecule. Since the center is a point, only one atom may be at the center. If there is an atom at the center, that atom is unique since it is the only one in the molecule which is not shifted when the inversion is performed. All other atoms must occur in pairs, since each must have a twin with which it is exchanged when the inversion is performed. From this it follows that we need not bother to look for a center of symmetry in molecules which contain an odd number of more than one species of atom.

The effect of carrying out the inversion operation n times may be written i^n. It should be easily seen that $i^n = E$ when n is even, and $i^n = i$ when n is odd.

Some examples of molecules having inversion centers are: octahedral AB_6 molecules, planar AB_4 molecules, planar and *trans* AB_2C_2, linear ABA, ethylene, benzene. Some examples of otherwise fairly symmetrical molecules which do not have centers of inversion are: $C_5H_5^-$ (plane pentagon), tetrahedral AB_4 (even though A is at the "center" and B's come in even numbers).

3.5   Proper Axes and Proper Rotations

Before discussing proper axes and rotations in a general way, let us take a specific case. A line drawn perpendicular to the plane of an equilateral triangle and intersecting it at its geometric center is a proper axis of rotation for that triangle. Upon rotating the triangle by 120° $(2\pi/3)$ about this axis, the triangle is brought into an equivalent configuration. It may be noted that a rotation by 240° $(2 \times 2\pi/3)$ also produces an equivalent configuration.

The general symbol for a proper axis of rotation is C_n where the subscript n denotes the *order* of the axis. By order is meant the value of n in $(2\pi/n)$ such that rotation through $2\pi/n$ gives an equivalent configuration. In the above example, the axis is a C_3 axis. Another way of defining the meaning of the order n of an axis is that it is the number of times that the smallest rotation capable of giving an equivalent configuration must be repeated in order to give a configuration not merely equivalent to the original but identical. The meaning of identical can be amplified if we attach numbers to each apex of the triangle in our example. Then the effects of rotating by $2\pi/3$, $2 \times 2\pi/3$, and $3 \times 2\pi/3$ are seen to be:

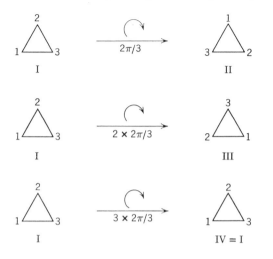

Configurations II and III are equivalent to I because without the labels (which are not real, but only our mental constructions) they are indistinguishable from I, although with the labels they are distinguishable. However, IV is not only indistinguishable from I without labels but also with labels. Hence, it is not merely equivalent, it is *identical*.

The C_3 axis is also called a threefold axis. Moreover, we use the symbol C_3 to represent the *operation* of rotation by $2\pi/3$ around the C_3 axis. For the rotation by $2 \times 2\pi/3$ we use the symbol $C_3{}^2$, and for the rotation by $3 \times 2\pi/3$ the symbol $C_3{}^3$. Symbolically we can write $C_3{}^4 = C_3$, and hence only C_3, $C_3{}^2$, and $C_3{}^3$ are separate and distinct operations. However, $C_3{}^3$ produces an identical configuration, and hence we may write $C_3{}^3 = E$.

After consideration of the above example, it is easy to accept some more general statements about proper axes and proper rotations. In general an n-fold axis is denoted C_n and a rotation by $2\pi/n$ is also represented by the symbol C_n. Rotation by $2\pi/n$ carried out successively m times is represented by the symbol $C_n{}^m$. Also, in any case, $C_n{}^n = E$, $C_n{}^{n+1} = C_n$, $C_n{}^{n+2} = C_n{}^2$, and so on.

In discussing planes of symmetry and inversion centers, attention was directed to the fact that only *one* operation, reflection, is generated by a symmetry plane, and only *one* operation, inversion, by an inversion center. A proper axis of order n, however, generates n operations, viz., C_n, $C_n{}^2$, $C_n{}^3$, ... $C_n{}^{n-1}$, $C_n{}^n(= E)$.

One last general consequence of the existence of a C_n axis concerns the requirement that there be certain numbers of each species of atom in a molecule containing the axis. Naturally, any atom which lies on a proper axis of symmetry is unshifted by any rotation about that axis. Thus there may be any number, even or odd, of each species of atom lying on an axis (unless other symmetry elements impose restrictions). However, if one atom of a certain species lies off a C_n axis, there must automatically be $n - 1$ more, or a total of n such atoms, since on applying C_n successively n times, the first atom is moved to altogether n different points. Had there not been identical atoms at all the other $n - 1$ points to begin with, the new configurations would not be equivalent configurations; this would mean that the axis would not be a C_n symmetry axis, contrary to the original assumption.

The symbol $C_n{}^m$ represents a rotation by $m \times 2\pi/n$. Let us consider the operation $C_4{}^2$, which is one of those generated by a C_4 axis. This is a rotation by $2 \times 2\pi/4 = 2\pi/2$, and can therefore be just as well written as C_2. Similarly, among the operations generated by a C_6 axis, we find $C_6{}^2$, $C_6{}^3$, and $C_6{}^4$, which may be written, respectively, as C_3, C_2, and $C_3{}^2$. It is frequent though not invariable practice to write an operation $C_n{}^m$ in what, by considering the fraction (m/n) in $(m/n)2\pi$, can be called lowest terms, and the reader should be familiar with this practice so that he immediately recognizes, for example, that the sequence C_6, C_3, C_2, $C_3{}^2$, $C_6{}^5$, E is identical in meaning with C_6, $C_6{}^2$, $C_6{}^3$, $C_6{}^4$, $C_6{}^5$, $C_6{}^6$.

Let us now consider some further illustrative examples chosen from among commonly encountered types of molecules. Again we may begin by considering extremes. Many molecules possess no axes of proper rotation. FClSO, for example, does not. (FClSO is actually a gratuitous example since it possesses no symmetry elements whatsoever.) Nor do Cl_2SO or F_2SO possess axes of proper rotation. At the other extreme are linear molecules which possess ∞-fold axes of proper rotation, colinear with the molecular axes. Since all atoms in a linear molecule lie on this axis, rotation by any angle whatever, and hence by all (∞ number) angles, leaves a configuration indistinguishable from the original. Again as with planes of symmetry, most small molecules possess one or a few axes, generally of low orders.

Among examples of molecules with a single axis of order 2 are H_2O and CH_2Cl_2. There are no molecules possessing just two twofold axes; this will be shown to be mathematically impossible in Section 3.7. There are many examples of molecules possessing three twofold axes, for example, ethylene, C_2H_4. One C_2 is colinear with the C—C axis. A second is perpendicular to the plane of the molecule and bisects the C—C line. The third is perpendicular to the first two and intersects both at the midpoint of the C—C line.

A regular tetrahedral molecule also possesses three twofold axes, as shown in the diagram below.

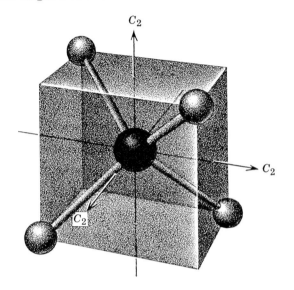

Threefold axes are quite common. Pyramidal and planar AB_3 molecules both possess threefold proper axes passing through the atom A and perpendicular to the plane of the three B atoms. A tetrahedral molecule, AB_4, possesses four threefold axes, each passing through the atom A and one of the B atoms. An octahedral molecule, AB_6, also possesses four threefold axes, each passing through the centers of two opposite triangular faces and the A atom.

The planar AB_3 molecule possesses three twofold axes perpendicular to the threefold axis as shown below:

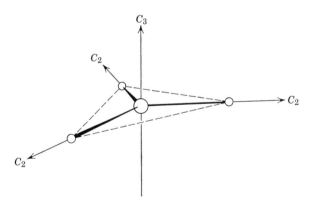

The existence of the C_3 axis and one C_2 axis perpendicular to the C_3 axis means that the other two C_2 axes, at angles of $2\pi/3$ and $4\pi/3$ to the first, *must* exist. For, on carrying out the rotation C_3, we generate the second C_2 axis from the first, and on carrying out the rotation $C_3{}^2$, we generate the third C_2 axis from the first.

The effect of the operations C_n, $C_n{}^2$ ... C_n^{m-1} in replicating other symmetry elements may profitably be discussed more fully at this point. The other symmetry elements of interest are planes and axes. It will also be sufficient to limit the discussion to axes perpendicular to the axis of the replicating rotations and to planes which contain the axis of the replicating rotations. A plane perpendicular to the axis of the replicating rotations is obviously not replicated since all rotations carry it into itself. While a completely general discussion might be given it seems more instructive to consider separately each of the replicating axes likely to be encountered in practice (C_n, $1 < n < 8$).

An axis perpendicular to or a plane containing a C_2 axis goes into itself on carrying out the operation C_2; hence no further axes or planes *of the same type* are required to exist in this case. We have just seen that from one axis perpendicular to a C_3 axis two similar ones are generated. The same is true for a plane of symmetry containing a C_3 axis. We may also deal with the C_5 and C_7 cases (and, indeed, any C_n where n is odd) for they all go in the same way. One axis perpendicular to or one plane containing a C_5 or C_7 axis will be made to generate four or six more separate and distinct axes or planes by the operations that the C_5 or C_7 axis makes possible. For cases where n in C_n is even, the results are less straightforward. Suppose we have one axis $C_2(1)$ perpendicular to a C_4 axis. On carrying out the rotation C_4, $C_2(1)$ is rotated by $2\pi/4$ and a second C_2 axis, $C_2(2)$, is thus produced. On carrying out the rotation $C_4{}^2(= C_2)$ about the C_4 axis, however, $C_2(1)$ merely goes into itself, and $C_2(2)$ also goes into itself. The operation $C_4{}^3$ takes $C_2(1)$ into $C_2(2)$ and $C_2(2)$ into $C_2(1)$. Hence, because $C_4{}^2$ is really only C_2 and $C_4{}^3$ is only C_4 followed by C_2, the C_4 axis only requires that the axis $C_2(1)$ be accompanied by one other such axis and not three others. A completely analogous argument holds regarding planes. In the C_6 case, using the same line of argument, it will easily be seen that if one axis perpendicular to a C_6 or one plane containing a C_6 exists, it must be accompanied by two more of the same type. We shall not consider even order axes C_8 and higher since at present no molecules containing axes of such orders are definitely known.

Continuing with examples of proper axes in typical molecules, we may cite the planar $PtCl_4{}^{2-}$ ion, which has a C_4 axis perpendicular to the plane of the ion and four C_2 axes in the plane of the ion.

$C_5H_5{}^-$, the cyclopentadienyl anion, possesses a C_5 axis perpendicular to the molecular plane and five C_2 axes in the molecular plane. Benzene possesses a C_6 axis and two sets of three C_2 axes. Probably the only known example of a molecule with a C_7 axis is the planar $[C_7H_7]^+$, the tropylium ion. The only example of a grouping with a C_8 axis is perhaps the $C_8H_8{}^{2-}$, although this is not yet completely certain.

3.6 Improper Axes and Improper Rotations

An improper rotation may be thought of as taking place in two steps: First a proper rotation and then a reflection through a plane perpendicular to the rotation axis. The axis about which this occurs is called an axis of improper rotation or, more briefly, an improper axis, and is denoted by the symbol S_n, where again n indicates the order. The operation of improper rotation by $2\pi/n$ is also denoted by the symbol S_n. Obviously, if an axis C_n and a perpendicular plane exist independently, then S_n exists. More important, however, is that an S_n may exist when neither the C_n nor the perpendicular σ exist separately. Perhaps this can best be emphasized by taking an example. Let us consider ethane in its staggered configuration. The C—C line defines a C_3 axis, but certainly not a C_6 axis. Also, there is no plane of symmetry perpendicular to the C_3 axis. Yet there is an S_6, as the following diagram shows.

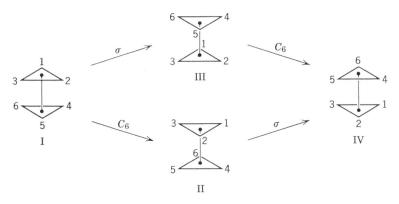

Observe that II and III are equivalent to each other but that neither is equivalent to I; that is, neither σ nor C_6 is by itself a symmetry operation. But the combination of both, in either order, which we call S_6, is a symmetry operation since it produces IV, which is equivalent to I.

As another important example of the occurrence of improper axes and rotations, let us consider a regular tetrahedral molecule. We have already noted in Section 3.5 that the tetrahedron possesses three C_2 axes. Now each of these C_2 axes is simultaneously an S_4 axis, as can be seen in the following diagram.

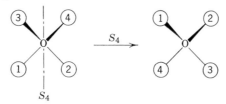

The element S_n in general generates a set of operations S_n, S_n^2, S_n^3 .... . However, there are some important features of these operations which should be noted. There are differences in the sets generated for even and odd n, so these two cases will be considered separately. Let us assume that our S_n axis is colinear with the z axis of a coordinate system and the plane to which the reflection part of the operation S_n is referred is the xy plane.

We shall discuss the even order S_n's first. The first S_n of even order, S_2, is not normally written as such. Let us consider any general point in a molecule or other body possessing an S_2 axis. Let the original coordinates of this point be $[x, y, z]$. If we first rotate the body about the z axis by $2\pi/2$, the coordinates of this point become $[-x, -y, z]$. If we then reflect through the plane perpendicular to the axis, $[-x, -y, z]$ becomes $[-x, -y, -z]$. Thus the overall effect of the operation S_2 on any point is to invert all of its coordinates. But this is precisely the effect of inversion in a center of symmetry. Hence, S_2 and i are identical, and by custom this element (and operation) is given the latter symbol. Obviously, $S_2^2 = i^2 = E$.

The even order S_n axes, where n is 4 or greater, all follow the same general pattern. The element S_n generates a set of operations S_n, S_n^2, $S_n^3 \ldots S_n^n$. Let us first show that (for n even) $S_n^n = E$. S_n^n means that we carry out the operations C_n, σ, C_n, σ ... until, in all, C_n and σ have each been carried out n times. Since n is an even number, n repetitions of σ is an identity operation, so that $S_n^n = C_n^n$; but C_n^n is also just E. Therefore $S_n^n = E$, and $S_n^{n+1} = S_n$, $S_n^{n+2} = S_n^2$, and so on. Now by the same argument S_n^m will be equal to C_n^m whenever m is even. Thus, in any set of operations generated by an even order S_n, certain of the S_n^m may be written in other ways. Consider, for example, the set S_6, S_6^2, S_6^3, S_6^4, S_6^5, S_6^6. S_6 can be written in no other way. $S_6^2 = C_6^2 = C_3$. $S_6^3 = S_2 = i$. $S_6^4 = C_3^2$. S_6^5 can be written in no other way. $S_6^6 = E$. Hence the complete set of operations generated by the element S_6 can be, and normally would be written: S_6, C_3, i, C_3^2, S_6^5, E. Having written the

set in this way, however, we can readily make another useful observation. This set contains C_3, $C_3{}^2$, and E, which are just the operations generated by a C_3 axis. Hence the existence of the S_6 axis automatically requires that the C_3 axis exists. It should not be difficult to see that, in general, the existence of an S_n axis of even order always requires the existence of a $C_{n/2}$ axis.

Let us turn now to improper axes of odd order. The most important property of these is that an odd order S_n requires that C_n and a σ perpendicular to it must exist independently. This is easily proved. The element S_n generates operations S_n, $S_n{}^2$, $S_n{}^3$, $S_n{}^4$ .... Let us examine the operation $S_n{}^n$ when n is odd. It must have the same effect as will application of $C_n{}^n$ followed by $\sigma^n = \sigma$. But since $C_n{}^n = E$, we see that $S_n{}^n = \sigma$. In other words, the element S_n generates a symmetry operation σ. But if the symmetry operation σ exists, the plane to which it is referred must be a symmetry element in its own right. Now, the operation S_n requires us to reflect in the plane σ, thus carrying a configuration I into another configuration, II, and then to rotate by $2\pi/n$, thus carrying II into III. Because S_n is a symmetry operation, I and III must be equivalent configurations. However, when n is odd, σ is itself a symmetry operation, so that II is also equivalent to I. II is then also equivalent to III, and we see that rotation by $2\pi/n$ has carried II into an equivalent configuration, III. Thus the operation C_n is also a symmetry operation in its own right.

To gain further familiarity with odd order improper axes, let us consider how many distinct operations are generated by some such axis, say S_5. The sequence begins S_5, $S_5{}^2$, $S_5{}^3$, $S_5{}^4$ .... Using relations and conventions previously developed, we can write certain of these in alternative ways, as shown below.

$$S_5 = C_5 \text{ then } \sigma \text{ (or } \sigma \text{ then } C_5)$$
$$S_5{}^2 = C_5{}^2$$
$$S_5{}^3 = C_5{}^3 \text{ then } \sigma$$
$$S_5{}^4 = C_5{}^4$$
$$S_5{}^5 = \sigma$$
$$S_5{}^6 = C_5$$
$$S_5{}^7 = C_5{}^2 \text{ then } \sigma$$
$$S_5{}^8 = C_5{}^3$$
$$S_5{}^9 = C_5{}^4 \text{ then } \sigma$$
$$S_5{}^{10} = E$$
$$S_5{}^{11} = C_5 \text{ then } \sigma$$

We see that for S_5 through S_5^{10} (in general, S_n through S_n^{2n}), the operations are all different ones, but commencing with S_n^{2n+1} repetition of the sequence begins. Of the ten operations, however, four plus E can only be expressed as a single operation by using symbols S_5^n, whereas the other five can be written either as C_5^n or as σ. Thus there are operations which, while they may be accomplished by using C_5^n and σ successively, cannot be represented as unit operations in any other way than S_5^n. We also see that in general the element S_n with n odd generates $2n$ operations.

3.7   Products of Symmetry Operations

In Sections 3.3–3.6 we have often discussed the question of how we may represent the net effect of applying one symmetry operation after another to a molecule, but only in a limited way. In this section we shall discuss this question with regard to a broader range of possibilities. First, we shall establish a conventional shorthand for stating that "operation X is carried out first and then operation Y, giving the same net effect as would the carrying out of the single operation Z." This we express symbolically as

$$YX = Z$$

Note that the order in which the operations are applied is the order in which they are written from *right to left*, that is, YX means X first and then Y. In general the order makes a difference although there are numerous cases where it does not. When the result of the sequence XY is the same as the result of the sequence YX, the two operations, X and Y, are said to *commute*. It is also normal to speak of an operation which produces the same result as does the successive application of two or more others as the *product* of the others.

We may approach the problem of finding one single operation which is the product of two others in this way. Suppose we consider a general point with coordinates $[x_1, y_1, z_1]$. On applying a certain operation, this point will be shifted to a new position with coordinates $[x_2, y_2, z_2]$, and, if still another operation is applied, it will again be shifted so that its coordinates are now $[x_3, y_3, z_3]$. The net effect of applying the two operations successively is to shift the point from $[x_1, y_1, z_1]$ to $[x_3, y_3, z_3]$. We now look for a way of doing this in one step. The operation which does so will be the product of the first two.

Let us illustrate this procedure by proving the statement made earlier that if there are two twofold axes at right angles to one another, there must necessarily be a third at right angles to both. Suppose the two given axes coincide with the x and y axes; we can designate them $C_2(x)$ and $C_2(y)$. On applying first $C_2(x)$ and then $C_2(y)$ to a general point, the following transformations of its coordinates take place:

$$[x_1, y_1, z_1] \xrightarrow{C_2(x)} [x_1, -y_1, -z_1] \xrightarrow{C_2(y)} [-x_1, -y_1, z_1]$$

That is, the value of x_3 is $-x_1$, the value of y_3 is $-y_1$, and the value of z_3 is z_1. If now we apply $C_2(z)$ to the general point, it is shifted to $[-x_1, -y_1, z_1]$. Thus we may write

$$C_2(y)C_2(x) = C_2(z)$$

Thus, whenever $C_2(x)$ and $C_2(y)$ exist, $C_2(z)$ must also exist, because it is their product.

As a second example of how the existence of two symmetry elements may automatically require that a third one exist, we shall consider a case having a C_4 axis and one plane containing this axis. We have already seen that the operation C_4 will generate a second plane from the first one at right angles to it. It is also true, however, though less obvious, that when the C_4 axis and one of these planes exist there must then be a second plane also containing C_4 at an angle of $45°$ to the first one. We can prove this by the method just used. The effect of reflecting a general point $[x_1, y_1, z_1]$ through the xz plane is given by

$$\sigma(xz)[x_1, y_1, z_1] \rightarrow [x_1, -y_1, z_1]$$

whereas the effect of a clockwise C_4 rotation about the z axis upon the point is given by

$$C_4(z)[x_1, y_1, z_1] \rightarrow [y_1, -x_1, z_1]$$

From these relations we can determine the effect of applying successively $\sigma(xz)$ and then $C_4(z)$, namely

$$C_4(z)\sigma(xz)[x_1, y_1, z_1] \rightarrow C_4(z)[x_1, -y_1, z_1] \rightarrow [-y_1, -x_1, z_1]$$

Now suppose we consider the effect of reflecting the point through a plane, σ_d, which also contains the z axis and bisects the angles between the $+y$ and $-x$ axes and the $+x$ and $-y$ axes. This transformation is

$$\sigma_d[x_1, y_1, z_1] \rightarrow [-y_1, -x_1, z_1]$$

We see then that

$$C_4(z)\sigma(xz) = \sigma_d$$

which means that the existence of $C_4(z)$ and $\sigma(xz)$ automatically requires that σ_d exist. The C_4 rotation then generates from σ_d another plane σ_d' which passes through the first and third quadrants. The final result then is that if there is one plane containing a C_4 axis, there is automatically a set of four planes.

It may be shown in a very similar way that if $C_4(z)$ and $C_2(y)$ axes exist a C_2 axis lying in the first and third quadrants of the xy plane at 45 degrees to $C_2(y)$ must also exist. This is left as an exercise.

In the above examples, where only C_2 and C_4 rotations and certain kinds of planes are concerned, the transformation of the coordinates, $[x_1, y_1, z_1]$ to $[x_1, -y_1, -z_1]$ by a twofold rotation about the x axis, for example, is fairly obvious by inspection. It is also obvious that a fourfold rotation about the x axis will transform the coordinates into $[x_1, -z_1, y_1]$. It is also easy to see by inspection the effects of the inversion operation, an improper rotation by $2\pi/2$ or $2\pi/4$ and reflection in a plane which is the xy, xz, or yz plane, or a plane rotated by 45 degrees from these. However, the transformations effected by more general symmetry operations such as rotation by $2\pi/n$ or $m2\pi/n$ and reflections in planes other than those mentioned above are not easily written down by inspection or in general easily handled by the simple methods and notation used above. Further discussion along this line will therefore be postponed to the next chapter where the more powerful methods of matrix algebra will be introduced.

3.8   Equivalent Symmetry Elements and Equivalent Atoms

If a symmetry element A is carried into the element B by an operation generated by a third element X, then of course B can be carried back into A by the application of X^{-1}. The two elements A and B are said to be equivalent. If A can be carried into still a third element, C, then there will also be a way of carrying B into C, and the three elements, A, B, and C form an equivalent set. In general, any set of symmetry elements chosen so that any member of the set can be transformed into each and every other member of the set by application of some symmetry operation is said to be a set of equivalent symmetry elements.

For example, in a plane triangular molecule such as BF_3, each of the twofold symmetry axes lying in the plane can be carried into coincidence with each of the others by rotations of $2\pi/3$ or $2 \times 2\pi/3$, which are symmetry operations. Thus all three twofold axes are said to be equivalent to one another. In a square planar AB_4 molecule, there are four twofold axes in the molecular plane. Two of them, C_2 and C_2', will lie along BAB axes, and the other two, C_2'' and C_2''', bisect BAB angles. Such a molecule also contains four symmetry planes, each of which is perpendicular to the molecular plane and intersects it along one of the twofold axes. Now it is easy to see that C_2 may be carried into C_2' and vice versa, and C_2'' may be carried into C_2''' and vice versa by rotations about the fourfold axis and by reflections in the symmetry planes mentioned, but there is no way to carry C_2 or C_2' into either C_2'' or C_2''' or vice versa. Thus C_2 and C_2' form one set of equivalent axes, and C_2'' and C_2''' form another. Similarly, two of the symmetry planes are equivalent to one another, but not to either of the other two, which are, however, equivalent to one another. As other illustrations of equivalence and non-equivalence of symmetry elements, we may note that all three of the symmetry planes in BF_3 which are perpendicular to the molecular plane are equivalent as are the three in NH_3, whereas the two planes in H_2O are not equivalent. The six twofold axes lying in the plane of the benzene molecule can be divided into two sets of equivalent axes, one set containing those which transect opposite carbon atoms and the other set containing those which bisect opposite edges of the hexagon.

Equivalent atoms in a molecule are those which may all be interchanged with one another by symmetry operations. Naturally, equivalent atoms must be of the same chemical species. As examples of equivalent atoms consider all of the hydrogen atoms in methane, ethane, benzene, or cyclopropane, all of the fluorine atoms in SF_6, and all of the carbon and oxygen atoms in $Cr(CO)_6$. Examples of chemically identical atoms which are not equivalent in molecular environment are the apical and equatorial fluorine atoms in PF_5; no symmetry operation possible for this molecule ever interchanges apical and equatorial fluorine atoms. The α and β hydrogen and carbon atoms of naphthalene are not equivalent. All six carbon atoms of cyclohexane are equivalent in the chair configuration, but four are different from the other two in the boat configuration.

3.9   The Symmetry Point Groups

Suppose that we have, by inspection, compiled a list of all of the symmetry elements possessed by a given molecule. We can then list all of the symmetry operations generated by each of these elements. Our first objective in this section is to demonstrate that such a *complete* list of symmetry *operations* satisfies the four criteria for a mathematical group. When this has been established, we shall then be free to use the theorems concerning the behavior of groups to assist in dealing with problems of molecular symmetry.

Let us first specify what we mean by a *complete* set of symmetry operations for a particular molecule. A complete set is one in which every possible product of two operations in the set is also an operation in the set. Let us consider as an example the set of operations which may be performed on a planar AB_3 molecule. These are E, C_3, $C_3{}^2$, C_2, C_2', C_2'', σ_v, σ_v', σ_v'', σ_h. It should be clear that no other symmetry operations are possible. If we number the B atoms as indicated, we can systematically work through all binary products. For example,

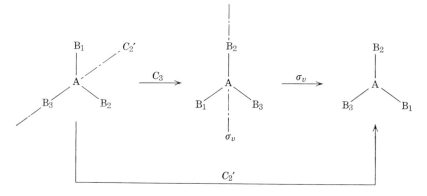

Hence we see that $\sigma_v C_3 = C_2'$. Proceeding in this way we can check all the combinations and we will find that the set given is indeed complete. This is suggested as a useful exercise.

Now, we can see that because our set of operations is complete in the sense defined above it satisfies the first requirement for mathematical groups, if we take as our law of combination of two symmetry operations the successive application of these operations.

The second requirement—that there must exist a group element E such that for every other element in the group, say X, $EX = XE = X$— is also seen to be satisfied. The "operation" of performing no operation at all, or that which results from a sequence of operations which sends the molecule into a configuration identical with the original (for example, σ^2, $C_n{}^n$) is our identity, E, and we have been calling it that all along.

The associative law is obviously valid for products of symmetry operations.

The final requirement, that every element of the group have an inverse, is also satisfied. For a group composed of symmetry operations, we may define the inverse of a given operation as that second operation which will exactly undo what the given operation does, or in more sophisticated terms, the reciprocal S of an operation R must be such that $RS = SR = E$. Let us consider each of the types of symmetry operation. For σ, reflection in a plane, the inverse is clearly σ itself: $\sigma \times \sigma = \sigma^2 = E$. For proper rotation, $C_n{}^m$, the inverse is $C_n{}^{n-m}$, for $C_n{}^m \times C_n{}^{n-m} = C_n{}^n = E$.

For an improper rotation, S_n^m, the reciprocal depends on whether m and n are even or odd, but a reciprocal exists in each of the four possible cases. When n is even the reciprocal of S_n^m is S_n^{n-m} whether m is even or odd. When n is odd and m is even, $S_n^m = C_n^m$, the reciprocal of which is C_n^{n-m}. For S_n^m with both n and m odd we may write $S_n^m = C_n^m \sigma$. The reciprocal would be the product $C_n^{n-m} \sigma$, which is equal to $C_n^{2n-m} \sigma$, and which in turn may be written as a single operation, S_n^{2n-m}.

Having shown that complete sets of symmetry operations do constitute groups, we shall now systematically consider what kinds of groups will be obtained from various possible collections of symmetry operations.

In the trivial case where there are no symmetry operations other than E, we have a group of order 1 called C_1.*

Let us next consider molecules whose sole symmetry element is a plane. This element generates only two operations, viz., σ and $\sigma^2 = E$. Hence the group is of order 2. The symbol normally given to this group is C_s. It is also possible to have a molecule whose sole symmetry element is an inversion center. The only operations generated by the inversion center are i and $i^2 = E$. Again we have a group of order 2; this one is conventionally designated C_i.

Let us consider now the cases where the only symmetry element is a proper axis, C_n. This generates a set of operations $C_n, C_n^2, C_n^3 \ldots C_n^n = E$. Hence a molecule with C_n as its only symmetry element would belong to a group of order n, which is designated C_n. It may be noted that a C_n group is a cyclic group (see Section 2.2) and hence also Abelian.

When an improper axis is present, we must consider whether it is even or odd. When the axis, S_n, is of even order, the group of operations it generates is called S_n and consists of the n elements $E, S_n, C_{n/2}, S_n^3 \ldots S_n^{n-1}$. The group S_2 is a special case because, as shown earlier, the symmetry element S_2 is equivalent to i. Thus the group which might be called the S_2 group is actually called C_i. The group of operations generated by an S_n axis when n is odd has been shown to consist of $2n$ elements, including σ_h and the operations generated by C_n. By convention such groups are denoted C_{nh}. This symbol emphasizes that there is a C_n axis and a horizontal plane, which combination of symmetry elements of course implies the existence of S_n just as S_n (n odd) implies the existence of C_n and σ_h. The C_{nh} groups will be discussed in more detail shortly.

* This and the other symbols for the symmetry groups, for example, C_n, D_n, C_{nh}, C_{nv}, D_{nh}, D_{nd} ..., which will be introduced are called the Schoenflies symbols after their inventor. The symmetry groups are also frequently called point groups since all symmetry elements in a molecule will intersect at a common point, which is not shifted by any of the symmetry operations. There are also symmetry groups called space groups which contain operations involving translatory motions. The latter are not considered in this book.

We have now listed all of the groups which can be thought of as generated by a single symmetry element. Next we turn to the groups which arise when two or more kinds of symmetry elements are present. We shall not pretend to be rigorous in showing that the final list is all-inclusive, but it can be taken that it is.

If a molecule possesses a proper axis, C_n, and also a twofold axis perpendicular to it, we have already seen that there must then necessarily be n such twofold axes. The n operations, E, C_n, C_n^2 ... C_n^{n-1}, plus the n twofold rotations constitute a complete set of symmetry operations, as may be verified by actually carrying through all of the binary products. Thus such a group consists of altogether $2n$ elements. The symbol for a group of this kind is D_n.

We have now reached a point of departure in the process of adding further symmetry elements to a C_n axis. We shall now consider (1) the addition of different kinds of symmetry planes to the C_n axis only, and (2) the addition of symmetry planes to a set of elements consisting of the C_n axis and the n C_2 axes perpendicular to it. In the course of this development it will be useful to have some symbols for several kinds of symmetry planes. In defining such symbols we shall consider the direction of the C_n axis, which we call the principal axis or reference axis, to be *vertical*. Hence, a symmetry plane perpendicular to this axis will be called a horizontal plane and denoted σ_h. Planes which include the C_n axis are generally called vertical planes, but there are actually two different types. In some molecules all vertical planes are equivalent and symbolized σ_v. In others there may be two different sets of vertical planes (as in $PtCl_4^{2-}$; cf. page 18), in which case those of one set will be called σ_v and those of the other set σ_d, the d standing for dihedral. It will be best to discuss these differences further as we meet them.

If to the C_n axis we add a horizontal plane, we expand the original group of n operations, C_n, C_n^2 ... E, to include all of the products $\sigma_h C_n$, $\sigma_h C_n^2$, $\sigma_h C_n^3$ ... $\sigma_h E = \sigma_h$, making $2n$ operations in all. Now the operation $\sigma_h C_n^m = C_n^m \sigma_h$ since σ affects only the z coordinate of a point while C_n^m affects only its x and y coordinates, so that the order in which σ and C_n^m are performed is inconsequential. Furthermore, all of the new operations of the type σC_n^m can be expressed as single operations, viz., as improper rotations. This new set of $2n$ operations can easily be shown to be a complete set and hence to constitute a group. Such a group has the general symbol C_{nh}.

Let us look next at the consequences of adding a vertical plane to the C_n axis. First we recall (Section 3.5) that the operations generated by C_n when n is odd will require that an entire set of n such vertical planes exist. All of these planes are properly called vertical planes and symbolized σ_v. When n is even, however, we have seen (Section 3.5) that only $n/2$ planes of the same type will exist as a direct consequence of the C_n axis. However, we have also shown (Section 3.7) that another set of $n/2$ vertical planes must exist as the various products $C_n{}^m \sigma_v$. These vertical planes in this second set are usually called dihedral planes, since they bisect the dihedral angles between members of the set of σ_v's, and they are denoted σ_d. Obviously, it is completely arbitrary which set is considered vertical and which dihedral. In either case, n even or n odd, the set of operations generated by the C_n and by all of the σ's constitute a complete set and such a group is called C_{nv}.

We might naturally ask now about what happens when we add both the horizontal plane and the set of n vertical planes to the C_n. This gives a group called D_{nh}, which we shall now develop by a different procedure.

We now consider the consequences of adding a σ_h to the group D_n. The group generated is denoted D_{nh}. We must first look at all of the products of σ_h with the operations generated by the C_2 axes and by the C_n axis. Suppose we choose a coordinate system such that the C_n axis coincides with the z axis, and one of the C_2 axes, $C_2(x)$, coincides with the x axis. We can indicate the effect of rotation about the $C_2(x)$ axis followed by σ_h on a general point $[x,\, y,\, z]$ thus:

$$[x,\, y,\, z] \xrightarrow{C_2(x)} [x,\, -y,\, -z] \xrightarrow{\sigma_h} [x,\, -y,\, z]$$

The effect of reflection in the xz plane on the same point will be

$$[x,\, y,\, z] \xrightarrow{\sigma(xz)} [x,\, -y,\, z]$$

Thus we can write

$$\sigma_h C_2(x) = \sigma(xz) = C_2(x)\sigma_h$$

where the second equality is easily proved in the same way. Of course, it now follows that if one of the C_2 axes lies in a vertical symmetry plane, so must all of the others. There must then be a set of n operations σ_v. We may now left-multiply the above equation by σ_h, obtaining

$$\sigma_h \sigma_h C_2 = \sigma_h \sigma_v = C_2$$

and we see that all of the products of σ_h with the σ_v's are C_2's. Thus we might also take the simultaneous existence of C_n, σ_h, and the σ_v's as the criterion for the existence of the group D_{nh}. It is only by reason of convention and not because of any mathematical requirement that we take instead the simultaneous existence of C_n, nC_2's and σ_h as the criterion.

We have now shown that the operations in a group D_{nh} include E, $(n-1)$ proper rotations about C_n, n reflections in vertical planes, σ_h, and n rotations about C_2 axes. These $3n+1$ operations still do not constitute the complete set, however. It will be found that among the products $C_n{}^m\sigma_h = \sigma_h C_n{}^m$ are $n - 1$ additional operations which are all improper rotations. For the general case where n is even, we obtain the new operations: S_n, $S_{n/2}$, ... i ($= C_n^{n/2}\sigma_h$), ... $S_{n/2}^{(n-2)/2}$, S_n^{n-1}. In the group D_{6h}, for example, we have S_6, S_3, i, $S_3{}^2$ and $S_6{}^5$. When n is odd we obtain in the general case the following $n - 1$ improper rotations: S_n, $S_n{}^3$, $S_n{}^5$ ... S_n^{2n-3}, S_n^{2n-1} except $S_n{}^n$ ($= \sigma_h$); all $S_n{}^m$ where m is even being, of course, either E or one of the proper rotations which we have already recognized. Thus, we now have a total of $4n$ operations in the group D_{nh}. Systematic examination will show that the set is now complete.

Our next and final task is to consider the consequences of adding to C_n and the nC_2's a set of dihedral planes, σ_d's. These are vertical planes which bisect the angles between adjacent pairs of C_2 axes. The groups generated by this combination of symmetry elements are denoted D_{nd}. The products of a σ_d with the various $C_n{}^m$ operations are all other σ_d operations. However, among the various products $\sigma_d C_2$ there are a set of n new operations generated by an S_{2n} axis colinear with C_n. These $4n$ operations now constitute the complete group D_{nd}.

Thus far our discussion has been reasonably systematic. A new group has been built up by adding an additional symmetry element to an existing set. In this way we have discovered the groups C_1, C_s, C_i, the C_n, S_n and D_n groups, the C_{nh} and C_{nv} groups, and the D_{nh} and D_{nd} groups.

There are, however, several other symmetry groups to which a number of real molecules belong. We shall not attempt to fit these into a systematic pattern but will simply describe them forthwith. These will be called "special" groups in this book.

The first of the special groups are the two to which linear molecules may belong. A linear molecule which does not have any symmetry plane perpendicular to the molecular axis belongs to the group $C_{\infty v}$, a group of infinite order consisting of rotations about the molecular axis and reflections in planes containing the molecular axis. Linear molecules which do have a plane of symmetry perpendicular to the molecular axis belong to another group of infinite order called $D_{\infty h}$. They also possess an infinite number of C_2 axes perpendicular to the molecular axis and an inversion center.

The second class of special groups to be described are the so-called cubic groups. There are several such groups but only two need be considered for our purposes. These are the groups to which the regular tetrahedron and the regular octahedron belong. Both of these figures may be inscribed in a cube, and for the tetrahedron this provides a particularly helpful way of looking at its symmetry properties.

It can be seen that the tetrahedron or any tetrahedral molecule possesses the following symmetry elements and operations.

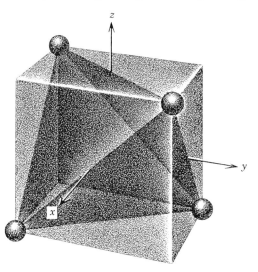

(i) Three S_4 axes coinciding with the x, y, and z axes. Each of these generates the operations S_4, $S_4{}^2 = C_2$ and $S_4{}^3$.

(ii) Three C_2 axes coinciding with the x, y, and z axes, each of which generates an operation C_2. These, however, have already been generated by the S_4's.

(iii) Four C_3 axes, each of which passes through one apex and the center of the opposite face. These each generate C_3 and $C_3{}^2$ operations, that is, eight operations in all.

(iv) Six planes of symmetry each of which generates a symmetry operation.

This entire set of operations then includes E, six improper rotations (S_4's and $S_4{}^3$'s), three twofold proper rotations, eight threefold proper rotations (C_3's and $C_3{}^2$'s), and six reflections, or twenty-four operations in all. This group is denoted T_d.

A regular octahedron has the following symmetry elements and operations.

(i) Three S_4 axes, each passing through a pair of opposite apices. Each generates the operations S_4, C_2, $S_4{}^3$.

(ii) Three C_2 axes colinear with the S_4's. The C_2 operations generated by these, however, are already accounted for under (i).

(iii) Three C_4 axes colinear with the S_4's and C_2's. Each generates a set of operations C_4, C_2, and $C_4{}^3$, but only C_4 and $C_4{}^3$ are new.

(iv) Six C_2' axes, which bisect opposite edges. Each generates an operation C_2'.

(v) Four S_6 axes, each passing through the centers of a pair of opposite triangular faces. Each generates a set of operations S_6, C_3, i, $C_3{}^2$, $S_6{}^5$.

(vi) Four C_3 axes colinear with the S_6's. Each generates two operations C_3 and $C_3{}^2$, which are also generated by the colinear S_6.

(vii) An inversion center which generates an operation i, which is also
generated by each of the S_6 axes.

(viii) Three planes of symmetry which pass through four of the six
apices. Each generates an operation σ.

(ix) Six planes of symmetry which pass through two apices and bisect
two opposite edges. Each of these generates an operation σ'.

Counting E and each of the above operations, we find a total of forty-
eight operations in this group, which is called O_h.

Finally, there is the point group of the regular icosahedron and regular
dodecahedron, which along with the tetrahedron, octahedron, and cube
constitute the five regular polyhedra. The regular dodecahedron has
twelve regular pentagonal faces and twenty apices. The regular icosahedron has twenty equilateral triangular faces each centered at one of the
twenty apices of the dodecahedron. Both of these polyhedra belong to
the group I_h. They have these kinds of symmetry elements: C_2, C_3, C_5,
i, σ, from which are obtained a total of 120 symmetry operations. The
character table is given in Appendix II, and we shall not enter into any
more explicit discussion here. At the time of writing only a few chemical
species belonging to the group I_h are known, namely icosahedral B_{12}
units in several elemental forms of boron and the $B_{12}H_{12}{}^{2-}$ ion.

3.10   Systematic Symmetry Classification of Molecules

In Section 3.9 we have shown that a complete and nonredundant set of
symmetry operations for any molecule constitutes a mathematical
group, and the various groups or kinds of groups (that is, C_n, D_n, S_n,
C_{nv}, C_{nh}, D_{nd}, T_d ...) we may expect to encounter among real molecules
have been described. In this section we shall describe a systematic procedure for deciding what point group any molecule belongs to. This
will be done in a practical and admittedly "how-to-do-it" manner, but
the close relation of this procedure to the arguments used in deriving the
various groups should be evident. The following sequence of steps will
lead systematically to a correct classification.

1. Determine whether or not the molecule belongs to any of the special
groups, that is, $C_{\infty v}$, $D_{\infty h}$, T_d, O_h, or I_h. Only a linear molecule can belong
to one of the first two. As for T_d, O_h, and I_h, the specially high symmetry
of a molecule belonging to these groups is usually fairly obvious. If the
molecule appears to belong to T_d, O_h, or I_h, however, this conclusion
should not be taken as final until one has verified, element by element,
that all of the required symmetry elements are indeed present.

2. If the molecule is found not to belong to any of the special groups, we then look to see if it has any proper axes of symmetry. If any are found, we proceed to step 3. If none can be found, we then look for a plane, in which case it belongs to the group C_s, or an inversion center, in which case it belongs to the group C_i. If no symmetry elements exist, the molecule belongs to the trivial group C_1, which contains only the identity operation. Of course, here and throughout, there is no certain defense, except perhaps skill and experience, against the human error of simply failing to notice a symmetry element.

3. If the molecule is found to possess one or more proper axes of symmetry, we select the one of highest order. It is possible that there will be no one axis of uniquely high order but instead three C_2 axes. In such a case, we look to see if one of them is geometrically unique in some sense, for example, in being colinear with a unique molecular axis. This occurs with the molecule allene which is one of the examples to be worked through later. If all of the axes appear quite similar to one another, then any one may be selected at random as the axis to which the vertical or horizontal character of planes will be referred. Suppose C_n is our reference or principal axis. We next look to see if there is, colinear with C_n, also an S_{2n}. If the S_{2n} exists but there are no other elements of symmetry whatever except possibly i, the molecule belongs to one of the S_n (n even) point groups. If we find the S_{2n} but also other symmetry elements, *or* if we do not find the S_{2n}, we proceed to step 4.

4. We next look to see if there is a set of n twofold axes lying in a plane perpendicular to C_n. If there is such a set, the molecule will belong to one of the groups D_n, D_{nh}, D_{nd}. If not, it can only belong to one of the groups C_n, C_{nv}, C_{nh}. If it must belong to one of the D groups, we proceed to step 5. If it must belong to one of the C groups, we skip to step 6.

5. For a molecule which must belong to one of the groups D_n, D_{nh}, or D_{nd}, we now decide which group. We first look for a σ_h, that is, a symmetry plane perpendicular to the C_n axis. If we find one, the point group must be D_{nh}. Failing this, we look for a set of $n\sigma_d$'s, that is, planes intersecting along the C_n axis, each of which bisects a pair of opposite angles formed by two of the C_2 axes. If we find such planes, the point group must be D_{nd}. If we find neither the σ_h nor the set of σ_d's, then the point group is simply D_n.

6. For a molecule which must belong to one of the groups, C_n, C_{nh}, or C_{nv}, we determine which by first looking for a σ_h. If one is found the point group must be C_{nh}. Failing this, we look for a set of n vertical planes, which, if found, place the molecule in the group C_{nv}. If neither the horizontal nor the vertical planes are found, the point group is simply C_n.

We shall now work through some illustrative examples.

Example I. H_2O

1. H_2O is not linear nor does it belong to any of the groups T_d, O_h, or I_h.

2. It does, however, possess a C_2 axis.

3. This C_2 axis is the highest order proper axis in the molecule, and there is no S_4 axis.

4. There are no C_2 axes perpendicular to the C_2 already considered; hence H_2O must belong to a C-type point group.

6. There is no σ_h so the C_{2h} group is ruled out. There are, however, two σ_v's; one is the molecular plane and the other is perpendicular to it. Hence, H_2O belongs to the point group C_{2v}.

Example II. NH_3

1. The molecule is not linear nor does it belong to one of the other special groups.

2. It is observed to possess a C_3 axis but none of any higher order.

3. There is no S_6 axis.

4. No C_2 axis perpendicular to the C_3 axis may be found. Therefore the point group must be one of the C types.

6. There is no σ_h so the possibility of C_{3h} is ruled out. There are, however, three σ_v's; therefore, the point group is C_{3v}.

Example III. Allene, $H_2C\!=\!\!C\!=\!\!CH_2$

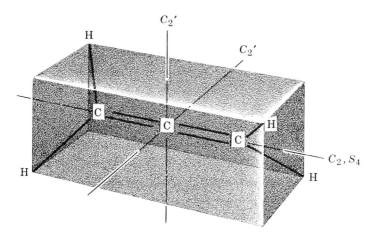

1. The molecule is not linear nor one of the other special types.

2. It is observed to possess several twofold axes, but the one which is colinear with the C=C=C line is perhaps the most obvious.

3. It is found to have an S_4 axis colinear with the C_2. However, it does not belong to the point group S_4 because there are symmetry elements in addition to the C_2 and S_4, of which the most obvious are two vertical planes of symmetry intersecting along the common C_2 and S_4 line, as well as other twofold axes.

4. A careful examination reveals that there are two more twofold axes, C_2'''s, perpendicular to the C=C=C line, as illustrated. Hence, the point group must be of the D type.

5. There is no σ_h, but, as already noted, there are two σ_v's. It can be seen also that these pass between the C_2'''s. Hence the group is D_{2d}.

It may be noted that any molecule which may be regarded as a tetrahedron which has been either squashed or elongated along one of the C_2 axes will belong to the group D_{2d}.

Example IV. H_2O_2

A. In its equilibrium configuration

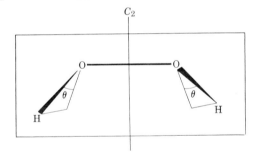

C_2

1. The molecule is not linear and clearly not a member of one of the other special groups.

2. It is observed to possess a C_2 axis (see drawing), thus ruling out C_1, C_i, and C_s. Moreover, this axis, which is a perpendicular bisector of both the O—O and H—H lines, is the only proper axis and hence is the reference axis.

3. There is no S_4 colinear with the C_2.

4. There are no C_2's perpendicular to the one mentioned or indeed any other symmetry elements whatever. Hence the point group is C_2.

Note that the C_2 symmetry is in no way related to the precise value of the angle θ, except when θ equals either $0°$ or $90°$, in which cases the symmetry is higher. We shall next determine the symmetries of these two *nonequilibrium* configurations of the molecule.

B. In a cis-planar configuration ($\theta = 0°$)

1. It does not belong to any of the special groups.

2. It has a C_2 axis, ruling out the groups C_1, C_i, and C_s. This is the only proper axis.

3. There is no S_4 colinear with the C_2.

4. There are no C_2's perpendicular to the one already noted.

5. There is no σ_h but there are two σ_v's. Hence the group is C_{2v}.

C. In a trans-planar configuration ($\theta = 90°$)

1. It does not belong to any of the special groups.

2. It is observed to possess a C_2 axis perpendicular to the molecular plane, thus ruling out the groups C_1, C_i, and C_s.

3. There is no S_4 axis colinear with the C_2 axis mentioned.

4. There are no C_2's perpendicular to the C_2 already noted.

5. There is a σ_h (the molecular plane); hence the point group is C_{2h}.

Example V. Benzene

1. The molecule does not belong to any of the special groups.

2. It is seen to possess a number of symmetry axes, but clearly the highest order axis is the C_6 which is perpendicular to the molecular plane, cutting it at the geometrical center of the molecule.

3. There is no S_{12} axis colinear with the C_6 axis.

4. Six C_2 axes, three of which bisect opposite C—C lines and are called C_2''s and three more which pass through opposite H—C ... C—H lines and are called C_2'''s can be found. Thus the point group is of the D type.

5. There is a plane of symmetry perpendicular to the C_6 axis. Hence the point group is D_{6h}. There are also six σ_v's, but note that these each *include* a C_2' or C_2'' axis; they do *not* pass between adjacent twofold axes.

Example VI. PCl₅ (Trigonal Bipyramid)

1. The molecule does not belong to any of the special groups.

2. The highest order proper axis it possesses is a C_3.

3. There is no S_6 colinear with this C_3.

4. There are three C_2 axes perpendicular to the C_3; hence it must belong to a group of the D type.

5. There is a σ_h so the group must be D_{3h}.

Example VII. [AuCl₄]⁻ *(Square)*

1. This ion does not belong to any of the special groups.
2. It possesses several symmetry axes, but the one of uniquely high order is a C_4 perpendicular to the molecular plane and passing through the gold atom.
3. There is no S_8 axis colinear with the C_4 axis.
4. There are four C_2 axes, two C_2' axes containing Cl—Au—Cl groups and two C_2'' axes bisecting Cl—Au—Cl angles. Thus the point group must be of the D type.
5. There is a σ_h (the molecular plane) so that the point group is D_{4h}.

Example VIIIA. Ferrocene, $(C_5H_5)_2Fe$ *(Pentagonal Antiprism)*

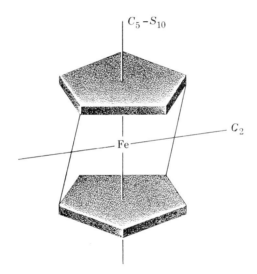

1. The molecule does not belong to any of the special groups.
2. There are a number of symmetry axes of which the one of uniquely high order is a C_5 passing through the iron atom, perpendicular to the planes of the rings.
3. There is an S_{10} axis colinear with the C_5, but the molecule also has other elements of symmetry (besides i) such as σ_v's.
4. There are five C_2 axes perpendicular to the C_5-S_{10} axis. These pass through the iron atom and are perpendicular bisectors of lines drawn from a carbon atom of one ring to one of the nearest carbon atoms of the other ring. Hence the group must be of the D type.

5. There is no σ_h. There are, however, five vertical planes of symmetry which pass between adjacent C_2's. Thus the group is D_{5d}.

Example VIIIB. Ruthenocene, $(C_5H_5)_2Ru$ (Pentagonal Prism)

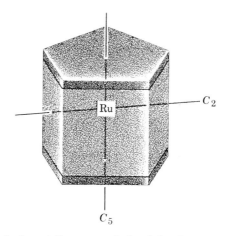

1. The molecule is not linear nor is it of I_d, O_h, or I_h symmetry.
2. There is a proper axis of uniquely high order, viz., a C_5 axis just as in ferrocene.
3. There is no S_{10} axis colinear with the C_5.
4. There are five twofold axes perpendicular to the C_5. Thus, like ferrocene, this molecule must belong to a D-type point group.
5. There is clearly a σ_h, so the group is D_{5h}. There are five vertical planes of symmetry, but each of these contains a C_2 axis; they do not pass between C_2 axes.

Some Practice Problems
Listed below are some further examples for practice; answers are given in a footnote at the bottom of page 46.
(1) 1,3,5-trichlorobenzene
(2) *trans*-Pt(NH$_3$)$_2$Cl$_2$ (ignore H's)
(3) SF$_5$Cl
(4) BFClBr

(5) 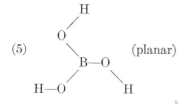 (planar)

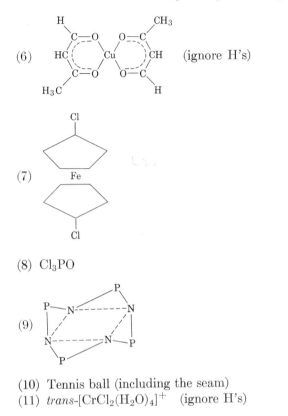

(6)   (ignore H's)

(7)

(8) Cl_3PO

(9)

(10) Tennis ball (including the seam)
(11) *trans*-$[CrCl_2(H_2O)_4]^+$ (ignore H's)

3.11 Classes of Symmetry Operations

In Section 2.4 the concept of classes of elements within a group was introduced. This concept is utilized in dealing with symmetry groups. As we shall see in Chapter 4, it is convenient and customary in writing what is called the character table of a group to consider all the elements of a given class together since they all behave identically in those properties covered by the character table. It is the purpose of this section to explain the manner in which the symmetry operations are arranged into classes and to discuss the geometrical significance of the classes.

Of course, the general definition of a class and the method of arranging the elements of a group into classes given in Section 2.4 is perfectly applicable to a symmetry group. Let us consider for example the group C_{4v}. This group of operations arises when the following symmetry elements are present: E, C_4, σ_v. There are eight operations in the complete set generated by these symmetry elements, viz., E, C_4, $C_4{}^2 = C_2$, $C_4{}^3$, $2\sigma_v$, $2\sigma_d$. The σ_v's are planes perpendicular to one another, intersecting along the C_4 axis and so are the σ_d's. The σ_d's make $45°$ angles with the σ_v's.

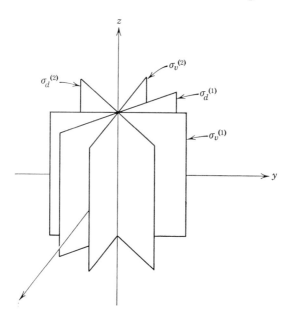

By methods previously explained and illustrated for determining the products of symmetry operations, a multiplication table for this group can be worked out.

Then, using this to carry out all of the possible similarity transformations, we find that there are the following classes:

$$E$$

$$C_4, C_4{}^3$$

$$C_2$$

$$\sigma_v^{(1)}, \sigma_v^{(2)}$$

$$\sigma_d^{(1)}, \sigma_d^{(2)}$$

It may be noted parenthetically that this result provides a good example of the fact that while the orders of all classes must be integral divisors of the group order, not *all* integral divisors of the group order need be

Answers to practice problems on page 44: (1) D_{3h} (2) D_{2h} (3) C_{4v} (4) C_s (5) C_{3h}
(6) C_{2h} (7) C_{2h} (8) C_{3v} (9) C_{2h} (10) D_{2d} (11) D_{4h}.

represented among the orders of the classes. Observe that while 4 is an integral divisor of 8, there is no class of order 4 in this group.

With symmetry groups the classes have a geometrical significance which may be stated as: Two operations belong to the same class when one may be replaced by the other in a new coordinate system *which is accessible by a symmetry operation.* The italicized part of this prescription is quite important. Let us consider the group C_{4v} and its subgroup C_4 to see what this means. The operation $C_4{}^3$ shifts every point in the molecule by $3 \times 2\pi/4$ in, let us say, the clockwise direction. This, however, is the same thing as shifting every point by $2\pi/4$ in the counterclockwise direction. Let us then for the moment think of the operation C_4 as rotation by $2\pi/4$ clockwise and $C_4' = C_4{}^3$ as rotation by $2\pi/4$ counterclockwise. Now suppose that the coordinate system in which we have been working is (*a*) so that clockwise rotation by $2\pi/4$ converts a point $[x, y]$

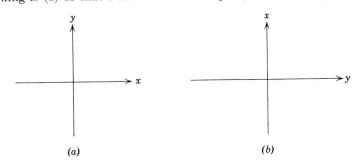

(a)   (b)

into $[y, -x]$ while counterclockwise rotation by $2\pi/4$ converts $[x, y]$ into $[-y, x]$. Symbolically

$$C_4(z)[x, y] \rightarrow [y, -x]$$

$$C_4'(z)[x, y] \rightarrow [-y, x]$$

In coordinate system (*b*), however, the effects of C_4 (clockwise) and C_4' (counterclockwise) are

$$C_4(z)[x, y] \rightarrow [-y, x]$$

$$C_4'(z)[x, y] \rightarrow [y, -x]$$

In short, the roles of C_4 and C_4' are interchanged in coordinate system (*b*) from what they are in coordinate system (*a*). Now, and this is the important point, there is a symmetry operation in the group C_{4v} which will convert coordinate system (*a*) into coordinate system (*b*), namely $\sigma_d^{(2)}$. Thus, in the group C_{4v}, C_4 and $C_4' = C_4{}^3$ are in the same class. However, in the group C_4 (which contains only the operations E, C_4, C_2, $C_4{}^3$, they are not in the same class because none of these four operations has the effect of transforming coordinate system (*a*) into system (*b*). Of course, since any C_n group is cyclic and hence Abelian, we can see that all operations must be of different classes, since each operation is conjugate only with itself in an Abelian group.

Returning to the group C_{4v} again, we note that C_2 is in a class by itself. This is so on geometrical grounds, because clearly there can be no way of shifting the coordinate system so that the effects of a rotation by $180°$ can be produced by a rotation by $90°$, or by a reflection of any kind. Also, the σ_v's and σ_d's form separate classes. Only a rotation by $2\pi/8$ could change the orientation of the coordinate system to a new one in which σ_d would accomplish what σ_v did in the old one, and rotation by $2\pi/8$ is not a symmetry operation which occurs in the group.

We may finally note that there is a close relationship between the classes of operations and the various sets of equivalent operations in a group. In fact the classes correspond directly to the sets of equivalent operations. The reason for this is easy to see. The geometrical criterion for putting two operations, A and B, in the same class is that there be some third operation, C, which can be applied to the coordinate system so that the operation B in the transformed coordinate system is analogous to operation A in the original coordinate system. At the same time, we say that operations A and B are equivalent if one is converted into the other (in the same coordinate system) by applying the operation C to the operations A and B. Now to say that operation C interchanges the operations A and B when applied to them, leaving the coordinate system fixed, is perfectly equivalent to saying that operation C interchanges the functions of A and B when applied to the coordinate system, leaving the operations fixed in space. Hence the simplest way of arranging the operations of a symmetry group into classes is to arrange them into sets of equivalent operations. These sets will be the classes.

A practical consequence of collecting all operations in the same class when writing down the complete set, for example, at the head of a character table, is that the notation used is a little different from what we have been using thus far. This new and final form of notation will now be explained and illustrated for the four kinds of symmetry operations.

(i) *Inversion.* Only one inversion operation is possible in a molecule. If one exists it is denoted i. It will always be in a class by itself.

(ii) *Reflections.* Reflection in a horizontal plane is denoted σ_h. This operation will always be in a class by itself. When there is a set of n vertical planes all in the same class, we write simply $n\sigma_v$, and for a set of σ_d's, $n\sigma_d$. When there are some vertical planes in one class and some in another, some may be called σ_v's and the set will be indicated by $n\sigma_v$, while the second set may be denoted $n\sigma_v'$ or $n\sigma_d$ (the use of σ_v' or σ_d for the second set is somewhat arbitrary).

(iii) *Proper rotations.* In the cyclic groups each of the operations, $C_n, C_n^2, C_n^3 \ldots C_n^{n-1}$ constitutes a class by itself and we continue to use this notation. However, in all other groups of higher symmetry, the number of classes spanned by these operations will be reduced in the following way. A C_n^m will fall into the same class with C_n^{n-m}. We have seen an example of this in the group C_{4v} where C_4 and C_4^3 are in the same class. In these cases, we use the notation illustrated below for the various operations generated by a C_7 and a C_6 axis.

OLD NOTATION
(Grouped by classes)   NEW NOTATION

$$C_7^{m}\text{'s}\begin{cases} C_7, C_7^6 \\ C_7^2, C_7^5 \\ C_7^3, C_7^4 \end{cases} \qquad \begin{matrix} 2C_7 \\ 2C_7^2 \\ 2C_7^3 \end{matrix}$$

$$C_6^{m}\text{'s}\begin{cases} C_6, C_6^5 \\ C_6^2, C_6^4 = C_3, C_3^2 \\ C_6^3 = C_2 \end{cases} \qquad \begin{matrix} 2C_6 \\ 2C_3 \\ C_2 \end{matrix}$$

In short, when two operations such as C_7 and C_7^6 are in the same class, one will be the same as the other only in the reverse direction, so that C_7 and C_7^6 are both called simply C_7, and so on.

(iv) *Improper rotations.* Just as with proper rotations, when two improper rotations fall in the same class it will be because one is really the same as the other except that the rotation is in the opposite sense. Thus S_6 and S_6^5 are both considered S_6's and are so written.

4

Representations of Groups

4.1   Some Properties of Matrices and Vectors

Because the representations of groups are in general made up of matrices, and because certain properties of representations can be advantageously formulated using certain properties of vectors, an account of those aspects of matrix and vector algebra essential to an understanding of the following discussion of representation theory will be given first.

Definition of a Matrix

In the most general sense a matrix is a rectangular array of numbers, or symbols for numbers, which may be combined with other such arrays according to certain rules. When a matrix is written out in full, it has an appearance of which the following is typical.

$$\begin{bmatrix} 4 & -7 & 6 & 0 \\ 2 & 9 & -1 & -8 \\ 2 & 0 & 5 & 4 \\ -8 & 7 & 0 & -3 \\ 6 & 3 & -4 & 7 \end{bmatrix}$$

Note the use of square brackets to enclose the array; this is a conventional way of indicating that the array is to be regarded as a matrix (instead of, perhaps, as a determinant).

In order to discuss matrices in a general way, certain general symbols are commonly used. Thus we may write a symbol for an entire matrix as a script letter, for example, $\mathcal{A}$, which stands for

$$\begin{bmatrix} a_{11} & a_{12} & a_{13} & \cdots & a_{1n} \\ a_{21} & a_{22} & a_{23} & \cdots & a_{2n} \\ a_{31} & a_{32} & a_{33} & \cdots & a_{3n} \\ \cdot & & & & \cdot \\ \cdot & & & & \cdot \\ \cdot & & & & \cdot \\ a_{m1} & a_{m2} & a_{m3} & \cdots & a_{mn} \end{bmatrix}$$

We may also represent the above matrix by $[a_{ij}]$. The vertical sets are called *columns* and the horizontal ones *rows*. The symbol a_{ij} represents that element of the matrix $\mathcal{A}$ which stands in the ith *row* and the jth *column*. The m and n tell us the order of the matrix; m gives the number of rows and n the number of columns. A matrix in which $m = n$ is called a *square matrix* and will be of special importance to us. The set of elements a_{ij} with $i = j$, that is, a_{11}, a_{22}, a_{33}, etc., in a square matrix are called the *diagonal elements* because they lie entirely on the line running diagonally from upper left to lower right corners. A square matrix in which all of the diagonal elements are equal to 1 and all of the other elements are equal to zero is called a *unit matrix* and conventionally represented by the symbol $\mathcal{E}$.

A type of matrix which is of considerable importance is the one-column matrix. To have the convenience of writing such a matrix all on one line, it is sometimes written out horizontally but enclosed in braces, { }, so as to distinguish it from a one-row matrix which would normally be written on one line in square brackets. The chief significance of the column matrix, at least for our purposes, is that it affords a way of representing a vector. Indeed it is sometimes actually called a vector.

Let us consider a vector in ordinary three-dimensional space. We can specify the length and direction of that vector in the following way. We arrange to have one end of the vector lie at the origin of a Cartesian coordinate system. The other end is then at a point which may be specified by its three Cartesian coordinates, x, y, and z. In fact, these three coordinates completely specify the vector itself provided it is understood that one end of the vector is at the origin of the coordinate system. We can then write these three coordinates as a column matrix, in this case one with three rows, $\{x \quad y \quad z\}$, and say that that matrix represents the vector in question.

This notation obviously can easily be generalized for vectors in abstract spaces of any dimension. In p-dimensional space a vector can be specified by a column vector of order $(p \times 1)$. The geometrical significance of the elements of this vector matrix is the same as in real space: they give the orthogonal (Cartesian in a general sense) coordinates of one end of the vector if the other end is at the origin of the coordinate system.

It should be noted that each of the coordinates of the outer terminus of the vector is numerically equal to the length of a projection of that vector on the axis concerned. Thus the set of numbers which define the vector in the sense discussed above may also be thought of as defining it in the sense of specifying its projections on a set of p orthogonal axes in the p-dimensional space in which it exists.

Combination of Matrices

There are certain rules for adding, subtracting and dividing matrices. These are the rules of *matrix algebra*. It should be noted first that two matrices are equal only if they are identical. If $\alpha = \mathfrak{B}$, then $a_{ij} = b_{ij}$ for all i and j.

To add or subtract two matrices, say α and $\mathfrak{B}$, to give a sum or difference $\mathcal{C}$, the three matrices must be of the same dimensions. The elements of $\mathcal{C}$ are given by

$$c_{pq} = a_{pq} \pm b_{pq}$$

A matrix may be multiplied by a scalar number or by another matrix. For multiplication of a matrix $[c_{ij}]$ by a scalar, α, we have

$$\alpha[c_{ij}] = [\alpha c_{ij}] = [c_{ij}\alpha] = [c_{ij}]\alpha$$

Multiplication of a matrix by a matrix is somewhat more complicated. In the first place, it can only be done if the two matrices are *conformable*. This means that if we wish to take the product $\alpha\mathfrak{B} = \mathcal{C}$, the number of columns in α must be equal to the number of rows in $\mathfrak{B}$. If this requirement is satisfied, so that α is of order $(n \times h)$ while $\mathfrak{B}$ is of order $(h \times m)$, then $\mathcal{C}$ will be of order $(n \times m)$. Each element of the product matrix is given by the following expression:

$$c_{il} = \sum_{k} a_{ik}b_{kl} \tag{4.1-1}$$

This sum may be written out explicitly as follows:

$$c_{il} = a_{i1}b_{1l} + a_{i2}b_{2l} + a_{i3}b_{3l} + a_{i4}b_{4l} \ldots a_{ih}b_{hl}$$

where a_{ih} is the last element in the ith row of α and b_{hl} is the last element in the lth column of $\mathfrak{B}$. Perhaps this will be still clearer if we explicitly write out the process of multiplying a 3×2 matrix into a 2×4 matrix.

$$\begin{bmatrix} a_{11} & a_{12} \\ a_{21} & a_{22} \\ a_{31} & a_{32} \end{bmatrix} \begin{bmatrix} b_{11} & b_{12} & b_{13} & b_{14} \\ b_{21} & b_{22} & b_{23} & b_{24} \end{bmatrix} = \begin{bmatrix} c_{11} & c_{12} & c_{13} & c_{14} \\ c_{21} & c_{22} & c_{23} & c_{24} \\ c_{31} & c_{32} & c_{33} & c_{34} \end{bmatrix}$$

$$c_{11} = a_{11}b_{11} + a_{12}b_{21} \qquad c_{21} = a_{21}b_{11} + a_{22}b_{21}$$

$$c_{12} = a_{11}b_{12} + a_{12}b_{22} \qquad c_{22} = a_{21}b_{12} + a_{22}b_{22}$$

$$c_{13} = a_{11}b_{13} + a_{12}b_{23} \qquad c_{23} = a_{21}b_{13} + a_{22}b_{23}$$

$$c_{14} = a_{11}b_{14} + a_{12}b_{24} \qquad c_{24} = a_{21}b_{14} + a_{22}b_{24}$$

$$c_{31} = a_{31}b_{11} + a_{32}b_{21}$$

$$c_{32} = a_{31}b_{12} + a_{32}b_{22}$$

$$c_{33} = a_{31}b_{13} + a_{32}b_{23}$$

$$c_{34} = a_{31}b_{14} + a_{32}b_{24}$$

A mnemonically helpful way of summarizing the process is to say that the ijth element of the product is obtained by taking the ith row of the first matrix into the jth column of the second, with emphasis on the "row-into-column" aspect. From this discussion of the process of multiplication, the conformability requirement is readily obvious. If a row of matrix $\mathcal{C}$ is to be multiplied into a column of $\mathcal{B}$, then clearly the number of elements in that row, which is the number of columns in the matrix $\mathcal{C}$, must be equal to the number of elements in a column of $\mathcal{B}$, which is the number of rows in the matrix $\mathcal{B}$.

It should be noted specifically that matrix multiplication is not in general commutative. If the matrices $\mathcal{C}$ and $\mathcal{B}$ are conformable in the sense $\mathcal{C}\mathcal{B}$, they need not necessarily be conformable in the sense $\mathcal{B}\mathcal{C}$. Indeed they can only be conformable both ways if both are square and of the same order. But even when the conformability requirement is satisfied, commutation is not in general possible. For example, consider the following two products.

$$\begin{bmatrix} 1 & 3 \\ 2 & 2 \end{bmatrix} \begin{bmatrix} 2 & 0 \\ 1 & 1 \end{bmatrix} = \begin{bmatrix} 5 & 3 \\ 6 & 2 \end{bmatrix}$$

$$\begin{bmatrix} 2 & 0 \\ 1 & 1 \end{bmatrix} \begin{bmatrix} 1 & 3 \\ 2 & 2 \end{bmatrix} = \begin{bmatrix} 2 & 6 \\ 3 & 5 \end{bmatrix}$$

Matrix multiplication does, however, always obey the associative law. This can easily be proved by extension of Equation 4.1-1, and working through this proof is a recommended exercise.

The quotient $\mathcal{Q}/\mathcal{B}$ may be equally well regarded as the product $\mathcal{Q}\mathcal{B}^{-1}$, that is, as $\mathcal{Q}$ multiplied into the inverse of $\mathcal{B}$. We thus reduce the question of how to carry out a division to the question of how to find an inverse. In order to find the inverse of a matrix certain properties of the corresponding determinant must be used. The subject is treated in detail in Appendix I for the interested reader; we shall simply state the main conclusions here. The expression for the inverse of a matrix contains the corresponding determinant in the denominator. Since division by zero is not defined, only matrices with nonvanishing determinants can have inverses, and since only square determinants can be nonzero we have the rule that only square matrices can have inverses. Of course, even some square matrices will have determinants equal to zero and hence their inverses will not be defined. A matrix $\mathcal{Q}$ having a determinant $|A|$ which equals zero is said to be *singular*. We shall only be interested in matrices which have inverses, that is, in so-called *nonsingular* matrices. The product of a matrix and its inverse is commutative and equals a unit matrix.

$$\mathcal{Q}\mathcal{Q}^{-1} = \mathcal{Q}^{-1}\mathcal{Q} = \mathcal{E}$$

A Special Case of Matrix Multiplication

A special case of matrix multiplication occurs when we deal with matrices having all nonzero elements in square blocks along the diagonal, such as the following two.

$$\begin{bmatrix} 1 & 0 & 0 & 0 & 0 & 0 \\ 1 & 2 & 0 & 0 & 0 & 0 \\ 0 & 0 & 3 & 0 & 0 & 0 \\ 0 & 0 & 0 & 1 & 3 & 2 \\ 0 & 0 & 0 & 1 & 2 & 2 \\ 0 & 0 & 0 & 4 & 0 & 1 \end{bmatrix} \begin{bmatrix} 4 & 1 & 0 & 0 & 0 & 0 \\ 2 & 3 & 0 & 0 & 0 & 0 \\ 0 & 0 & 1 & 0 & 0 & 0 \\ 0 & 0 & 0 & 0 & 1 & 2 \\ 0 & 0 & 0 & 3 & 0 & 2 \\ 0 & 0 & 0 & 2 & 1 & 1 \end{bmatrix}$$

The product of these two matrices taken in the above order is

$$\begin{bmatrix} 4 & 1 & 0 & 0 & 0 & 0 \\ 8 & 7 & 0 & 0 & 0 & 0 \\ 0 & 0 & 3 & 0 & 0 & 0 \\ 0 & 0 & 0 & 13 & 3 & 10 \\ 0 & 0 & 0 & 10 & 3 & 8 \\ 0 & 0 & 0 & 2 & 5 & 9 \end{bmatrix}$$

The most conspicuous feature of this product matrix is that it is blocked out in exactly the same way as are its factors. It is not difficult to see that this sort of result must always be obtained. Moreover, it should also easily be seen that the elements of a given block in the product matrix are determined only by the elements in the corresponding blocks in the factors. Thus, when two matrices which are blocked out in the same way are to be multiplied, the corresponding blocks in each may be considered independently of the remaining blocks in each. Specifically, in the above case,

$$\begin{bmatrix} 1 & 0 \\ 1 & 2 \end{bmatrix} \begin{bmatrix} 4 & 1 \\ 2 & 3 \end{bmatrix} = \begin{bmatrix} 4 & 1 \\ 8 & 7 \end{bmatrix}$$

$$[3] \times [1] = [3]$$

$$\begin{bmatrix} 1 & 3 & 2 \\ 1 & 2 & 2 \\ 4 & 0 & 1 \end{bmatrix} \begin{bmatrix} 0 & 1 & 2 \\ 3 & 0 & 2 \\ 2 & 1 & 1 \end{bmatrix} = \begin{bmatrix} 13 & 3 & 10 \\ 10 & 3 & 8 \\ 2 & 5 & 9 \end{bmatrix}$$

We shall have use for this property of blocked-out matrices presently.

Characters of Conjugate Matrices

An important property of a square matrix is its *character*. This is simply the sum of its diagonal elements, and it is usually given the symbol χ (Greek chi). Thus

$$\chi_{\mathfrak{A}} = \sum_j a_{jj}$$

We shall now prove two important theorems concerning the behavior of characters.

If $\mathfrak{C} = \mathfrak{A}\mathfrak{B}$ *and* $\mathfrak{D} = \mathfrak{B}\mathfrak{A}$, *the characters of* $\mathfrak{C}$ *and* $\mathfrak{D}$ *are equal.*

PROOF:

$$\chi_{\mathfrak{C}} = \sum_j c_{jj} = \sum_j \sum_k a_{jk} b_{kj}$$

$$\chi_{\mathfrak{D}} = \sum_k d_{kk} = \sum_k \sum_j b_{kj} a_{jk}$$

$$= \sum_j \sum_k b_{kj} a_{jk} = \sum_j \sum_k a_{jk} b_{kj} = \chi_{\mathfrak{C}}$$

Conjugate matrices have identical characters. Conjugate matrices are related by a similarity transformation in the same way as are conjugate elements of a group. Thus, if matrices $\mathcal{R}$ and $\mathcal{P}$ are conjugate, there is some other matrix, $\mathcal{Q}$, such that

$$\mathcal{R} = \mathcal{Q}^{-1}\mathcal{P}\mathcal{Q}$$

Since the associative law holds for matrix multiplication, the theorem is proved in the following way.

PROOF.

$$\chi \text{ of } \mathcal{R} = \chi \text{ of } \mathcal{Q}^{-1}\mathcal{P}\mathcal{Q} = \chi \text{ of } (\mathcal{Q}^{-1}\mathcal{P})\mathcal{Q}$$
$$= \chi \text{ of } \mathcal{Q}(\mathcal{Q}^{-1}\mathcal{P}) = \chi \text{ of } (\mathcal{Q}\mathcal{Q}^{-1})\mathcal{P}$$
$$= \chi \text{ of } \mathcal{P}$$

Matrix Notation for Geometric Transformations

One of the most important uses of matrices is in dealing with transformations. Suppose we have a point in the xy plane with coordinates x_1 and y_1. This point defines a vector, r_1, between itself and the origin. Now suppose this vector is rotated through an angle θ so that a new vector, r_2, is produced with a terminus at the point x_2 and y_2. We now inquire about how the final coordinates x_2 and y_2 are related to the original coordinates x_1 and y_1 and the angle θ. This relationship is not difficult to work out. When the x component of r_1, x_1, is rotated by θ it becomes a vector x' which has an x component of $x_1 \cos \theta$ and a y component of $x_1 \sin \theta$.

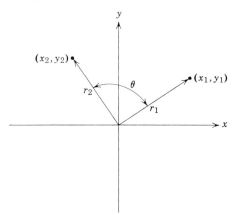

Similarly, the y component of r_1, y_1, upon rotation by θ becomes a new vector y' which has an x component of $-y_1 \sin \theta$ and a y component of y_1 $\cos \theta$. Now, x_2 and y_2, the components of r_2, must be equal to the sums of the x and y components of x' and y', so we write

$$x_2 = x_1 \cos \theta - y_1 \sin \theta$$

$$y_2 = x_1 \sin \theta + y_1 \cos \theta$$

(4.1-2)

The transformation expressed by Equations 4.1-2 can be written in matrix notation in the following way.

$$\begin{bmatrix} \cos \theta & -\sin \theta \\ \sin \theta & \cos \theta \end{bmatrix} \begin{bmatrix} x_1 \\ y_1 \end{bmatrix} = \begin{bmatrix} x_2 \\ y_2 \end{bmatrix}$$

(4.1-3)

We have written the vectors r_1 and r_2 as column matrices and the array of coefficients of x_1 and y_1 in Equations 4.1-2 as a matrix. By using the law for matrix multiplication, it is seen that 4.1-3 is equivalent to 4.1-2.

Suppose we now consider what happens to the vector r_1 if we reflect it through the xz plane. A new vector r_3 with components x_3 and y_3 will be produced, and it is obvious by inspection that

$$x_3 = x_1 + 0y_1$$

$$y_3 = 0x_1 - y_1$$

(4.1-4)

and Equations 4.1-4 can be expressed in matrix notation as follows:

$$\begin{bmatrix} 1 & 0 \\ 0 & -1 \end{bmatrix} \begin{bmatrix} x_1 \\ y_1 \end{bmatrix} = \begin{bmatrix} x_3 \\ y_3 \end{bmatrix}$$

(4.1-5)

Now let us suppose that we take the vector r_2 and reflect it across the xz plane. This gives us a new vector r_4 whose components are

$$x_4 = x_1 \cos \theta - y_1 \sin \theta$$

$$y_4 = -x_1 \sin \theta - y_1 \cos \theta$$

(4.1-6)

which may be expressed in matrix notation as

$$\begin{bmatrix} \cos \theta & -\sin \theta \\ -\sin \theta & -\cos \theta \end{bmatrix} \begin{bmatrix} x_1 \\ y_1 \end{bmatrix} = \begin{bmatrix} x_4 \\ y_4 \end{bmatrix}$$

(4.1-7)

Thus the square matrix in Equation 4.1-7 represents the total effect on r_1 of rotating by θ and then reflecting in the xz plane. The matrix in Equation 4.1-3 represents the rotation alone; the matrix in Equation 4.1-5 represents the effect of reflection through the xz plane alone. Let us now multiply the matrices from Equations 4.1-3 and 4.1-5 together, in the order shown.

$$\begin{bmatrix} 1 & 0 \\ 0 & -1 \end{bmatrix} \begin{bmatrix} \cos \theta & -\sin \theta \\ \sin \theta & \cos \theta \end{bmatrix} = \begin{bmatrix} \cos \theta & -\sin \theta \\ -\sin \theta & -\cos \theta \end{bmatrix}$$

(4.1-8)

We see that their product is just that matrix which represents the combined effect of successively applying first rotation by θ and then reflection through the xz plane.

The specific instance treated above illustrates the general conclusion that a series of matrices, each representing one of a series of geometrical transformations, when multiplied together give a matrix which represents a single geometrical operation having the same effect as the successive application of all those operations in the series. Symbolically, if a set of geometrical operations, $A, B, C, D \ldots$, applied successively give the same net effect as a single operation X, that is,

$$\cdots DCBA = X$$

then the products of the matrices representing these operations will multiply together in the same order to give a matrix corresponding to X, viz.,

$$\cdots \mathcal{DCBA} = \mathcal{X}$$

Vectors and Their Scalar Products. For future use, a few further properties of vectors will be developed here. As noted earlier, a vector in p-dimensional space may be defined by the lengths of its projections on each of a set of p orthogonal axes in that space. For instance, a vector, **A**, in real space, with the coordinates x_1, y_1, z_1 for its outer terminus, has a projection, A_x, of length x_1 on the x axis, a projection A_y, of length y_1 on the y axis, and a projection A_z, of length z_1 on the z axis.

One type of product of two vectors is called the scalar product because it is merely a number, a scalar. This may be defined as the product of the lengths of the two vectors times the cosine of the angle between them. The scalar product is indicated by placing a dot between the symbols. We denote a vector as **A**, its length by A and its projections on coordinate axes by, for example, A_x, A_y . . . .

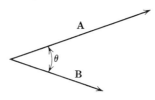

$$\mathbf{A} \cdot \mathbf{B} = AB \cos \theta$$

If two vectors **C** and **D** are orthogonal, their scalar or "dot" product will be zero, for

$$\mathbf{C} \cdot \mathbf{D} = CD \cos 90° = 0$$

If they are parallel or colinear, their scalar product is equal to the product of their lengths since $\cos 0 = 1$.

There is an equivalent but more generally useful way of writing the scalar product of two vectors. Suppose we have two vectors **A** and **B**, both lying in the xy plane. Let **A** make an angle ϕ to the x axis and **B** a greater angle ψ. The angle between **A** and **B**, θ, is then $(\psi - \phi)$. Thus

$$\mathbf{A} \cdot \mathbf{B} = AB \cos \theta = AB \cos (\psi - \phi) \tag{4.1-9}$$

Now the components of **A**, that is, its projections on the x and y axes, are

$$A_x = A \cos \phi$$
$$A_y = A \sin \phi \tag{4.1-10}$$

and similarly for **B**

$$B_x = B \cos \psi$$
$$B_y = B \sin \psi \tag{4.1-11}$$

Using a trigonometric identity, Equation 4.1-9 can be written

$$\mathbf{A} \cdot \mathbf{B} = AB(\cos \phi \cos \psi + \sin \phi \sin \psi)$$

which may be rearranged to

$$\mathbf{A} \cdot \mathbf{B} = A \cos \phi \, B \cos \psi + A \sin \phi \, B \sin \psi$$

On substituting the relations 4.1-10 and 4.1-11 we get

$$\mathbf{A} \cdot \mathbf{B} = A_x B_x + A_y B_y$$

Thus the scalar product of vectors **A** and **B** in two-dimensional space is equal to the sum of the products of their components with no cross terms (for example, $A_x B_y$). This result is actually only a special case of the general rule in p-dimensional space:

$$\mathbf{A} \cdot \mathbf{B} = \sum_{i=1}^{p} A_i B_i \tag{4.1-12}$$

We can now restate the rule for orthogonality of two vectors in p-dimensional space as requiring that

$$\sum_{i=1}^{p} A_i B_i = 0 \tag{4.1-13}$$

and the square of the length of a vector may be written

$$A^2 = \sum_{i=1}^{p} A_i^2 \tag{4.1-14}$$

4.2   Representations of Groups

A representation of a group of the type we shall be interested in may be defined as a set of matrices, each corresponding to a single operation in the group, which can be combined among themselves in a manner parallel to the way the group elements—in this case, the symmetry operations—combine. Thus, if two symmetry operations in a symmetry group, say C_2 and σ, combine to give a product C_2', then the matrices corresponding to C_2 and σ must multiply together to give the matrix corresponding to C_2'. But we have already seen that if the matrices corresponding to each of the operations have been correctly written down, they will naturally have this property.

Let us, for example, work out a representation of the group C_{2v}. This group consists of the operations E, C_2, σ_v, σ_v'. Let us say that the C_2 axis coincides with the z axis of a Cartesian coordinate system, and let σ_v be the xz plane and σ_v' be the yz plane. The matrices representing the transformations effected on a general point can easily be seen to be as follows:

$$E:\begin{bmatrix} 1 & 0 & 0 \\ 0 & 1 & 0 \\ 0 & 0 & 1 \end{bmatrix} \qquad C_2:\begin{bmatrix} -1 & 0 & 0 \\ 0 & -1 & 0 \\ 0 & 0 & 1 \end{bmatrix}$$

$$\sigma_v:\begin{bmatrix} 1 & 0 & 0 \\ 0 & -1 & 0 \\ 0 & 0 & 1 \end{bmatrix} \qquad \sigma_v':\begin{bmatrix} -1 & 0 & 0 \\ 0 & 1 & 0 \\ 0 & 0 & 1 \end{bmatrix}$$

We have then, for example,

$$\begin{bmatrix} -1 & 0 & 0 \\ 0 & -1 & 0 \\ 0 & 0 & 1 \end{bmatrix}\begin{bmatrix} x \\ y \\ z \end{bmatrix} = \begin{bmatrix} -x \\ -y \\ z \end{bmatrix}$$

which is entirely equivalent to saying that rotation by $2\pi/2$ about z changes the signs of x and y coordinates but leaves z coordinates unaltered. Now the group multiplication table is as follows:

	E	C_2	σ_v	σ_v'
E	E	C_2	σ_v	σ_v'
C_2	C_2	E	σ_v'	σ_v
σ_v	σ_v	σ_v'	E	C_2
σ_v'	σ_v'	σ_v	C_2	E

It can easily be shown that the matrices multiply together in the same fashion. For example:

$$\sigma_v C_2 = \sigma_v'$$

and

$$\begin{bmatrix} 1 & 0 & 0 \\ 0 & -1 & 0 \\ 0 & 0 & 1 \end{bmatrix} \begin{bmatrix} -1 & 0 & 0 \\ 0 & -1 & 0 \\ 0 & 0 & 1 \end{bmatrix} = \begin{bmatrix} -1 & 0 & 0 \\ 0 & 1 & 0 \\ 0 & 0 & 1 \end{bmatrix}$$

Again, each element in the group C_{2v} is its own inverse, so this must be true of the matrices. This is easily shown to be so; for example:

$$\begin{bmatrix} 1 & 0 & 0 \\ 0 & -1 & 0 \\ 0 & 0 & 1 \end{bmatrix} \begin{bmatrix} 1 & 0 & 0 \\ 0 & -1 & 0 \\ 0 & 0 & 1 \end{bmatrix} = \begin{bmatrix} 1 & 0 & 0 \\ 0 & 1 & 0 \\ 0 & 0 & 1 \end{bmatrix}$$

We have now, by one procedure, namely by considering the transformations of a general point, generated a set of matrices which form a representation for the group C_{2v}. We might next ask, how many representations can be found for this group. The answer is: a very large number, limited only by our ingenuity in devising ways to generate them. There are first some very simple ones, obtained by assigning 1 or -1 to each operation, viz.,

E	C_2	σ_v	σ_v'
1	1	1	1
1	-1	1	-1
1	-1	-1	1
1	1	-1	-1

Then there are many of high order. For example, if we were to assign three small unit vectors directed along x, y, and z axes to each of the atoms in H_2O and write down matrices representing the changes and interchanges of these upon applying the operations, a set of four 9×9 matrices constituting a representation of the group would be obtained. Using CH_2Cl_2 in the same way, a representation consisting of 15×15 matrices could be obtained. However, for any group, only a limited number of representations are of fundamental significance, and we shall now discuss the origin and properties of these.

Suppose we have a set of matrices, $\mathcal{E}$, $\mathcal{A}$, $\mathcal{B}$, $\mathcal{C}$ ... which form a representation of a group. If we make the same similarity transformation on each matrix, we obtain a new set of matrices, viz.,

$$\mathcal{E}' = \mathcal{Q}^{-1}\mathcal{E}\mathcal{Q}$$

$$\mathcal{A}' = \mathcal{Q}^{-1}\mathcal{A}\mathcal{Q}$$

$$\mathcal{B}' = \mathcal{Q}^{-1}\mathcal{B}\mathcal{Q}$$

$$\cdots$$

It is easy to prove that the new set of matrices is also a representation of the group. Suppose

$$\mathcal{A}\mathcal{B} = \mathcal{D}$$

then

$$\mathcal{A}'\mathcal{B}' = (\mathcal{Q}^{-1}\mathcal{A}\mathcal{Q})(\mathcal{Q}^{-1}\mathcal{B}\mathcal{Q}) = \mathcal{Q}^{-1}\mathcal{A}(\mathcal{Q}\mathcal{Q}^{-1})\mathcal{B}\mathcal{Q}$$

$$= \mathcal{Q}^{-1}(\mathcal{A}\mathcal{B})\mathcal{Q} = \mathcal{Q}^{-1}\mathcal{D}\mathcal{Q} = \mathcal{D}'$$

Clearly all products in the set of matrices $\mathcal{E}'$, $\mathcal{A}'$, $\mathcal{B}'$ ... will run parallel to those in the representation $\mathcal{E}$, $\mathcal{A}$, $\mathcal{B}$ ... so the primed set also constitutes a representation.

Let us now suppose that when the matrix $\mathcal{A}$ is transformed to $\mathcal{A}'$ using $\mathcal{Q}$ or some other matrix, we find $\mathcal{A}'$ to be a blocked out matrix, namely

$$\mathcal{A}' = \mathcal{Q}^{-1}\mathcal{A}\mathcal{Q} = \begin{bmatrix} \mathcal{A}'_1 & & & & \\ & \mathcal{A}'_2 & & & \\ & & \mathcal{A}'_3 & & \\ & & & \mathcal{A}'_4 & \\ & & & & \mathcal{A}'_5 \end{bmatrix}$$

for example. If now each of the matrices $\mathcal{A}'$, $\mathcal{B}'$, $\mathcal{C}'$, and so forth, are all blocked out in the same way, then, as shown earlier (page 54), corresponding blocks of each matrix can be multiplied together separately. Thus we can write such equations as:

$$\mathcal{A}'_1\mathcal{B}'_1 = \mathcal{D}'_1$$

$$\mathcal{A}'_2\mathcal{B}'_2 = \mathcal{D}'_2$$

$$\mathcal{A}'_4\mathcal{B}'_4 = \mathcal{D}'_4$$

$$\cdots$$

Therefore the various sets of matrices

$$\mathcal{E}'_1, \ \mathcal{A}'_1, \ \mathcal{B}'_1, \ \mathcal{C}'_1, \ \mathcal{D}'_1 \ \ldots$$

$$\mathcal{E}'_2, \ \mathcal{A}'_2, \ \mathcal{B}'_2, \ \mathcal{C}'_2, \ \mathcal{D}'_2 \ \ldots$$

$$\ldots$$

are in themselves representations of the group. We then call the set of matrices, $\mathcal{E}$, $\mathcal{A}$, $\mathcal{B}$, $\mathcal{C}$, $\mathcal{D}$ ... , a *reducible* representation, because it is possible, using some matrix, $\mathcal{Q}$ in this case, to transform each matrix in the set into a new one so that the new ones can all be taken apart in the same way to give two or more representations of smaller dimension. (The dimension of a representation is the order of the square matrices which constitute it.) If it is not possible to find a similarity transformation which will reduce all of the matrices of a given representation in the above manner, that representation is said to be *irreducible*. It is the irreducible representations of a group which are of fundamental importance, and their main properties will now be described.

4.3   Properties of the Characters of Representations

All of the properties of group representations and their characters which are important in dealing with problems in valence theory and molecular dynamics can be derived from one basic theorem concerning the elements of the matrices which constitute the irreducible representations of a group. In order to state this theorem, which we shall do without proof,[*] some notation must be introduced. The order of a group will, as before, be denoted by h. The dimension of the ith representation, which is the order of each of the matrices which constitute it, will be denoted l_i. The various operations in the group will be given the generic symbol R. Finally, the element in the mth row and nth column of the matrix corresponding to an operation R in the ith irreducible representation will be denoted $\Gamma_i(R)_{mn}$. The theorem may then be stated as follows:

$$\sum_R \Gamma_i(R)_{mn}\Gamma_j(R)_{m'n'} = \frac{h}{\sqrt{l_i l_j}} \, \delta_{ij}\delta_{mm'}\delta_{nn'} \qquad (4.3\text{-}1)$$

This means that in the set of matrices constituting any one irreducible representation, any set of corresponding matrix elements, one from each matrix, behave as the components of a vector in h-dimensional

[*] The proof, which is not trivial, may be found in other places, e.g., in *Quantum Chemistry*, by H. Eyring, J. Walter and G. E. Kimball, Wiley, New York, 1944, p. 371.

space such that all these vectors are mutually orthogonal, and each is normalized so that the square of its length equals h/l_i. This interpretation of Equation 4.3-1 will perhaps be more obvious if we, as it were, take 4.3-1 apart into three simpler equations, each of which is contained within it. These are

$$\sum_R \Gamma_i(R)_{mn}\Gamma_j(R)_{mn} = 0 \text{ if } i \neq j \tag{4.3-2}$$

$$\sum_R \Gamma_i(R)_{mn}\Gamma_i(R)_{m'n'} = 0 \text{ if } m \neq m' \text{ and/or } n \neq n' \tag{4.3-3}$$

$$\sum_R \Gamma_i(R)_{mn}\Gamma_i(R)_{mn} = h/l_i \tag{4.3-4}$$

Thus, if the vectors differ by being chosen from matrices of different representations, they are orthogonal (4.3-2). If they are chosen from the same representation but from different sets of elements in the matrices of this representation, they are orthogonal (4.3-3). Finally, 4.3-4 expresses the fact that the square of the length of any such vector equals h/l_i.

We shall now discuss five important rules about irreducible representations and their characters.

(1) *The sum of the squares of the dimensions of the irreducible representations of a group is equal to the order of the group, that is,*

$$\Sigma l_i^2 = l_1^2 + l_2^2 + l_3^2 \cdots = h \tag{4.3-5}$$

PROOF. A complete proof is quite lengthy and will not be given. It is, however, easy to show the $\Sigma l_i^2 \leqslant h$. In a matrix of order l there are l^2 elements. Thus each irreducible representation, Γ_i, will provide l_i^2 h-dimensional vectors. The basic theorem requires this set of $l_1^2 + l_2^2 + l_3^2 \cdots$ vectors to be mutually orthogonal. Since there can be no more than h orthogonal h-dimensional vectors, the sum $l_1^2 + l_2^2 + l_3^2 \cdots$ may not exceed h. Since $\chi_i(E)$, the character of the representation of E in the ith irreducible representation, is equal to the order of the representation, we can also write this rule as

$$\sum_i [\chi_i(E)]^2 = h \tag{4.3-5a}$$

(2) *The sum of the squares of the characters in any irreducible representation equals h, that is,*

$$\sum_R [\chi_i(R)]^2 = h \tag{4.3-6}$$

PROOF. From 4.3-1 we may write

$$\sum_R \Gamma_i(R)_{mm}\Gamma_i(R)_{m'm'} = \frac{h}{l_i} \delta_{mm'}$$

Summing the left side over m and m' we obtain

$$\sum_{m'} \sum_{m} \sum_{R} \Gamma_i(R)_{mm} \Gamma_i(R)_{m'm'} = \sum_{R} [(\sum_{m} \Gamma_i(R)_{mm})(\sum_{m'} \Gamma_i(R)_{m'm'})]$$

$$= \sum_{R} \chi_i(R)\chi_i(R)$$

$$= \sum_{R} [\chi_i(R)]^2$$

while summing the right side over m and m' we obtain

$$\frac{h}{l_i} \sum_{m'} \sum_{m} \delta_{mm'} = \frac{h}{l_i} l_i = h$$

thus proving the equality 4.3-6.

(3) *The vectors whose components are the characters of two different irreducible representations are orthogonal, that is,*

$$\sum_{R} \chi_i(R)\chi_j(R) = 0 \text{ when } i \neq j \tag{4.3-7}$$

PROOF. Setting $m = n$ in 4.3-2, we get

$$\sum_{R} \Gamma_i(R)_{mm} \Gamma_j(R)_{mm} = 0 \text{ if } i \neq j$$

$$\sum_{R} \chi_i(R)\chi_j(R) = \sum_{R} (\sum_{m} \Gamma_i(R)_{mm} \sum_{m} \Gamma_j(R)_{mm})$$

$$= \sum_{m} (\sum_{R} \Gamma_i(R)_{mm} \Gamma_j(R)_{mm}) = 0$$

(4) *In a given representation (reducible or irreducible) the characters of all matrices belonging to operations in the same class are identical.*
PROOF. Since all elements in the same class are conjugate to one another, all matrices corresponding to elements in the same class in any representation must be conjugate. But we have shown on page 55 that conjugate matrices have identical characters.

(5) *The number of irreducible representations of a group is equal to the number of classes in the group.*
PROOF. As for rule 1, a complete proof will not be given; we can, however, easily prove that the number of classes sets an upper limit on the number of irreducible representations. We can combine Equations 4.3-6 and 4.3-7 into one equation, viz.,

$$\sum_{R} \chi_i(R)\chi_j(R) = h\delta_{ij} \tag{4.3-8}$$

If now we denote the number of elements in the mth class by g_m, the number in the nth class by g_n, and so on, and if there are k classes altogether, 4.3-8 can be rewritten:

$$\sum_{p=1}^{k} \chi_i(R_p)\chi_j(R_p)g_p = h\delta_{ij} \qquad (4.3\text{-}9)$$

R_p refers to any one of the operations in the pth class. Equation 4.3-9 implies that the k quantities, $\chi_l(R_p)$ in each representation Γ_l behave like the components of a k-dimensional vector and that these k vectors are mutually orthogonal. Since only k k-dimensional vectors *can* be mutually orthogonal, there can be no more than k irreducible representations in a group which has k classes.

Let us now consider the irreducible representations of several typical groups to see how these rules apply. The group C_{2v} consists of four elements, and each is in a separate class. Hence (rule 5) there are four irreducible representations for this group. But it is also required (rule 1) that the sum of the squares of the dimensions of these representations equal h. Thus we are looking for a set of four positive integers, l_1, l_2, l_3, and l_4 which satisfy the relation

$$l_1{}^2 + l_2{}^2 + l_3{}^2 + l_4{}^2 = 4$$

Clearly the only solution is

$$l_1 = l_2 = l_3 = l_4 = 1$$

Thus the group C_{2v} has four one-dimensional irreducible representations.

We can actually work out the characters of these four irreducible representations—which are in this case the representations themselves because the dimensions are 1—on the basis of the vector properties of the representations and the rules derived above. One suitable vector in 4-space which has a component of 1 corresponding to E will obviously be

for

	E	C_2	σ_v	σ_v'
Γ_1	1	1	1	1

$$\sum_R [\chi_1(R)]^2 = 1^2 + 1^2 + 1^2 + 1^2 = 4$$

thus satisfying rule 2. Now all other representations will have to be such that

$$\sum_R [\chi_i(R)]^2 = 4$$

which can only be true if each $\chi_i(R) = \pm 1$. Moreover, in order for each of the other representations to be orthogonal to Γ_1 (rule 3 and Equation 4.3-7), there will have to be two $+1$'s and two -1's. Thus

$$(1)(-1) + (1)(-1) + (1)(1) + (1)(1) = 0$$

Thus we will have

	E	C_2	σ_v	σ_v'
Γ_1	1	1	1	1
Γ_2	1	-1	-1	1
Γ_3	1	-1	1	-1
Γ_4	1	1	-1	-1

All of these are also orthogonal to one another. For example, taking Γ_2 and Γ_4, we have

$$(1)(1) + (-1)(1) + (-1)(-1) + (1)(-1) = 0$$

and so on. These are then the four irreducible representations of the group C_{2v}.

As another example of the working of the rules, let us consider the group C_{3v}. This consists of the following elements, listed by classes:

$$E \quad 2C_3 \quad 3\sigma_v$$

We therefore know at once that there are three irreducible representations. If we denote their dimensions by l_1, l_2, and l_3, we have (rule 1)

$$l_1{}^2 + l_2{}^2 + l_3{}^2 = h = 6$$

The only values of the l_i which will satisfy this requirement are 1, 1, and 2. Now once again, and always in any group, there will be a one-dimensional representation whose characters are all equal to 1. Thus we have

	E	$2C_3$	$3\sigma_v$
Γ_1	1	1	1

Note that (from Equation 4.3-9)

$$1^2 + 2(1)^2 + 3(1)^2 = 6$$

We now look for a second vector in 6-space all of whose components are equal to ± 1 which is orthogonal to Γ_1. The components of such a vector must consist of three $+1$'s and three -1's. Since $\chi(E)$ must always be positive and since all elements in the same class must have representations with the same character, the only possibility here is:

	E	$2C_3$	$3\sigma_v$
Γ_1	1	1	1
Γ_2	1	1	-1

Now our third representation will be of dimension 2. Hence $\chi_3(E) = 2$. In order to find out the values of $\chi_3(C_3)$ and $\chi_3(\sigma_v)$ we make use of the orthogonality relationships (rule 3, Equation 4.3-7):

$$\sum_R \chi_1(R)\chi_3(R) = [1][2] + 2[1][\chi_3(C_3)] + 3[1][\chi_3(\sigma_v)] = 0$$

$$\sum_R \chi_2(R)\chi_3(R) = [1][2] + 2[1][\chi_3(C_3)] + 3[-1][\chi_3(\sigma_v)] = 0$$

Solving these we get

$$2\chi_3(C_3) + 3\chi_3(\sigma_v) = -2$$

$$-[2\chi_3(C_3) - 3\chi_3(\sigma_v) = -2]$$

$$\overline{\qquad\qquad\qquad 6\chi_3(\sigma_v) = 0}$$

$$\chi_3(\sigma_v) = 0$$

and

$$2\chi_3(C_3) + 3(0) = -2$$

$$\chi_3(C_3) = -1$$

Thus the complete set of characters of the irreducible representations is

	E	$2C_3$	$3\sigma_v$
Γ_1	1	1	1
Γ_2	1	1	-1
Γ_3	2	-1	0

We may note that there is still a check on the correctness of Γ_3: the square of the length of the vector it defines should be equal to h (rule 2), and we see that this is so:

$$2^2 + 2(-1)^2 + 3(0)^2 = 6$$

We will conclude this section by deriving a relationship between any reducible representation of a group and the irreducible representations of that group. In terms of practical application of group theory to molecular problems, this relationship is of pivotal importance. We know already that for any reducible representation, it is possible to find some similarity transformation which will reduce each matrix to one consisting of blocks along the diagonal, each of which belongs to an irreducible representation of the group. We also know that the character of a matrix is not changed by any similarity transformation. Thus we can write

$$\chi(R) = \sum_j a_j \chi_j(R) \tag{4.3-10}$$

where $\chi(R)$ is the character of the matrix corresponding to operation R in the reducible representation, and a_j represents the number of times the block constituting the jth irreducible representation will appear along the diagonal when the reducible representation is completely reduced by the necessary similarity transformation. Now we do not need to bother about the difficult question of how to find out what matrix is required to reduce completely the reducible representation in order to find the values of the a_j. We can obtain the required relationship by working only with the characters of all representations in the following way. We multiply each side of 4.3-10 by $\chi_i(R)$ and then sum each side over all operations, viz.,

$$\sum_R \chi(R)\chi_i(R) = \sum_R \sum_j a_j \chi_j(R)\chi_i(R)$$

$$= \sum_j \sum_R a_j \chi_j(R)\chi_i(R)$$

Now for each of the terms in the sum over j, we have from Equation 4.3-8

$$\sum_R a_j \chi_j(R)\chi_i(R) = a_j \sum_R \chi_j(R)\chi_i(R) = a_j h \delta_{ij}$$

since the sets of characters $\chi_j(R)$ and $\chi_i(R)$ define orthogonal vectors, the squares of whose lengths equal h. Thus, in summing over all j, only that sum over R in which $i = j$ can survive, and in that case we have

$$\sum_R \chi(R)\chi_i(R) = ha_i$$

which we rearrange to read

$$a_i = \frac{1}{h} \sum_R \chi(R)\chi_i(R) \tag{4.3-11}$$

Thus we can readily determine the number of times the ith irreducible representation occurs in a reducible representation knowing only the characters of each representation.

Let us take an example. For the group C_{3v} we give below the characters of the irreducible representations Γ_1, Γ_2, and Γ_3, and the characters for two reducible representations, Γ_a and Γ_b.

C_{3v}	E	$2C_3$	$3\sigma_v$
Γ_1	1	1	1
Γ_2	1	1	-1
Γ_3	2	-1	0
Γ_a	5	2	-1
Γ_b	7	1	-3

Using 4.3-11, we find for Γ_a

$$a_1 = \tfrac{1}{6}[1(1)(5) + 2(1)(2) + 3(1)(-1)] = 1$$

$$a_2 = \tfrac{1}{6}[1(1)(5) + 2(1)(2) + 3(-1)(-1)] = 2$$

$$a_3 = \tfrac{1}{6}[1(2)(5) + 2(-1)(2) + 3(0)(-1)] = 1$$

and for Γ_b

$$a_1 = \tfrac{1}{6}[1(1)(7) + 2(1)(1) + 3(1)(-3)] = 0$$

$$a_2 = \tfrac{1}{6}[1(1)(7) + 2(1)(1) + 3(-1)(-3)] = 3$$

$$a_3 = \tfrac{1}{6}[1(2)(7) + 2(-1)(1) + 3(0)(-3)] = 2$$

The numbers in italics are the numbers of elements in each class. The results obtained above will be found to satisfy 4.3-10, as of course they must. For Γ_a we have:

	E	$2C_3$	$3\sigma_v$
Γ_1	1	1	1
Γ_2	1	1	-1
Γ_2	1	1	-1
Γ_3	2	-1	0
Γ_a	5	2	-1

and for Γ_b

	E	$2C_3$	$3\sigma_v$
Γ_2	1	1	-1
Γ_2	1	1	-1
Γ_2	1	1	-1
Γ_3	2	-1	0
Γ_3	2	-1	0
Γ_b	7	1	-3

Indeed, in simple cases, a reducible representation may often be reduced very quickly by using Equation 4.3-10, that is, by looking for those rows of characters which add up to the correct total in each column. For more complicated cases, it is usually best to use Equation 4.3-11; however, Equation 4.3-10 then provides a valuable check on the results.

4.4 Character Tables

(i) Throughout all of our applications of group theory and molecular symmetry we will utilize devices called character tables. A set of these for all symmetry groups likely to be encountered among real molecules is given in Appendix II.* In this section we shall explain the meaning and indicate the source of the information given in these tables. For this purpose we shall examine in detail a representative character table, one for the group C_{3v}, reproduced below. The four † main areas of the table have been assigned Roman numerals for reference in the following discussion.

C_{3v}	E	$2C_3$	$3\sigma_v$		
A_1	1	1	1	z	$x^2 + y^2, z^2$
A_2	1	1	-1	R_z	
E	2	-1	0	$(x, y)(R_x, R_y)$	$(x^2 - y^2, xy)(xz, yz)$
II		I		III	IV

In the top row are these entries: In the upper left corner is the Schoenflies symbol for the group. Then, along the top row of the main body of the table, are listed the elements of the group, gathered into classes; the notation is the kind explained in Section 3.11.

Area I. In area I of the table are the characters of the irreducible representations of the group. These have been fully discussed in preceding sections of this chapter and require no additional comment here.

Area II. We have previously designated the ith representation, or its set of characters, by the symbol Γ_i in a fairly arbitrary way. While this practice is still to be found in some places, and is common in older literature, most books and papers—virtually all those by English-speaking authors—use the kind of symbols found in the C_{3v} table above and all those in Appendix II. This nomenclature was proposed by R. S. Mulliken and the symbols are normally called Mulliken symbols. Their meanings are as follows:

* Appendix IIA will be found as a separate booklet in a pocket in the back of this book.
† In some books areas III and IV are combined.

(1) All one-dimensional representations are designated either A or B; two-dimensional representations are designated E; three-dimensional species are designated T (or sometimes F).

(2) One-dimensional representations which are symmetric with respect to rotation by $2\pi/n$ about the principal C_n axis (symmetric meaning: $\chi(C_n) = 1$) are designated A while those antisymmetric in this respect $(\chi(C_n) = -1)$ are designated B.

(3) Subscripts 1 and 2 are usually attached to A's and B's to designate, respectively, those which are symmetric or antisymmetric with respect to a C_2 perpendicular to the principal axis or, if such a C_2 axis is lacking, to a vertical plane of symmetry.

(4) Primes and double primes are attached to all letters, when appropriate, to indicate those which are, respectively, symmetric and antisymmetric with respect to σ_h.

(5) In groups with a center of inversion, the subscript g (from the German *gerade*, meaning even) is attached to symbols for representations which are symmetric with respect to inversion and the subscript u (from the German *ungerade*, meaning uneven) is used for those which are antisymmetric to inversion.

(6) The use of numerical subscripts for E's and T's also follows certain rules, but these cannot be easily stated precisely without some mathematical development. It will be satisfactory here to regard them as arbitrary labels.

Area III. In area III we will always find six symbols, viz., x, y, z, R_x, R_y, R_z. The first three represent the coordinates x, y, and z, while the R's stand for rotations about the axes specified in the subscripts. We shall now show in an illustrative but by no means thorough way why these symbols are assigned to certain representations in the group C_{3v}, and this should suffice to indicate the basis for the assignments in other groups.

Any set of algebraic functions or vectors may be used as the *basis* for a representation of a group. In order to use them for a basis, we consider them to be the components of a vector and then determine the matrices which show how that vector is transformed by each symmetry operation. The resulting matrices, naturally, constitute a representation of the group. We have previously used the coordinates x, y, and z as a basis for forming a representation of the group C_{2v}. We shall now use them in the same way for the group C_{3v}.

Writing

$$E \begin{bmatrix} x \\ y \\ z \end{bmatrix} = \begin{bmatrix} x' \\ y' \\ z' \end{bmatrix}$$

the new coordinates, x', y', z' are seen to be related to the original co-ordinates x, y, and z as follows:

$$x' = x + 0y + 0z$$

$$y' = 0x + y + 0z$$

$$z' = 0x + 0y + z$$

Similarly, on performing $C_3(z)$, we have

$$x' = (\cos 2\pi/3)x - (\sin 2\pi/3)y + 0z$$

$$y' = (\sin 2\pi/3)x + (\cos 2\pi/3)y + 0z$$

$$z' = \qquad 0x + \qquad\qquad 0y + z$$

On performing $\sigma_v(xz)$ we get

$$x' = x + 0y + 0z$$

$$y' = 0x - y + 0z$$

$$z' = 0x + 0y + z$$

The matrices for these three transformations are then

$$E: \qquad\qquad\qquad C_3: \qquad\qquad\qquad \sigma_v:$$

$$\begin{bmatrix} 1 & 0 & 0 \\ 0 & 1 & 0 \\ 0 & 0 & 1 \end{bmatrix} \quad \begin{bmatrix} \cos 2\pi/3 & -\sin 2\pi/3 & 0 \\ \sin 2\pi/3 & \cos 2\pi/3 & 0 \\ 0 & 0 & 1 \end{bmatrix} \quad \begin{bmatrix} 1 & 0 & 0 \\ 0 & -1 & 0 \\ 0 & 0 & 1 \end{bmatrix}$$

Now the first thing we can observe about these matrices is that they never mix z with x or y. That is, z' is always a function of z only. Hence z by itself forms an independent representation of the group. On the other hand C_3 mixes up x and y to give x' and y', so x and y jointly form a representation. This is equivalent to observing that the three matrices are all blocked out in the same way, namely into the following sub-matrices:

$$E \qquad\qquad\qquad C_3 \qquad\qquad\qquad \sigma_v$$

$$\Gamma_{x,y} \begin{bmatrix} 1 & 0 \\ 0 & 1 \end{bmatrix} \qquad \begin{bmatrix} \cos 2\pi/3 & -\sin 2\pi/3 \\ \sin 2\pi/3 & \cos 2\pi/3 \end{bmatrix} \qquad \begin{bmatrix} 1 & 0 \\ 0 & -1 \end{bmatrix}$$

$$\Gamma_z \qquad 1 \qquad\qquad\qquad\qquad 1 \qquad\qquad\qquad\qquad 1$$

We see that Γ_z is the A_1 irreducible representation. This means that the coordinate z forms a basis for the A_1 representation, or, as we also say, "z transforms as (or according to) A_1." If we examine the characters of $\Gamma_{x,y}$ we find them to be those of the E representation ($2 \cos 2\pi/3 = -1$), so that the coordinates x and y *together* transform as or according to the E representation. It is important to grasp that x and y are inseparable in this respect since the representation for which they form a basis is irreducible.

A rigorous and general treatment of how the transformation properties of the rotations are determined would be an unnecessary digression from this discussion. In simple cases we can get the answer in a semipictorial way by letting a curved arrow about the axis stand for a rotation. Thus such an arrow around the z axis is transformed into itself by E, into itself by C_3, and its direction is reversed by σ_v. Thus it is the basis for a representation with the characters 1, 1, -1, and so we see that R_z transforms as A_2.

Area IV. In this part of the table are listed all of the squares and binary products of coordinates according to their transformation properties. These results are quite easy to work out using the same procedure as that used for x, y, and z, except that the amount of algebra increases considerably.

(ii) It will be seen upon inspection of the character tables in Appendix II that in quite a few groups there are representations which have imaginary or complex characters. We shall therefore give here some discussion of these and of how representations with imaginary characters apply to physical problems in which the coordinates and functions are all real. All of the complex characters are expressed in terms of a quantity ϵ. For a group in which the order of the reference axis is n, the value of ϵ is

$$\epsilon = \exp (2\pi i/n)$$

The utility of this notation becomes evident if we recall an equality from the theory of infinite series. We have

$$\exp (\theta i) = \cos \theta + i \sin \theta$$

Thus we may write our ϵ's as

$$\epsilon_n = \cos \frac{2\pi}{n} + i \sin \frac{2\pi}{n}$$

Then $\epsilon_n{}^m$ takes the form

$$\epsilon_n{}^m = \cos \frac{2\pi m}{n} + i \sin \frac{2\pi m}{n}$$

The manner in which $\epsilon_n{}^m$ can be written for various values of m relative to n can be summarized as follows:

(1) When $m = n$, or $m = 0$

$$\epsilon_n{}^0 = \epsilon_n{}^n = \cos 2\pi + i \sin 2\pi = 1 + 0 = 1$$

(2) When $m = n/2$

$$\epsilon_n^{n/2} = \cos \pi + i \sin \pi = -1 + 0 = -1$$

(3) When $m = n/4$

$$\epsilon_n^{n/4} = \cos \pi/2 + i \sin \pi/2 = 0 + i = i$$

(4) When $m < n/2$

$$\epsilon_n{}^m \text{ is written as } \epsilon_n{}^m$$

(5) When $m > n/2$

$$\epsilon_n{}^m = \exp [n\ 2\pi i/n] \exp [(m - n)2\pi i/n]$$
$$= \exp [(m - n)2\pi i/n] = \exp [-(n - m)2\pi i/n]$$
$$= \epsilon_n^{(n-m)*}$$

and is usually so written, for example, $\epsilon_6{}^5 = \epsilon_6{}^*$, $\epsilon_7{}^4 = \epsilon_7^{3*}$, and so on.

It will be seen that in every case where representations with complex characters occur, they occur in pairs, such that the elements of one are the complex conjugates of the corresponding elements of the other; such pairs are enclosed in braces and the pair is given only one Mulliken symbol, E_i. Each member of such a pair must, for mathematical reasons, be considered as a separate representation. This enables us to satisfy the requirements as to the numbers and dimensions of representations of a group. However, for purposes of applying these to physical problems, we add the corresponding members of each representation. We thus obtain a set of characters for representations of dimension 2, and moreover all characters are now real, for the sum of a complex number and its complex conjugate is always a real number. We can then use these real, two-dimensional representations for the solution of certain physical problems.

Let us take the group C_3 as an example. Its correct character table is, in part,

C_3	E	C_3	$C_3{}^2$	
A	1	1	1	
E	$\left\{\begin{matrix} 1 \\ 1 \end{matrix}\right.$	$\begin{matrix} \epsilon \\ \epsilon^* \end{matrix}$	$\left.\begin{matrix} \epsilon^* \\ \epsilon \end{matrix}\right\}$	$\epsilon = \exp (2\pi i/3)$

and when we combine the two parts of the "E representation" we get

C_3	E	C_3	$C_3{}^2$
A	1	1	1
E	2	$2 \cos 2\pi/3$	$2 \cos 2\pi/3$

To show that the table in this form is serviceable for physical problems, let us work out the transformation properties of the x, y, and z coordinates in the same way as we did above for the group C_{3v}. Here we get the matrices

$$
\overset{E}{\begin{bmatrix} 1 & 0 & 0 \\ 0 & 1 & 0 \\ 0 & 0 & 1 \end{bmatrix}}
\overset{C_3}{\begin{bmatrix} \cos 2\pi/3 & -\sin 2\pi/3 & 0 \\ \sin 2\pi/3 & \cos 2\pi/3 & 0 \\ 0 & 0 & 1 \end{bmatrix}}
\overset{C_3{}^2}{\begin{bmatrix} \cos 4\pi/3 & -\sin 4\pi/3 & 0 \\ \sin 4\pi/3 & \cos 4\pi/3 & 0 \\ 0 & 0 & 1 \end{bmatrix}}
$$

Again we see that these matrices give a reducible representation which can be reduced on inspection to two representations having the following characters:

	E	C_3	$C_3{}^2$
Γ_z	1	1	1
$\Gamma_{x,y}$	2	$2 \cos 2\pi/3$	$2 \cos 2\pi/3$

Thus x and y transform according to E, and z transforms according to A_1, which are the results stated in the complete form of the mathematically correct table (Appendix II).

Group Theory and
Quantum Mechanics

5

5.1 Wave Functions as Bases for Irreducible Representations

It will be appropriate to give first a brief discussion of the wave equation.
It is not necessary that the reader have any very extensive knowledge of
wave mechanics in order to follow the development in this chapter, but
the information given here is essential. The wave equation for any
physical system is

$$\mathcal{H}\Psi = E\Psi \tag{5.1-1}$$

$\mathcal{H}$ is the Hamiltonian operator which indicates that certain operations are
to be carried out on a function written to its right. The wave equation
states that, if the function is an *eigenfunction*, the result of performing the
operations indicated by $\mathcal{H}$ will yield the function itself multiplied by a
constant which is called an *eigenvalue*. Eigenfunctions are conventionally
denoted Ψ, and the eigenvalue, which is the energy of the system, is denoted E. The Hamiltonian operator is obtained by writing down the expression for the classical energy of the system, which is simply the sum of
potential and kinetic energy for systems of interest to us, and then replacing the momentum terms by differential operators according to the
postulates of wave mechanics. We need not concern ourselves with this
construction of the Hamiltonian operator in any detail. The only
property of it which we shall have to use explicitly concerns its symmetry
with respect to the interchange of like particles in the system to which it
applies. The particles in the system will be electrons and atomic nuclei.
If any two or more particles are interchanged by carrying out a symmetry operation on the system, the Hamiltonian must be *unchanged*.
A symmetry operation carries the system into an equivalent configuration and the definition of an equivalent configuration is that it is in-

distinguishable from the original. Clearly then, the energy of the system must be the same before and after carrying out the symmetry operation. Thus we say that any symmetry operation commutes with the Hamiltonian and we can write

$$R\mathcal{3C} = \mathcal{3C}R \qquad (5.1\text{-}2)$$

It has been more or less implied up to this point that for any eigenvalue E_i there is one appropriate eigenfunction Ψ_i. This is often true, but there are also many cases in which several eigenfunctions give the same eigenvalue, for example,

$$\mathcal{3C}\Psi_{i1} = E_i\Psi_{i1}$$

$$\mathcal{3C}\Psi_{i2} = E_i\Psi_{i2}$$

$$\begin{matrix} \cdot & & \cdot \\ \cdot & & \cdot \\ \cdot & & \cdot \end{matrix} \qquad (5.1\text{-}3)$$

$$\mathcal{3C}\Psi_{ik} = E_i\Psi_{ik}$$

In such cases we say that the eigenvalue is *degenerate,* and in the particular case given above we would say that the energy E_i is k-fold degenerate. Now in the case of a degenerate eigenvalue, not only does the initial set of eigenfunctions provide correct solutions to the wave equation, but any linear combination of these is also a solution giving the same eigenvalue. This is easily shown as follows:

$$\mathcal{3C}\sum_j a_{ij}\Psi_{ij} = \mathcal{3C}a_{i1}\Psi_{i1} + \mathcal{3C}a_{i2}\Psi_{i2} + \cdots \mathcal{3C}a_{ik}\Psi_{ik}$$

$$= E_ia_{i1}\Psi_{i1} + E_ia_{i2}\Psi_{i2} + \cdots E_ia_{ik}\Psi_{ik}$$

$$= E_i\sum_j a_{ij}\Psi_{ij} \qquad (5.1\text{-}4)$$

Finally, an important property of eigenfunctions must be mentioned. Eigenfunctions are so constructed as to be *orthonormal,* which means that

$$\int \Psi_i{}^*\Psi_j \, d\tau = \delta_{ij} \qquad (5.1\text{-}5)$$

where the integration is to be carried out over all of the coordinates, collectively represented by τ, which occur in Ψ_i and Ψ_j. When an eigenfunction belonging to the eigenvalue E_i is expressed as a linear combination of a set of eigenfunctions, we have, from 5.1-5

$$\int \Psi_i^* \Psi_i \, d\tau = \int \left(\sum_j a_{ij} \Psi_{ij}^* \right) \left(\sum_{j'} a_{ij'} \Psi_{ij'} \right) d\tau$$

Now all products where $j \neq j'$ will vanish, for example,

$$\int a_{ij} \Psi_{ij}^* a_{ij'} \Psi_{ij'} \, d\tau = a_{ij} a_{ij'} \int \Psi_{ij}^* \Psi_{ij'} \, d\tau = 0$$

and assuming that each Ψ_{ij} is normalized, we are left with

$$\int \sum_j a_{ij} \Psi_{ij}^* a_{ij} \Psi_{ij} \, d\tau = \sum_j a_{ij}^2 = 1 \tag{5.1-6}$$

We can now show that the eigenfunctions for a molecule are bases for irreducible representations of the symmetry group to which the molecule belongs. Let us take first the simple case of nondegenerate eigenvalues. If we take the wave equation for the molecule and carry out a symmetry operation, R, upon each side, then, from 5.1-1 and 5.1-2 we have

$$\mathcal{H} R \Psi_i = E_i R \Psi_i \tag{5.1-7}$$

Thus $R\Psi$ is itself an eigenfunction. Since Ψ is normalized we must require, in order that $R\Psi$ also be normalized,

$$R\Psi_i = \pm 1 \Psi_i$$

Hence, by applying each of the operations in the group to an eigenfunction Ψ_i belonging to a nondegenerate eigenvalue, we generate a representation of the group with each matrix, $\Gamma_i(R)$, equal to ± 1. Since the representations are one-dimensional, they are obviously irreducible.

If we take the wave equation for the case where E_i is k-fold degenerate, then we must write, in analogy to 5.1-7

$$\mathcal{H} R \Psi_{il} = E_i R \Psi_{il} \tag{5.1-8}$$

But here $R\Psi_{il}$ may in general be any linear combination of the Ψ_{ij}, that is,

$$R\Psi_{il} = \sum_{j=1}^{k} r_{jl} \Psi_{ij}$$

For some other operation, S, we have, similarly,

$$S\Psi_{ij} = \sum_{m=1}^{k} s_{mj} \Psi_{im}$$

Because R and S are members of a symmetry group, there must be an element $T = SR$ and its effect on one of the functions in the set can be expressed as follows:

$$SR\Psi_{il} = T\Psi_{il} = \sum_{m=1}^{k} t_{ml}\Psi_{im} = S\sum_{j=1}^{k} r_{jl}\Psi_{ij}$$

$$= \sum_{j=1}^{k}\sum_{m=1}^{k} s_{mj}r_{jl}\Psi_{im} \qquad (5.1\text{-}9)$$

Comparing the third and fifth terms in 5.1-9, we see that

$$t_{ml} = \sum_{j=1}^{k} s_{mj}r_{jl}$$

But this is just the expression which gives the elements of a matrix $\mathfrak{I}$ which is the product, $\mathfrak{SR}$, of two other matrices. Thus the matrices which describe the transformations of a set of k eigenfunctions corresponding to a k-fold degenerate eigenvalue are a k-dimensional representation for the group. Moreover, these representations are irreducible. If they were reducible we could divide the k eigenfunctions $\Psi_{i1}, \Psi_{i2} \dots \Psi_{ik}$, or k linear combinations thereof, up into smaller sets such that the symmetry operations would send one member of the set into a linear combination of only members of its own set. Then the eigenvalue for members of one set *could* be different from the eigenvalue for members of another set. But this contradicts our original assumption that all of the Ψ_{il} *must* have the same eigenvalue.

To illustrate this explicitly, let us consider the $2p_x$ and $2p_y$ orbitals of the nitrogen atom in ammonia, which belongs to the group C_{3v}. These orbitals are represented or described by the following eigenfunctions:

$$p_x = R \sin \theta \cos \phi$$

$$p_y = R \sin \theta \sin \phi$$

where R is a constant insofar as symmetry operations are concerned, and θ and ϕ are angles in a polar coordinate system.* θ stands for an angle measured down from a reference axis, say the z axis, and ϕ denotes an angle measured in the counterclockwise direction from the x axis in the xy plane. Let us now work out the matrices which represent the transformations of these functions by each of the symmetry operations in the group C_{3v}. We consider what happens to a line whose direction is fixed initially by the angles θ_1 and ϕ_1. First of all we note that none of the operations in the group will affect θ so that θ_2, the value of θ after appli-

* See Figure 6.1, page 90.

cation of a symmetry operation, will always equal θ_1. Hence

$$\sin \theta_2 = \sin \theta_1$$

If we rotate by $2\pi/3$ about the z axis, however, we have

$$\phi_2 = \phi_1 + 2\pi/3$$

and hence

$$\cos \phi_2 = \cos(\phi_1 + 2\pi/3) = \cos \phi_1 \cos 2\pi/3 - \sin \phi_1 \sin 2\pi/3$$

$$= -\tfrac{1}{2} \cos \phi_1 - \frac{\sqrt{3}}{2} \sin \phi_1$$

$$\sin \phi_2 = \sin(\phi_1 + 2\pi/3) = \sin \phi_1 \cos 2\pi/3 + \cos \phi_1 \sin 2\pi/3$$

$$= -\tfrac{1}{2} \sin \phi_1 + \frac{\sqrt{3}}{2} \cos \phi_1$$

If we reflect in the xz plane, we have

$$\phi_2 = -\phi_1$$

and hence

$$\cos \phi_2 = \cos \phi_1$$

$$\sin \phi_2 = - \sin \phi_1$$

We can now use this information to work out the required matrices:

E:

$$E p_x = E(R \sin \theta_1 \cos \phi_1) = R \sin \theta_2 \cos \phi_2 = R \sin \theta_1 \cos \phi_1 = p_x$$

$$E p_y = E(R \sin \theta_1 \sin \phi_1) = R \sin \theta_2 \sin \phi_2 = R \sin \theta_1 \sin \phi_1 = p_y$$

C_3:

$$C_3 p_x = C_3(R \sin \theta_1 \cos \phi_1) = R \sin \theta_2 \cos \phi_2$$

$$= R(\sin \theta_1)(-\tfrac{1}{2})(\cos \phi_1 + \sqrt{3} \sin \phi_1)$$

$$= -\tfrac{1}{2} R \sin \theta_1 \cos \phi_1 - \frac{\sqrt{3}}{2} R \sin \theta_1 \sin \phi_1$$

$$= -\tfrac{1}{2} p_x - \frac{\sqrt{3}}{2} p_y$$

$$C_3 p_y = C_3(R \sin \theta_1 \sin \phi_1) = R \sin \theta_2 \sin \phi_2$$

$$= R(\sin \theta_1)(-\tfrac{1}{2})(\sin \phi_1 - \sqrt{3} \cos \phi_1)$$

$$= \frac{\sqrt{3}}{2} R \sin \theta_1 \cos \phi_1 - \tfrac{1}{2} R \sin \theta_1 \sin \phi_1$$

$$= \frac{\sqrt{3}}{2} p_x - \tfrac{1}{2} p_y$$

σ_v:

$$\sigma_v p_x = \sigma_v(R \sin \theta_1 \cos \phi_1) = R \sin \theta_2 \cos \phi_2 = R \sin \theta_1 \cos \phi_1 = p_x$$

$$\sigma_v p_y = \sigma_v(R \sin \theta_1 \sin \phi_1) = R \sin \theta_2 \sin \phi_2 = -R \sin \theta_1 \sin \phi_1 = -p_y$$

Expressing these results in matrix notation we write

$$\begin{bmatrix} 1 & 0 \\ 0 & 1 \end{bmatrix} \begin{bmatrix} p_x \\ p_y \end{bmatrix} = E \begin{bmatrix} p_x \\ p_y \end{bmatrix} \qquad \chi(E) = 2$$

$$\begin{bmatrix} -\dfrac{1}{2} & -\dfrac{\sqrt{3}}{2} \\ \dfrac{\sqrt{3}}{2} & -\dfrac{1}{2} \end{bmatrix} \begin{bmatrix} p_x \\ p_y \end{bmatrix} = C_3 \begin{bmatrix} p_x \\ p_y \end{bmatrix} \qquad \chi(C_3) = -1$$

$$\begin{bmatrix} 1 & 0 \\ 0 & -1 \end{bmatrix} \begin{bmatrix} p_x \\ p_y \end{bmatrix} = \sigma_v \begin{bmatrix} p_x \\ p_y \end{bmatrix} \qquad \chi(\sigma_v) = 0$$

The characters are seen to be those of the E representation of C_{3v}. Thus we see that the p_x and p_y orbitals, as a pair, provide a basis for the E representation. It will be noted that the coordinates x and y are shown as transforming according to the E representation in the character table for the group C_{3v}. Thus the functions $\sin \theta \cos \phi$ and $\sin \theta \sin \phi$ transform in the same way as x and y. This is why the p orbital which has an eigenfunction $\sin \theta \cos \phi$ is called p_x and the one which has an eigenfunction $\sin \theta \sin \phi$ is called p_y.

5.2   The Direct Product

Suppose that R is an operation in the symmetry group of a molecule and $X_1, X_2 \ldots X_m$ and $Y_1, Y_2 \ldots Y_n$ are two sets of functions (perhaps eigenfunctions of the wave equation for the molecule) which are bases for representations of the group. As shown earlier, we may write

$$RX_i = \sum_{j=1}^{m} x_{ji} X_j$$

$$RY_k = \sum_{l=1}^{n} y_{lk} Y_l$$

It is also true that

$$RX_i Y_k = \sum_{j=1}^{m} \sum_{l=1}^{n} x_{ji} y_{lk} X_j Y_l = \sum_{j} \sum_{l} z_{jl,ik} X_j Y_l$$

Thus the set of functions $X_i Y_k$, called the direct product of X_i and Y_k, also forms a basis for a representation of the group. The $z_{jl,ik}$ are the elements of a matrix Z of order $(mn) \times (mn)$.

We now have a very important theorem about the character of the Z matrices for the various operations in the group:

The characters of the representation of a direct product are equal to the products of the characters of the representations based on the individual sets of functions.

PROOF. This theorem is easily proved as follows:

$$\chi_\mathsf{Z}(R) = \sum_{jl} z_{jl,jl} = \sum_{j=1}^{m} \sum_{l=1}^{n} x_{jj} y_{ll} = \chi_\mathfrak{x}(R) \chi_\mathfrak{y}(R)$$

Thus, if we want to know the characters $\chi(R)$ of a representation which is the direct product of two other representations with characters $\chi_1(R)$ and $\chi_2(R)$, these are given by

$$\chi(R) = \chi_1(R) \chi_2(R) \tag{5.2-1}$$

for each operation R in the group.

For example, the direct products of some irreducible representations of the group C_{4v} are shown below.

C_{4v}	E	C_2	$2C_4$	$2\sigma_v$	$2\sigma_d$
A_1	1	1	1	1	1
A_2	1	1	1	-1	-1
B_1	1	1	-1	1	-1
B_2	1	1	-1	-1	1
E	2	-2	0	0	0
$A_1 A_2$	1	1	1	-1	-1
$B_1 E$	2	-2	0	0	0
$A_1 E B_2$	2	-2	0	0	0
E^2	4	4	0	0	0

It should be clear from the associative property of matrix multiplication that what has been said above regarding direct products of two representations can be extended to direct products of any number of representations.

In general, though not invariably, the direct product of two or more irreducible representations will be a reducible representation. For example, the direct product representations of the group given above reduce in the following way:

$$A_1 A_2 = A_2 \qquad E^2 = A_1 + A_2 + B_1 + B_2$$

$$B_1 E = E$$

$$A_1 E B_2 = E$$

We shall now explain the importance of direct products in the solution of problems in molecular physics. Whenever we have an integral of the product of two functions, for example,

$$\int f_A f_B \, d\tau$$

the value of this integral will be equal to zero unless the integrand is invariant under all operations of the symmetry group to which the molecule belongs or unless some term in it, if it can be expressed as a sum of terms, remains invariant. This is a generalization of the familiar case in which an integrand is a function of only one variable. In that case, if $y = f(x)$, the integral

$$\int_{-\infty}^{\infty} y \, dx$$

equals zero if y is an odd function, that is, if $f(x) = -f(-x)$. In this simple case we say that y is not invariant to the operation of reflecting all points in the second and third quadrants into the first and fourth quadrants and vice versa.

Now when we say that the integrand $f_A f_B$ is invariant to all symmetry operations, this means it forms a basis for the totally symmetric representation of the group, or if some term in the expanded form of $f_A f_B$ is invariant, then that term forms a basis for the totally symmetric representation. But from what has been said above, we know how to determine the irreducible representations occurring in the representation Γ_{AB} for which $f_A f_B$ forms a basis if we know the irreducible representations for which f_A and f_B separately form bases. In general:

$$\Gamma_{AB} = \text{a sum of irreducible representations}$$

Only if one of the irreducible representations occurring in the sum is the totally symmetric one will the integral have a value other than zero. There is a theorem concerning whether the totally symmetric representation will be present in this sum.

The representation of a direct product, Γ_{AB}, *will contain the totally symmetric representation only if the irreducible* Γ_A = *the irreducible* Γ_B.

PROOF. Equation 4.3-11 tells us that the number of times, a_i, the ith irreducible representation, Γ_i, occurs in a reducible representation, say Γ_{AB}, is given by

$$a_i = \frac{1}{h} \sum_R \chi_{AB}(R)\chi_i(R)$$

If a_1 and χ_1 refer to the totally symmetric representation, for which all $\chi_1(R)$ equal 1, we have

$$a_1 = \frac{1}{h} \sum_R \chi_{AB}(R)$$

But from 5.2-1

$$\chi_{AB}(R) = \chi_A(R)\chi_B(R)$$

hence

$$a_1 = \frac{1}{h} \sum_R \chi_A(R)\chi_B(R)$$

According to the properties of characters of irreducible representations as components of vectors (Equation 4.3-8), we get

$$a_1 = \delta_{AB} \qquad \text{Q.E.D.}$$

We also see that if Γ_1 occurs at all it will occur only once. It is very easy to check this theorem using the character tables in Appendix II and doing so will perhaps help to develop familiarity with the manipulation of direct products.

From the foregoing discussion of the integrals of products of two functions it is easy to derive some important rules regarding integrands which are products of three, four, or more functions. The case of a triple product is of particular importance. In order for the integral

$$\int f_A f_B f_C \, d\tau$$

to be nonzero, the direct product of the representations of f_A, f_B, and f_C must be or contain the totally symmetric representation. This can only occur if the representation of the direct product of any two of the functions is or contains the same representation as is given by the third function. This follows directly from the above theorem. The applicability of this corollary is chiefly in dealing with matrix elements of the type

$$\int \psi_i P \psi_j \, d\tau$$

where ψ_i and ψ_j are wave functions and P is some quantum mechanical operator. For the specially important case in which P is the Hamiltonian operator, viz.,

$$\int \psi_i \mathcal{H} \psi_j \, d\tau$$

we conclude that the integral can be nonzero only if the representation of $\psi_i \psi_j$ is or contains the totally symmetric representation. This is because the Hamiltonian operator itself must have the full symmetry of the molecule; it is only an operator expression for the energy of the molecule, and clearly the energy of the molecule cannot change in either sign or magnitude as a result of a symmetry operation. Our final conclusion, then, is that ψ_i and ψ_j must belong to the same irreducible representation if the integral is not to vanish.

Part II

Applications

Construction of Hybrid Orbitals *

6.1   The Transformation Properties of Atomic Orbitals

In this chapter we will show how to determine what combination of
atomic orbitals on an atom can be used to construct a set of hybrid orbitals capable of forming bonds to a set of other atoms arranged in some
symmetric manner. For example, it will be shown why it is the sets sp^3
and sd^3 which give tetrahedrally directed orbitals. It will further be
shown that the question of which set is used is not in general a question
of the either-or variety but rather a question of how much of each set
contributes to the actual hybrids. The discussion will make clear the
basis for the frequently encountered hybridization schemes, but also the
reader will then be in a position to deduce hybridization schemes to suit
any new situation not already treated. The whole process is actually of
the utmost simplicity.

First, however, it is necessary to discuss briefly the symmetry or transformation properties of atomic orbitals. We shall restrict ourselves to s,
p, and d orbitals, but the discussion will expose all of the principles required to deal with f orbitals in the relatively rare cases where that may
be necessary.

The wave functions for the hydrogen atom are known exactly. They
are functions of the three spatial coordinates of the electron and take
their most simple form when we choose these coordinates to be the polar
coordinates shown in Figure 6.1 in relation to a set of Cartesian axes.
The point at x, y, and z in Cartesian coordinates is fixed by r, the radial
distance OP, from the origin of the coordinate system (always considered
positive), θ, the angle between the z axis and the line OP, and ϕ, the
angle between the x axis and the projection of OP on the xy plane.

---

* The first general discussion and broad application of the methods treated in this
chapter was given by G. E. Kimball, *J. Chem. Phys.*, **8**, 188 (1940), although the
principles were understood earlier.

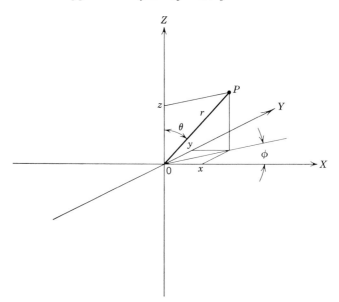

Figure 6.1   Diagram showing the relation of polar coordinates, r, θ, ϕ to Cartesian coordinates for the point P.

The wave functions for the electron in the hydrogen atom are all products of two functions. First there is the radial function, $R(n, r)$ which depends on the principal quantum number, n, and the coordinate, r. Then there is the angular part, $A(\theta, \phi)$, which is independent of both n and r but a function of θ and ϕ. Both $R(n, r)$ and $A(\theta, \phi)$ are assumed to be separately normalized * to unity, that is,

$$\int_0^\infty [R(n, r)]^2 r^2 \, dr = 1$$

$$\int_0^{2\pi} \int_0^\pi [A(\theta, \phi)]^2 \sin \theta \, d\theta \, d\phi = 1$$

Their product, the complete orbital wave function, is then also normalized to unity.

Because no symmetry operation can alter the value of $R(n, r)$, we need not consider the radial wave functions any further. Symmetry operations do alter the angular wave functions, so we shall now examine them in more detail. It should be noted that since $A(\theta, \phi)$ does not depend on n,

* It should be recalled that the differential element of volume in polar coordinates is $r^2 \sin \theta \, dr \, d\theta \, d\phi$.

the angular wave function for all s, all p, all d, etc., orbitals of a given type are the same regardless of the principal quantum number of the shell to which they belong. Table 6.1 lists the angular wave functions for s, p, and d orbitals.

In an example worked out at the end of Section 5.2 it was noted in passing that the p orbital with an angular dependence on $\sin \theta \cos \phi$ was called a p_x orbital because the function $\sin \theta \cos \phi$ has the same transformation properties as does the Cartesian coordinate x. At this point we shall discuss the transformation properties and hence the notation for the various orbitals more fully. To do so we should recognize that the x, y, and z coordinates of a point (see Figure 6.1) are related to its polar coordinates in the following way:

$$\left. \begin{array}{l} x = r \sin \theta \cos \phi \\ y = r \sin \theta \sin \phi \\ z = r \cos \theta \end{array} \right\} \tag{6.1-1}$$

These relations mean that since x is equal to $\sin \theta \cos \phi$ times a constant, which is of course unaltered by any transformation of the kind occurring in a point group, $\sin \theta \cos \phi$ must transform in the same way as does x. On this basis the assignment of the subscripts x, y, and z to the p orbitals is clear.

The notation of the d orbitals is also deduced using the relations 6.1-1. For example:

$$\begin{aligned} (1) \quad \sin^2 \theta \sin 2\phi &= 2 \sin^2 \theta \sin \phi \cos \phi \\ &= 2(\sin \theta \cos \phi)(\sin \theta \sin \phi) \\ &= 2(x/r)(y/r) = (2/r^2)xy \\ &= \text{constant} \cdot xy \end{aligned}$$

Table 6.1   Angular Wave Functions, $A(\theta, \phi)$ of s, p, and d Orbitals (Normalized to Unity)

ORBITAL TYPE	$A(\theta, \phi)$
s	$1/2 \sqrt{\pi}$
p_z	$(\sqrt{3}/2 \sqrt{\pi}) \cos \theta$
p_x	$(\sqrt{3}/2 \sqrt{\pi}) \sin \theta \cos \phi$
p_y	$(\sqrt{3}/2 \sqrt{\pi}) \sin \theta \sin \phi$
$d_{z^2}(= d_{2z^2 - x^2 - y^2})$	$(\sqrt{5}/4 \sqrt{\pi})(3 \cos^2 \theta - 1)$
d_{xz}	$(\sqrt{15}/2 \sqrt{\pi})(\sin \theta \cos \theta \cos \phi)$
d_{yz}	$(\sqrt{15}/2 \sqrt{\pi})(\sin \theta \cos \theta \sin \phi)$
$d_{x^2 - y^2}$	$(\sqrt{15}/4 \sqrt{\pi})(\sin^2 \theta \cos 2\phi)$
d_{xy}	$(\sqrt{15}/4 \sqrt{\pi})(\sin^2 \theta \sin 2\phi)$

(2) $3 \cos^2 \theta - 1 = 3 \cos^2 \theta - \cos^2 \theta - \sin^2 \theta$
$$= 2 \cos^2 \theta - \sin^2 \theta$$

now
$$(x/r)^2 = \sin^2 \theta \cos^2 \phi$$
$$(y/r)^2 = \sin^2 \theta \sin^2 \phi$$

hence
$$(1/r^2)(x^2 + y^2) = \sin^2 \theta \, (\sin^2 \phi + \cos^2 \phi)$$
$$= \sin^2 \theta$$

Hence we can write

$$3 \cos^2 \theta - 1 = 2(z^2/r^2) - (1/r^2)(x^2 + y^2)$$

$$= \text{constant} \cdot (2z^2 - x^2 - y^2)$$

Thus the d orbital whose angular wave function is a constant times $3 \cos^2 \theta - 1$ should be written $d_{2z^2-x^2-y^2}$. Since in most groups z^2 and $x^2 + y^2$ transform in the same way, $2z^2 - x^2 - y^2$ will transform in the same way as z^2 and the shorter notation d_{z^2} is used.

As a result of the fact that the subscript to an orbital symbol tells us that the orbital transforms in the same way as the subscript, we can immediately determine the transformation properties of any orbital on an atom lying at the center of the coordinate system by looking up its subscript in the appropriate column on the right of a character table. Consider for example the phosphorus atom in PCl_3. By looking at the character table for the group C_{3v} we immediately learn that the phosphorus orbitals belong to the following representations:

A_1: s, p_z, d_{z^2}
A_2: none
E: $(d_{xy}, d_{x^2-y^2})$, (d_{xy}, d_{yz}), (p_x, p_y)

It should be recalled that when we say a certain orbital (or group of orbitals) "belongs" to a certain irreducible representation we mean that it is a basis for that irreducible representation.

The preceding discussion of the symmetry properties of atomic orbitals has referred explicitly to the one-electron orbitals of the hydrogen atom. However, the principles can be carried over to the treatment of many-electron atoms. The wave functions for these atoms may be written as products of one-electron wave functions. For each electron in a many-electron atom we write a wave function consisting of an angular function which is the same as the angular function of an analogous electron in the hydrogen atom, and a radial function which differs from the radial function the electron would have in a hydrogen atom because of mutual shielding and repulsion effects among the electrons. The important point is that since the angular properties of an electron in a many-electron atom can be taken as being the same as those of a corresponding hydrogen electron, the symmetry properties of the one-electron wave functions used to build up the total wave functions for atoms have the same transformation properties as the simple and exact one-electron wave functions obtained by solving the wave equation for the hydrogen atom.

6.2 Hybridization Schemes for σ Orbitals

It is perhaps easiest to explain this subject by going directly to an example. Let us take as a typical but relatively simple one, the case of tetrahedral hybridization. We wish to know what atomic orbitals on atom A in the tetrahedral molecule AB_4 are required to construct a set of four σ orbitals on atom A which have their lobes directed to the B atoms, that is, toward the apices of a tetrahedron. This set of four hybrid orbitals will form a basis for a representation of the symmetry group of the molecule, in this case the group T_d. We may represent each hybrid orbital by a vector pointing in the appropriate direction and number these vectors r_1, r_2, r_3, r_4, as shown in Figure 6.2. Let us now determine the characters of the representation for which this set of vectors forms a basis.

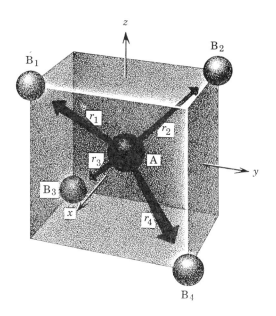

Figure 6.2 A set of vectors, r_1, r_2, r_3, and r_4 representing the four hybrid σ orbitals used by atom A to bond the four B atoms in a tetrahedral AB_4 molecule.

Applying the identity operation we get

$$r_1 \rightarrow r_1 \;\; + 0r_2 + 0r_3 + 0r_4$$
$$r_2 \rightarrow 0r_1 + r_2 \;\; + 0r_3 + 0r_4$$
$$r_3 \rightarrow 0r_1 + 0r_2 + r_3 \;\; + 0r_4$$
$$r_4 \rightarrow 0r_1 + 0r_2 + 0r_3 + r_4$$

The matrix of the coefficients on the right is a unit matrix of dimension 4 and hence $\chi(E) = 4$.

If we rotate the set of vectors by $2\pi/3$ about that C_3 axis which is co-incident with r_1, we get

$$r_1 \rightarrow r_1 \;\; + 0r_2 + 0r_3 + 0r_4$$
$$r_2 \rightarrow 0r_1 + 0r_2 + r_3 \;\; + 0r_4$$
$$r_3 \rightarrow 0r_1 + 0r_2 + 0r_3 + r_4$$
$$r_4 \rightarrow 0r_1 + r_2 \;\; + 0r_3 + 0r_4$$

The character of the matrix of the coefficients here, $\chi(C_3)$, is equal to 1.

Proceeding in the same way with a C_2, an S_4, and a σ_d, we shall get the following set of characters for the representation generated:

	E	$8C_3$	$3C_2$	$6S_4$	$6\sigma_d$
Γ_{tetra}	4	1	0	0	2

Reference to the T_d character table shows that this representation is not one of the irreducible ones but that it can be reduced in the following way:

$$\Gamma_{\text{tetra}} = A_1 + T_2$$

This means that the four atomic orbitals which are combined to make the set of four hybrid orbitals must be chosen so as to include one orbital of A_1 symmetry and a set of three orbitals belonging to the T_2 representation. The character table also tells us that atomic orbitals of atom A falling into these categories are as follows:

A_1 ORBITALS	T_2 ORBITALS
s	(p_x, p_y, p_z)
	(d_{xy}, d_{xz}, d_{yz})

Hence our set of hybrid orbitals may be sp^3 or sd^3 (where, of course, the d^3 means specifically d_{xy}, d_{xz}, d_{yz}, and no others). From the point of view of symmetry there is no difference between sp^3 and sd^3 hybrids.

Because the sp^3 and sd^3 hybrids have exactly the same symmetry properties it is impossible for any atom A in a tetrahedral molecule AB_4 to use purely one set or the other. It must always use a mixture of both. However, in many cases, other reasoning based on knowledge or estimates of the energies of the various orbitals may lead us to believe that the contribution of one set is of minor or perhaps totally negligible magnitude. For example, carbon can form a set of sp^3 hybrid orbitals using its $2s$ and $2p$ orbitals. The most stable, that is, lowest energy, d orbitals available to it are its $3d$ orbitals, so the most stable sd^3 hybrids it could form would be constructed from $2s$, $3d_{xy}$, $3d_{xz}$, and $3d_{yz}$. However, in carbon, the $3d$ orbitals lie some 230 Kcal/mole higher than the $2p$ orbitals. Therefore, in order for the bonds formed using an sd^3 set of hybrids to be more stable than a set using sp^3 hybrids, each sd^3 bond would have to be some $3 \times \frac{230}{4} \sim 170$ Kcal/mole stronger than each sp^3 bond. This is quite impossible, and we can be sure that carbon will not use an sd^3 set. In fact the $3d$ orbitals are so high in energy relative to the $2p$ orbitals that even partial usage of the d orbitals is unlikely to be important. Thus we can correctly say that carbon (and any other element in the first short period, Li–F) will form a set of four tetrahedrally directed bonds using $2s2p^3$ hybrid orbitals. But it should be borne in mind that this is for reasons of energy and not for reasons of symmetry.

In contrast, it is quite likely that the sd^3 set is important if not dominant in the formation of four σ bonds by Mn and Cr in the ions MnO_4^-, MnO_4^{2-}, and CrO_4^{2-}. Here the lowest usable d orbitals are $3d$, and the lowest usable p orbitals are $4p$, and the $3d$ orbitals are probably of somewhat lower energy than the $4p$ orbitals.

Before proceeding to some other illustrative examples we shall develop a rule that will simplify the process of working out the characters of the reducible representation for which a set of hybrid orbitals is a basis. If, on carrying out a symmetry operation on a set of hybrid orbitals or the set of vectors representing them, a certain vector remains unshifted, there appears in the matrix a diagonal element equal to 1. If, however, that vector and some other one are interchanged by the operation, two corresponding diagonal elements are equal to 0. Hence, to determine the character of the matrix corresponding to a given operation we can use the following simple rule:

The character is equal to the number of vectors which are unshifted by the operation.

Suppose we wish to find what atomic orbitals phosphorus may use to form the σ bonds to five fluorine atoms in PF_5, assuming PF_5 to have a trigonal bipyramid structure. The symmetry group is then D_{3h}. The set of five σ orbitals on phosphorus forms a basis for a representation with the following characters:

D_{3h}	E	$2C_3$	$3C_2$	σ_h	$2S_3$	$3\sigma_v$
Γ_σ	5	2	1	3	0	3

These numbers were obtained as follows, where Figure 6.3 shows the coordinate system and numbering of the bonds. All bonds are unshifted upon performing E; hence $\chi(E) = 5$. Only (4) and (5) remain unshifted on performing a C_3; hence $\chi(C_3) = 2$. On performing a C_2, only one bond remains unshifted; if the C_2 is $C_2(x)$ only (1) remains fixed; hence $\chi(C_2) = 1$. σ_h leaves (1), (2) and (3) unshifted; hence $\chi(\sigma_h) = 3$. S_3 leaves no bonds unshifted; the rotation part of it shifts (1), (2), and (3), and the reflection part then interchanges (4) and (5); hence $\chi(S_3) = 0$. A σ_v leaves three bonds unshifted; for example $\sigma(xz)$ interchanges (2) and (3) but does not shift (1), (4), or (5); hence $\chi(\sigma_v) = 3$.

Now it is easily shown that

$$\Gamma_\sigma = 2A'_1 + A''_2 + E'$$

Orbitals falling into these symmetry classes are

A'_1	A''_2	E'
s	p_z	(p_x, p_y)
d_{z^2}		$(d_{xy}, d_{x^2-y^2})$

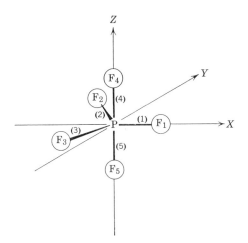

Figure 6.3   Coordinate axes and numbering system for PF_5.

Thus any of the following combinations could be used:

$$(1) \quad ns, \ (n+1)s, \ p_z, \ \begin{cases} p_x, \ p_y & (a) \\ d_{xy}, \ d_{x^2-y^2} & (b) \end{cases}$$

$$(2) \quad nd_{z^2}, \ (n+1)d_{z^2}, \ p_z, \ \begin{cases} p_x, \ p_y & (a) \\ d_{xy}, \ d_{x^2-y^2} & (b) \end{cases}$$

$$(3) \quad s, d_{z^2}, p_z, \ \begin{cases} p_x, \ p_y & (a) \\ d_{xy}, \ d_{x^2-y^2} & (b) \end{cases}$$

In molecules which are known to have or might have a trigonal bipyramid structure, it is rather unlikely, for energetic reasons, that combinations (1) or (2) would be used. In PF_5 for example, the combination (3a) seems likely to be a good description of the composition of the hybrid orbitals used. On the other hand, in gaseous $MoCl_5$ it is probable that some mixture of schemes (3a) and (3b) is required to represent the situation faithfully since the Mo $4d$ orbitals are of energy comparable to its $5p$ orbitals. In short notation, schemes (3a) and (3b) can be written dsp^3 and d^3sp, but it should be remembered when appropriate that only certain d and p orbitals are referred to.

To emphasize this, let us determine what combinations of atomic orbitals can hybridize to give the σ orbitals required in the other commonly occurring shape for an AB_5 molecule, viz., a tetragonal pyramid. Such a molecule belongs to the group C_{4v}, and the characters of the representation, Γ_σ, for which the five σ orbitals of atom A form a basis are

C_{4v}	E	$2C_4$	C_2	$2\sigma_v$	$2\sigma_d$
Γ_σ	5	1	1	3	1

Γ_σ reduces as

$$\Gamma_\sigma = 2A_1 + B_1 + E$$

There are the following orbitals in the required symmetry classes:

A_1	B_1	E
s	$d_{x^2-y^2}$	(p_x, p_y)
p_z		(d_{xz}, d_{yz})
d_{z^2}		

One way in which we can select two A_1 orbitals, one B_1 orbital and one pair of E orbitals is s, p_z, $d_{x^2-y^2}$, p_x, p_y, which set may be abbreviated dsp^3. In this C_{4v} case it must be understood that the d refers specifically and only to $d_{x^2-y^2}$ while in the dsp^3 set discussed above for the D_{3h} case, d must be understood to mean specifically and only d_{z^2}. In a situation where the atom A in AB_5 will be likely for energetic reasons to use hybrids composed of an s, three p, and one d orbitals, the geometry of the molecule will depend on whether a $d_{x^2-y^2}$ or a d_{z^2} orbital is used. Of course, for the C_{4v} case, other possible hybridization schemes, written in abbreviated notation, are

$$sd^4, \; spd^3, \; sd^2p^2, \; pd^4, \; p^3d^2$$

The type of analysis discussed rather fully for several important cases above will now be presented in summary form for several other important cases.

AB$_3$ (planar): symmetry D_{3h}. Examples: BF$_3$, AlR$_3$, NO$_3^-$, SO$_3$.

D_{3h}	E	$2C_3$	$3C_2$	σ_h	$2S_3$	$3\sigma_v$
Γ_σ	3	0	1	3	0	1

$$\Gamma_\sigma = A_1' + E'$$

Possible combinations: $(s, \; p_x, \; p_y)$, $(s, \; d_{xy},$ $d_{x^2-y^2})$, $(d_{z^2}, \; p_x, \; p_y)$, $(d_{z^2}, \; d_{xy}, \; d_{x^2-y^2})$ which are, in brief notation, sp^2, sd^2, dp^2, d^3

AB$_4$ (planar): symmetry D_{4h}. Examples: AuCl$_4^-$, XeF$_4$, Ni(CN)$_4^{-2}$.

D_{4h}	E	$2C_4$	C_2	$2C_2'$	$2C_2''$	i	$2S_4$	σ_h	$2\sigma_v$	$2\sigma_d$
Γ_σ	4	0	0	2	0	0	0	4	2	0

$$\Gamma_\sigma = A_{1g} + B_{1g} + E_u$$

Possible combinations: $(s, \; d_{x^2-y^2}, \; p_x, \; p_y)$, $(d_{z^2}, \; d_{x^2-y^2},$ $p_x, \; p_y)$ which are, in brief notation, dsp^2 and d^2p^2.

AB$_6$ (octahedral): symmetry O_h. Examples: SF$_6$, PF$_6^-$, Fe(CN)$_6^{-3}$.

O_h	E	$8C_3$	$6C_2$	$6C_4$	$3C_2$	i	$6S_4$	$8S_6$	$3\sigma_h$	$6\sigma_d$
Γ_σ	6	0	0	2	2	0	0	0	4	2

$$\Gamma_\sigma = A_{1g} + E_g + T_{1u}$$

Possible combination: *only s, p_x, p_y, p_z, d_{z^2}, $d_{x^2-y^2}$*, which is, in brief notation, d^2sp^3.

6.3   Hybridization Schemes for π Bonding

We begin by discussing in detail the characteristics of π orbitals as compared to σ orbitals. This difference can be stated in terms of the number of nodal planes possessed by each. A nodal plane—or surface, more generally—is the locus of all points at which the wave function has zero amplitude as a result of its changing sign on passing from one side of the surface to the other. A σ orbital or bond is defined as one having *no* nodal surface which contains the bond axis. A π orbital or bond is defined as one which has *one* nodal surface or plane containing the bond axis. This system of classification extends further, to include, for example, δ orbitals and δ bonds which have *two* nodal surfaces intersecting along the bond axis, but we shall not go beyond the π case here.

To illustrate these definitions, Figure 6.4 shows some cross sections of orbitals or bonds. The closed curves are lines of constant value of the wave function, those nearest the center generally representing higher amplitudes, though this is not necessary since there may also be nodal surfaces concentric around the bond axis. (*a*) Shows a section through a σ

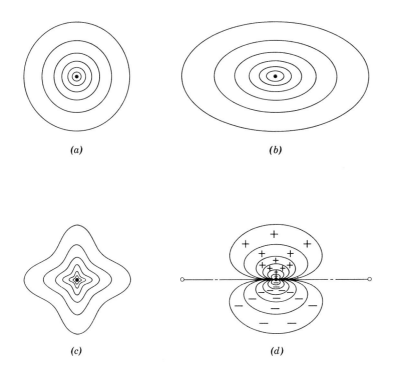

Figure 6.4   (*a*), (*b*), (*c*) Sections through σ bonds or σ orbitals perpendicular to the internuclear axis. Note absence of nodal planes. (*d*) Section through a π bond or π orbital. ○— – — – —○ is the trace of a nodal plane. The curves are loci of all points with the same value of the electronic wave function.

orbital which is circularly symmetric. This might be a pure s orbital, a pure p_q orbital viewed along the q axis, or the main lobe of a d_{z^2} orbital viewed along the z axis. (b) Shows a cross section of a σ orbital which has elliptical symmetry, and (c) shows a section which is even more complex in its shape. All, however, have the defining property of a σ orbital: if we follow a circle concentric about the bond axis, there is never any change in sign of the wave function. Note further that for a σ orbital or bond, there is a finite value of the wave function along the bond axis.

Figure 6.4d shows a cross section through a π orbital. The nodal plane passing through the bond axis is easily seen. If such a bond is to be formed by overlap of two atomic orbitals (AO's), one on each of the two bonded atoms, it is obviously necessary that each AO have π character with respect to the internuclear axis (that is, have a nodal plane containing the axis), *and* that these two nodal planes be the same plane. These considerations are illustrated in Figure 6.5.

Finally, it may also be easily seen that it is possible to have two, and only two, orthogonal π bonds between the same two atoms. These two π bonds will have their nodal planes mutually perpendicular as shown in Figure 6.6. It can be seen that the positive overlap of the positive lobe of the first π bond with the positive lobe of the second will be exactly canceled by overlap of the positive lobe of the first one with the negative lobe of the second one. An analogous cancellation occurs in the overlaps of the negative lobe of the first orbital with the lobes of the second. However, no third π orbital which has net zero overlap with both of the first two is possible.

In consequence of the properties of π bonds discussed above, the question of what orbitals are required on a central atom in order to form π bonds to each of a set of atoms surrounding it can be approached in the following way. We want to have altogether $2n$ π-type hybrid orbitals on atom A in the molecule AB$_n$, two for each B atom. These $2n$ hybrids on A

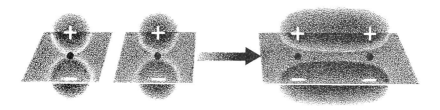

Figure 6.5   Schematic diagram showing formation of a π bond from two atomic or hybrid orbitals with a common nodal plane.

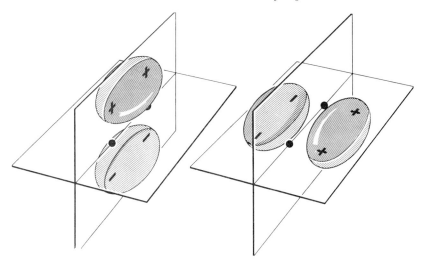

Figure 6.6   Schematic diagram showing two π bonds between the same pair of atoms with the nodal planes of the two orbitals mutually perpendicular.

must include an orbital to match (in the sense discussed above and shown in Figure 6.5) each one of the π orbitals on the atoms B. Thus the set of $2n$ hybrids on A and the $2n$ π atomic orbitals on the B atoms will both form bases for the same representation of the symmetry group of the molecule. Moreover, each π atomic orbital on one of the B atoms can be represented by a vector perpendicular to the nodal plane and pointing in the direction of the positive values of the wave function. There may be two such vectors at right angles on each B atom. Rather than attempting to carry the discussion further on a general basis, let us turn to a specific example.

Suppose we consider a planar, symmetrical AB_3 molecule, such as BF_3 or NO_3^-, belonging to the group D_{3h}. The six A—B π bonds which are, in principle, possible will transform, as noted above, in the same way as a set of six vectors attached to the B atoms. The two vectors on a B atom need only be perpendicular to one another and be in a plane perpendicular to the A—B axis. Their orientation within that plane can, in principle, be chosen arbitrarily. However, in cases such as the present one where there is a molecular plane, it is usually advantageous both in working out the results and in grasping their significance if we orient one vector on each B atom perpendicular to the molecular plane, and then, necessarily, have the other one lying in the molecular plane, as shown in

Figure 6.7. This set of six vectors is now used as the basis for a representation Γ_π, of the group D_{3h}. Again we can use the simple rule that any vectors shifted by a symmetry operation contribute zero to the character and any which are left unchanged contribute $+1$. Here we shall also find that a vector may not be shifted to a new position but will have its direction reversed. Thus it is transformed into the negative of itself and therefore contributes -1 to the character. In this way Γ_π is easily obtained. However, in carrying out the various symmetry operations, it will be found that in no case are any of the vectors perpendicular to the plane ever interchanged with those in the plane. This means then that each set gives rise to a representation independently of the other. Let us call the representation given by those perpendicular to the plane $\Gamma_\pi(\perp)$ and the representation given by the set in the plane $\Gamma_\pi(\|)$. The entire body of results, including reduction of the several representations, is as follows:

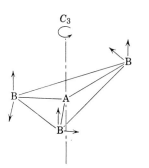

Figure 6.7 Six vectors representing π orbitals on the B atoms in an AB_3 molecule belonging to the group D_{3h}.

D_{3h}	E	$2C_3$	$3C_2$	σ_h	$2S_3$	$3\sigma_v$
Γ_π	6	0	-2	0	0	0
$\Gamma_\pi(\perp)$	3	0	-1	-3	0	1
$\Gamma_\pi(\|)$	3	0	-1	3	0	-1

$$\Gamma_\pi = \Gamma_\pi(\perp) + \Gamma_\pi(\|)$$
$$\Gamma_\pi(\perp) = A_2'' + E''$$
$$\Gamma_\pi(\|) = A_2' + E'$$

Thus, in order for atom A to form a π bond perpendicular to the molecular plane (a $\pi(\perp)$ bond) to each of the B atoms, it must use three hybrid orbitals built of one atomic orbital transforming as A_2'' and a degenerate pair of atomic orbitals transforming as E''. Reference to the D_{3h} character table shows that s, p, or d orbitals meeting these requirements are:

$$A_2'': p_z$$
$$E'': (d_{xz}, d_{yz})$$

Thus a set of three equivalent hybrid orbitals constructed from these is the only possible set for forming the $\pi(\perp)$ bonds.

Turning now to the $\pi(\|)$ bonds, we find that atomic orbitals of the necessary types are as follows:

$$A_2': \text{none}$$
$$E'': (p_x, p_z) \text{ and } (d_{x^2-y^2}, d_{xy})$$

Since there are no atomic orbitals of A_2' symmetry, it is impossible to form a set of *three* equivalent $\pi(\|)$ A—B bonds. This general situation, that is, lack of a complete set of AO's to form a complete set of π bonds, arises very frequently, as we shall see in several subsequent examples. The conclusion stated here will therefore be of general value.

The unavailability of the A_2' orbital does not mean that no $\pi(\|)$ bonds can be formed, nor does it mean that only two of the B atoms can be $\pi(\|)$ bonded. It means rather that *there can be only two $\pi(\|)$ bonds shared equally among the three B atoms.* The discussion of the octahedral AB_6 molecule which follows immediately will provide an opportunity to discuss this concept more fully.

We shall now treat several more of the important cases, starting with the octahedral AB_6 molecule. To determine the representation of O_h for which the twelve possible A—B π bonds form a basis, we attach two vectors to each B atom as shown in Figure 6.8, and consider the effects of the group operations upon them. It should be noted that each vector is exchanged with each of the other eleven by one symmetry operation or another. This means that all twelve π bonds and hence all twelve orbitals

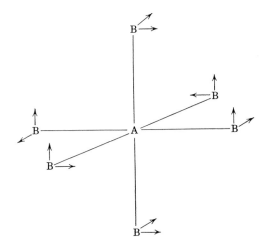

Figure 6.8   An octahedral AB_6 molecule with a set of twelve vectors representing the π orbitals of the B atoms.

required on atom A fall in the same set. The results are as follows:

O_h	E	$8C_3$	$6C_2$	$6C_4$	$3C_2\ (=C_4{}^2)$	i	$6S_4$	$8S_6$	$3\sigma_h$	$6\sigma_d$
Γ_π	12	0	0	0	-4	0	0	0	0	0

$$\Gamma_\pi = T_{1g} + T_{2g} + T_{1u} + T_{2u}$$

Referring again to the O_h character table, we find that the atom A will possess, among its s, p, and d orbitals, the following members of each of the above symmetry classes:

$$T_{1g}:\ \text{none}$$
$$T_{2g}:\ (d_{xy},\ d_{xz},\ d_{yz})$$
$$T_{1u}:\ (p_x,\ p_y,\ p_z)$$
$$T_{2u}:\ \text{none}$$

The first conclusion to be drawn from these results is that it is impossible for the entire set of twelve A—B π bonds to subsist, since the A atom does not have all of the necessary orbitals. Moreover, the only T_{1u} orbitals are the p orbitals. If we assume that a full set of A—B σ bonds has been formed, then these p orbitals are already fully used for that purpose (See page 98) and cannot be of any use for π bonding. The correctness of this assumption is not of *a priori* certainty, but in most cases at least it would seem a reasonable one. Thus there are only three orbitals on atom A, the T_{2g} d orbitals, which are available for π bonding, and, as before, the correct interpretation is to conceive of three π bonds shared equally among the six A—B pairs.

In this octahedral case, it is easy to see geometrically the correctness of this interpretation. If we look at the d_{xy} orbital, we see (Figure 6.9b) that it can form π bonds with B atoms 1, 2, 3, and 4 equally well. There is no reason why it should form a π bond exclusively to one and not to the others. Similarly, the d_{xz} orbital can form π bonds with B atoms 1, 2, 5, and 6 equally well (Figure 6.9c), and the d_{yz} can form π bonds equally well with B atoms 3, 4, 5, and 6 (Figure 6.9d). Looking at the situation from the opposite direction, so to speak, each B atom has the same prospects for forming π bonds with each of two d orbitals on atom A. Thus we must regard the π bonding as being shared equally among all six A—B bonds, giving, in effect, one-half of a π bond per A—B pair.

We shall next consider the square planar AB_4 molecule, which belongs to the point group D_{4h}. Here, as in the planar AB_3, we may divide the eight possible π bonds into two subsets, four perpendicular to the molecular plane and four lying in the molecular plane. When the representa-

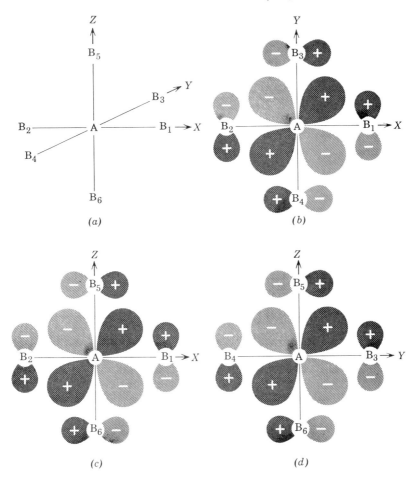

Figure 6.9   Drawings showing the relation of the $d\pi$ orbitals of atom A to the B atoms in an octahedral AB_6 molecule.

tions for which these two sets form bases are worked out and reduced, the following results are obtained:

D_{4h}	E	$2C_4$	C_2	$2C_2'$	$2C_2''$	i	$2S_4$	σ_h	$2\sigma_v$	$2\sigma_d$
$\Gamma_\pi(\perp)$	4	0	0	-2	0	0	0	-4	2	0
$\Gamma_\pi(\|)$	4	0	0	-2	0	0	0	4	-2	0

$$\Gamma_\pi(\perp) = A_{2u} + B_{2u} + E_g$$
$$\Gamma_\pi(\|) = A_{2g} + B_{2g} + E_u$$

The D_{4h} character table also tells us that for each of the required representations there are the following s, p, or d orbitals on atom A:

$$
\begin{array}{ll}
A_{2u}: p_z & A_{2g}: \text{none} \\
B_{2u}: \text{none} & B_{2g}: d_{xy} \\
E_g: (d_{xz}, d_{yz}), & E_u: (p_x, p_y)
\end{array}
$$

Thus neither of the sets of π bonds can possibly be complete since the required B_{2u} and A_{2g} orbitals on atom A simply do not exist (among s, p, and d orbitals). There may, however, be as many as three perpendicular π bonds shared among the four A—B sets, for the p_z, d_{xz}, and d_{yz} orbitals cannot be used at all in A—B sigma bonding (see Section 6.2). Since the A—B sigma bonds require the use of s, p_x, p_y, $d_{x^2-y^2}$ hybrid orbitals on atom A, however, and we usually assume that the formation of sigma bonds takes precedence, there is only the d_{xy} orbital to form one in-plane π bond shared equally (see Figure 6.9b) between all four A—B pairs.

We shall conclude this section by working out the π bonding possibilities in a tetrahedral AB_4 molecule. Following the usual practice, we assign a pair of vectors to each B atom, so oriented that they will transform identically with the A—B π bonds which may be formed and hence identically with the required orbitals on atom A. We obtain the following characters of the representation for which these vectors form a basis:

T_d	E	$8C_3$	$3C_2$	$6S_4$	$6\sigma_d$
Γ_π	8	-1	0	0	0

which reduces to

$$\Gamma_\pi = E + T_1 + T_2$$

It will be noted that all eight vectors belong to the same set, since any one is interchanged with each of the others by one operation or another.

Again referring to the T_d character table, we find that there are the following s, p, and d orbitals belonging to the irreducible representations which constitute Γ_π:

$$
\begin{array}{l}
E: (d_{x^2-y^2}, d_{xy}) \\
T_1: \text{none} \\
T_2: (p_x, p_y, p_z) \quad \text{and} \quad (d_{xy}, d_{xz}, d_{yz})
\end{array}
$$

Thus the first conclusion is that of the eight physically conceivable A—B π bonds, only five may be formed when atom A has only s, p, and d

orbitals at its disposal. Only one set of T_2 orbitals may be used. This set may be the three pure p orbitals or the three pure d orbitals, *or* a set of three p-d hybrids constructed from the two limiting sets.

In this case we have a particularly important example of the phenomenon already encountered, namely, the requirement of orbitals belonging to the same representation for both σ bonding and π bonding. In the case that there is only one orbital or one set of orbitals of the required type, we usually assume, as noted already, that the formation of σ bonds takes precedence. In this case, however, the matter is a little more complex. As shown in Section 6.2, a set of tetrahedrally directed σ orbitals on atom A requires atomic orbitals belonging to the representations A_1 and T_2. Thus both the σ and π sets require a group of T_2 orbitals. Since there are two sets of T_2 orbitals available, each may satisfy its requirement, but it is impossible, purely on the basis of symmetry, to make any definite allocation of one set of orbitals to σ bonding and another set to π bonding. Three cases may be considered, however. If the metal uses pure sp^3 hybrids for σ bonding, then it can use a pure d^5 set for π bonding. There is then the other limiting case in which atom A will use a pure sd^3 set for σ bonding. It will then use a p^3d^2 set for π bonding. Finally, there is the whole range of intermediate cases where the σ orbitals are a mixture of the sp^3 and sd^3 limiting cases, and the π orbitals are a complementary mixture of the d^5 and p^3d^2 limiting cases. Symmetry considerations alone can tell us no more than that these are the possibilities.

6.4   Hybrid Orbitals as Linear Combinations of Atomic Orbitals

Sets of Equivalent Orbitals

We have seen how to determine the sets of atomic orbitals which may be used to construct sets of hybrid orbitals of any desired spatial distribution. It is possible to write down algebraic expressions for the hybrid orbitals as linear combinations of the atomic orbitals, and this process is facilitated by taking account, formally or informally, of the symmetry properties which the hybrids must have. A knowledge of the actual algebraic expressions for hybrid orbitals is required, for example, in order to make numerical computations of overlap integrals, which are roughly proportional to bond strengths. In this section we will outline and illustrate the procedure for doing this in a few important cases and quote the results for certain others. The deduction of these latter may be undertaken by the reader for practice.

We shall use capital phi, Φ_i, to denote the ith hybrid orbital, and write it as a linear combination of atomic orbitals, ϕ_j, thus:

$$\Phi_i = a_i\phi_1 + b_i\phi_2 + c_i\phi_3 + \cdots$$

Our problem then is to find the proper values of the a_i, b_i, c_i ... in each Φ_i. There are three guides to working out a set of simultaneous equations which may be solved for the numerical values of these coefficients.

(1) The coefficients must be so adjusted that each of the hybrid orbitals will transform into one of the others which is supposed to be equivalent to it when the appropriate symmetry operations are performed.

(2) Each Φ_i must be normalized. We use ϕ_j's which are themselves orthonormal so that this requirement enables us to write the following equation for each of the Φ_i's:

$$a_i{}^2 + b_i{}^2 + c_i{}^2 + \cdots = 1$$

In general there will be fewer such equations than there are hybrid orbitals, for several may be identical.

(3) Every pair of hybrid orbitals, say Φ_i and Φ_k, must be orthogonal. Again, because the ϕ_j's are members of an orthonormal set, this requirement enables us to write an equation of the following type for each pair of hybrid orbitals:

$$a_ia_k + b_ib_k + c_ic_k + \cdots = 0$$

Just as in the case of the equations derived from the normalization requirement, not all of these equations will in general be different.

It may happen that not all of the equations obtained using the above criteria will be linearly independent, but there will always be a sufficiency of equations which are linearly independent to provide a complete set of coefficients.

As a first example of the use of this procedure, let us construct a set of equivalent trigonal sp^2 hybrids in the xy plane. This set of orbitals has D_{3h} symmetry, and the symmetry operations of this group which cause interchanges of them are C_3, $C_3{}^2$, the three σ_v's, and the three C_2's. We may select the direction of the first orbital arbitrarily and then require that the others be related to it by one or another of the symmetry operations. Let us have the first one directed along the positive extension of the x axis. We can write, then

$$\Phi_1 = a_1s + b_1p_x + c_1p_y$$

and immediately set c_1 equal to zero since the p_y orbital has zero amplitude along the x axis. The remaining two orbitals will be in the second and third quadrants and will have contributions from both p_x and p_y as well as from s. Thus we write

$$\Phi_2 = a_2 s - b_2 p_x + c_2 p_y$$

$$\Phi_3 = a_3 s - b_3 p_x - c_3 p_y$$

The use of $+$ and $-$ signs is dictated by the following consideration. We want to consider only the large positive lobes of the hybrid orbitals. For Φ_2, in the second quadrant, the signs of the s and p_y orbitals are positive, but the sign of the p_x orbital is negative. In order to assure that we obtain a positive contribution from each atomic orbital, we will adopt the procedure of making all coefficients positive and adjusting the $+$ and $-$ signs to allow for the sign of the atomic orbitals. Thus the p_x orbital is subtracted instead of added.

We now invoke some symmetry requirements to find relationships between the various coefficients. One way to do this is to require that both Φ_2 and Φ_3 be transformed into Φ_1 when an appropriate symmetry operation is performed. A convenient one to choose is rotation about the threefold axis. If we rotate Φ_2 by $2\pi/3$ in the clockwise direction, it must become identical with Φ_1. We can express this in the equation

$$C_3 \times \{a_2 s - b_2 p_x + c_2 p_y\} = a_1 s + b_1 p_x + 0 p_y \qquad (6.4\text{-}1)$$

The left side of this equation can be rewritten as

$$a_2 [C_3 \times s] - b_2 [C_3 \times p_x] + c_2 [C_3 \times p_y]$$

Since an s orbital has spherical symmetry, $[C_3 \times s] = s$. We have previously shown (page 91) that a p_x orbital has the same transformation properties as a unit vector $\mathbf{x}$ and p_y those of a unit vector $\mathbf{y}$, and thus we may write that

$$C_3 \times p_x = p_x \cos \theta - p_y \sin \theta = p_x \cos 120° - p_y \sin 120°$$

$$= -\tfrac{1}{2} p_x - \frac{\sqrt{3}}{2} p_y$$

$$C_3 \times p_y = p_x \sin \theta + p_y \cos \theta = p_x \sin 120° + p_y \cos 120°$$

$$= \frac{\sqrt{3}}{2} p_x - \tfrac{1}{2} p_y$$

On substituting these results into Equation 6.4-1 and then collecting terms, we obtain

$$a_2 s + (\tfrac{1}{2} b_2 + \frac{\sqrt{3}}{2} c_2) p_x + \left(\frac{\sqrt{3}}{2} b_2 - \tfrac{1}{2} c_2 \right) p_y = a_1 s + b_1 p_x + 0 p_y$$

In order for this equation to hold, it is necessary that the coefficients of a particular atomic orbital have the same value on both sides of the equation and we can thus write the following relations:

$$a_1 = a_2$$

$$c_2 = \sqrt{3} b_2$$

$$b_1 = 2 b_2$$

Although we could repeat the above procedure in order to require that Φ_3 transform upon rotation into Φ_1, it is equally satisfactory and rather easier to carry out a reflection of Φ_3 through the plane of symmetry (the xz plane) which should transform it into Φ_2, and by adjusting the coefficients a_3, b_3, and c_3 obtain relations between these and a_2, b_2, and c_2. Thus we may write

$$\sigma_{xz} \times \{a_3 s - b_3 p_x - c_3 p_y\} = a_2 s - b_2 p_x + c_2 p_y \qquad (6.4\text{-}2)$$

But on reflecting each of the atomic orbitals in the xy plane, we obtain

$$\sigma_{xz} \times s = s$$

$$\sigma_{xz} \times p_x = p_x$$

$$\sigma_{xz} \times p_y = -p_y$$

Thus Equation 6.4-2 becomes

$$a_3 s - b_3 p_x + c_3 p_y = a_2 s - b_2 p_x + c_2 p_y$$

By equating coefficients of the atomic orbitals we obtain

$$a_2 = a_3$$

$$b_2 = b_3$$

$$c_2 = c_3$$

Symmetry requirements have thus provided six equations connecting the eight coefficients. In order to obtain two more equations we invoke the normalization and orthogonality requirements. Normalization of Φ_2 requires that

$$a_2{}^2 + b_2{}^2 + c_2{}^2 = 1$$

and the orthogonality of Φ_2 to Φ_3 requires

$$a_2 a_3 + b_2 b_3 - c_2 c_3 = 0$$

The eight equations can easily be solved to give the following values of the coefficients:

$$a_1 = a_2 = a_3 = 1/\sqrt{3}$$
$$b_1 = 2/\sqrt{6}$$
$$b_2 = b_3 = 1/\sqrt{6}$$
$$c_2 = c_3 = 1/\sqrt{2}$$

Thus the final expressions for the desired hybrid orbitals are the following:

$$\Phi_1 = \frac{1}{\sqrt{3}} s + \frac{2}{\sqrt{6}} p_x$$

$$\Phi_2 = \frac{1}{\sqrt{3}} s - \frac{1}{\sqrt{6}} p_x + \frac{1}{\sqrt{2}} p_y$$

$$\Phi_3 = \frac{1}{\sqrt{3}} s - \frac{1}{\sqrt{6}} p_x - \frac{1}{\sqrt{2}} p_y$$

Before proceeding to discuss some other examples, a few *ex post facto* observations may be made on the one just treated. First, we note that the coefficients of the s orbital are all the same. An s orbital must always make exactly the same contribution to all members of an equivalent set of hybrid orbitals because of its isotropic nature. Thus we could immediately have set down the equality $a_1 = a_2 = a_3$. Similarly, since Φ_2 and Φ_3 are equivalent in their orientation to the x axis, and the p_x orbital is symmetric about the x axis, the coefficients b_2 and b_3 could also have been set equal at the outset. The contributions of p_y to Φ_2 and Φ_3 can also be seen to be necessarily of the same magnitude but of opposite sign because of the spatial relationship of these hybrid orbitals to the p_y orbital. Had these equalities in coefficients been noted at the outset it would have been unnecessary to carry out the transformation of Φ_2 into Φ_3 by reflection in the xz plane. The important general point here is that we need not be completely mechanical in working out the expressions for hybrid orbitals, but instead, with a little practice, it becomes advantageous to make direct use of any immediately obvious relations between coefficients.

The practice of using negative signs as needed in order to keep all coefficients intrinsically positive is convenient since it eliminates ambiguity about which sign to use when one of the coefficients is obtained as the root of a quadratic equation.

As an example of a case in which the correct expressions can be written down without any *formal* use of symmetry operators, we next consider the set of square planar hybrids composed of s, p_x, p_y, $d_{x^2-y^2}$ atomic orbitals. The completely general expressions will be

$$\Phi_1 (+x) = a_1 s + b_1 p_x + c_1 p_y + d_1 d_{x^2-y^2}$$

$$\Phi_2 (-x) = a_2 s + b_2 p_x + c_2 p_y + d_2 d_{x^2-y^2}$$

$$\Phi_3 (+y) = a_3 s + b_3 p_x + c_3 p_y + d_3 d_{x^2-y^2}$$

$$\Phi_4 (-y) = a_4 s + b_4 p_x + c_4 p_y + d_4 d_{x^2-y^2}$$

The symbol $\Phi_1 (+x)$ refers to the orbital having its positive lobe directed along the positive extension of the x axis. All the orbitals of this set are equivalent, being permuted among themselves by the symmetry operations of the group D_{4h}.

We can thus immediately write the equality

$$a_1 = a_2 = a_3 = a_4$$

Since the p_x orbital can make no contribution to a hybrid directed along the y or $-y$ axes and the p_y orbital can make no contribution to a hybrid directed along the x or $-x$ axes, we can also write

$$c_1 = c_2 = b_3 = b_4 = 0$$

Next, we can see that the contribution of p_x to $\Phi_1 (+x)$ must be positive while its contribution to $\Phi_2 (-x)$ must be of the same magnitude but negative, with a similar situation prevailing in regard to the contributions of p_y to $\Phi_3 (+y)$ and $\Phi_4 (-y)$. These requirements are expressed as

$$0 < b_1 = -b_2$$

$$0 < c_3 = -c_4$$

Moreover, the p_x and p_y orbitals are entirely equivalent to one another except for orientation so that the contribution of p_x to the orbital directed along $+x$ must be equal to the contribution of p_y to the orbital directed along $+y$. Therefore

$$b_1 = c_3$$

Finally, because the four lobes of a $d_{x^2-y^2}$ orbital are all of the same amplitude but with the signs $+$ along $+x$ and $-x$, and $-$ along $+y$ and $-y$, we can write

$$0 < d_1 = d_2 = -d_3 = -d_4$$

Rewriting the completely general expressions to incorporate all this information we obtain

$$\Phi_1\,(+x) = a_1 s + b_1 p_x + d_1 d_{x^2-y^2}$$

$$\Phi_2\,(-x) = a_1 s - b_1 p_x + d_1 d_{x^2-y^2}$$

$$\Phi_3\,(+y) = a_1 s + b_1 p_y - d_1 d_{x^2-y^2}$$

$$\Phi_4\,(-y) = a_1 s - b_1 p_y - d_1 d_{x^2-y^2}$$

Thus there are only three independent coefficients, a_1, b_1, d_1 to be evaluated, and the normalization and orthogonality requirements suffice to do this. For all four orbitals, the normalization condition is

$$a_1{}^2 + b_1{}^2 + d_1{}^2 = 1$$

For the orthogonality of Φ_1 to Φ_2 we have

$$a_1{}^2 - b_1{}^2 + d_1{}^2 = 0$$

and for the orthogonality of Φ_1 to Φ_3

$$a_1{}^2 - d_1{}^2 = 0$$

All other orthogonality conditions will be identical with one of the two mentioned. Solving these three equations, we obtain

$$a_1 = \frac{1}{2}$$

$$b_1 = \frac{1}{\sqrt{2}}$$

$$d_1 = \frac{1}{2}$$

Two other important sets of hybrid orbitals in which all members are equivalent are the tetrahedral, sp^3, and octahedral, sp^3d^2, sets. Using the methods described and illustrated above, but with somewhat more cumbersome algebra, the following expressions may be derived for these:

For tetrahedral, sp^3, oriented with the axis of each hybrid forming equal angles with the Cartesian axes (numbered as in Figure 6.2):

$$\Phi_1 = \tfrac{1}{2}(s + p_x - p_y + p_z)$$

$$\Phi_2 = \tfrac{1}{2}(s - p_x + p_y + p_z)$$

$$\Phi_3 = \tfrac{1}{2}(s - p_x - p_y - p_z)$$

$$\Phi_4 = \tfrac{1}{2}(s + p_x + p_y - p_z)$$

For octahedral, sp^3d^2 orbitals, directed along Cartesian axes:

$$\Phi_1 = \frac{1}{\sqrt{6}} s + \frac{1}{\sqrt{2}} p_z + \frac{1}{\sqrt{3}} d_{z^2}$$

$$\Phi_2 = \frac{1}{\sqrt{6}} s - \frac{1}{\sqrt{2}} p_z + \frac{1}{\sqrt{3}} d_z$$

$$\Phi_3 = \frac{1}{\sqrt{6}} s + \frac{1}{\sqrt{2}} p_x - \frac{1}{\sqrt{12}} d_{z^2} + \tfrac{1}{2} d_{x^2-y^2}$$

$$\Phi_4 = \frac{1}{\sqrt{6}} s - \frac{1}{\sqrt{2}} p_x - \frac{1}{\sqrt{12}} d_{z^2} + \tfrac{1}{2} d_{x^2-y}$$

$$\Phi_5 = \frac{1}{\sqrt{6}} s + \frac{1}{\sqrt{2}} p_y - \frac{1}{\sqrt{12}} d_{z^2} - \tfrac{1}{2} d_{x^2-y^2}$$

$$\Phi_6 = \frac{1}{\sqrt{6}} s - \frac{1}{\sqrt{2}} p_y - \frac{1}{\sqrt{12}} d_{z^2} - \tfrac{1}{2} d_{x^2-y^2}$$

The derivation of the octahedral set is an excellent exercise in applying the procedure. In so doing it should be noted that the amplitude of the d_{z^2} orbital in any direction in the xy plane is only half its amplitude at the same distance from the origin along the z axis (cf. the wave function in Table 6.1).

Sets Containing Nonequivalent Orbitals

There are two subdivisions in this category, the one requiring no new considerations, the other requiring additional precautions in constructing the linear combinations.

If the orbitals in one subset are constructed entirely from atomic orbitals which cannot be used at all to construct those in the other subset and vice versa, the two subsets can be treated entirely independently of one another. For example, if we wish to construct a set of hybrid sigma orbitals to be used by atom A in a trigonal bipyramidal AB_5 molecule, we might construct the two axial orbitals using a d_{z^2} and a p_z orbital and the three equatorial orbitals using s, p_x, and p_y, obtaining for the latter the same expressions previously derived for the sp^2 set alone and for the former the two expressions:

$$\Phi_4 = \frac{1}{\sqrt{2}}(p_z + d_{z^2})$$

$$\Phi_5 = \frac{1}{\sqrt{2}}(-p_z + d_{z^2})$$

In doing this, however, we would be making assumptions not required by pure symmetry arguments and unlikely to be fully correct. The d_{z^2} orbital is capable of contributing to the equatorial hybrids, and the s orbital is capable of contributing to the axial hybrids. Indeed, we could equally well write the following expressions:

$$\Phi_1 = \frac{1}{\sqrt{3}}d_{z^2} + \frac{2}{\sqrt{6}}p_x$$

$$\Phi_2 = \frac{1}{\sqrt{3}}d_{z^2} - \frac{1}{\sqrt{6}}p_x + \frac{1}{\sqrt{2}}p_y \quad \left.\right\} \text{Equatorial}$$

$$\Phi_3 = \frac{1}{\sqrt{3}}d_{z^2} - \frac{1}{\sqrt{6}}p_x - \frac{1}{\sqrt{2}}p_y$$

$$\Phi_4 = \frac{1}{\sqrt{2}}(p_z + s)$$

$$\Phi_5 = \frac{1}{\sqrt{2}}(-p_z + s) \quad \left.\right\} \text{Axial}$$

These embody the extreme opposite assumption about the contributions of s and d_{z^2} to the two inequivalent sets.

The nature of the difficulty is very fundamental, inhering in the essential symmetry requirements of the problem. Both the axial and equatorial sets require the use of an orbital of A_1' symmetry, so to construct the entire set of five, two of these must be present. However, symmetry considerations cannot say which A_1' orbital is to be used in which set, so that by symmetry considerations alone no choice between the two limiting cases is possible. Indeed, there is no reason based on symmetry why each subset cannot use part of each A_1' orbital, and the most general expressions for a set of sp^3d trigonal hybrids must allow for this.

It is relatively easy to obtain this most general set of expressions from those of the limiting sets above. The coefficients of the p orbitals, which are required by symmetry to belong exclusively to one subset or the other, remain unaltered. Taking advantage of the trigonometric identity $\sin^2 \alpha + \cos^2 \alpha = 1$, we may write this most general set as follows:

$$\Phi_1 = \frac{1}{\sqrt{3}} (s \sin \alpha - d_{z^2} \cos \alpha) + \frac{2}{\sqrt{6}} p_x$$

$$\Phi_2 = \frac{1}{\sqrt{3}} (s \sin \alpha - d_{z^2} \cos \alpha) - \frac{1}{\sqrt{6}} p_x + \frac{1}{\sqrt{2}} p_y$$

$$\Phi_3 = \frac{1}{\sqrt{3}} (s \sin \alpha - d_{z^2} \cos \alpha) - \frac{1}{\sqrt{6}} p_x - \frac{1}{\sqrt{2}} p_y$$

$$\Phi_4 = \frac{1}{\sqrt{2}} (s \cos \alpha + d_{z^2} \sin \alpha) + \frac{1}{\sqrt{2}} p_z$$

$$\Phi_5 = \frac{1}{\sqrt{2}} (s \cos \alpha + d_{z^2} \sin \alpha) - \frac{1}{\sqrt{2}} p_z$$

It can easily be seen that each of these orbitals is still normalized since, for example,

$$\int (s \sin \alpha - d_{z^2} \cos \alpha)^2 \, d\tau = \sin^2 \alpha + \cos^2 \alpha = 1$$

and, similarly, it is also apparent that they are orthogonal.

The question of the actual distribution of the s and d_{z^2} orbitals among the two subsets, that is, the question of the magnitude of α, in a real molecule can only be settled by solution of an appropriate wave equation, or, approximately, by some simpler procedure such as calculating the magnitude of overlap of the general set with a suitable set of orbitals on the atoms B and selecting the value of α which minimizes the energy of the system or maximizes the total overlap.

Symmetry Aspects of Molecular Orbital Theory

7

7.1 General Principles

In the valence bond theory as developed by Slater, Pauling, and others, all bonds are considered to be two-center bonds, that is, to subsist between two atoms. It is only as an afterthought, more or less, that account is taken of any interaction between such bonds. In addition, there is no *a priori* way to decide which pairs of atoms should be considered as bonded and which nonbonded; we make choices which are supported by chemical knowledge. The molecular orbital theory begins, at least in principle, with the idea that all orbitals in a molecule extend over the entire molecule, which means therefore that electrons occupying these orbitals may be delocalized over the entire molecule. The theory does, naturally, admit of the possibility that one or more of these *molecular orbitals*, MO's, may have significantly large values of the wave function only in certain parts of the molecule. That is, localized bonding is a special case which is adequately covered by MO theory, but localization is not "built in" as a postulate at the outset as in the VB treatment.

Because MO theory treats orbitals which are in general spread over the entirety of a molecule, considerations of molecular symmetry properties are extremely useful in MO theory. They make it possible to determine the symmetry properties of the MO wave functions. With these known, it is often possible to draw many useful conclusions about bonding without doing any actual quantum computations at all, or only very simple ones. If elaborate calculations are to be carried out, the use of MO symmetry properties can immensely alleviate the labor involved by showing that many integrals must be identically equal to zero. This may be appreciated if we examine the equation that must be solved in order to calculate the energies of the molecular orbitals.

The Secular Equation

If a set of electronic wave functions for a molecule are denoted ψ_1, $\psi_2 \ldots \psi_i \ldots \psi_n$, the energies of eigenstates of the molecule can be obtained by solving the following determinantal equation:

$$
\begin{vmatrix}
H_{11} - ES_{11} & H_{12} - ES_{12} & \cdots & H_{1i} - ES_{1i} & \cdots & H_{1n} - ES_{1n} \\
H_{21} - ES_{21} & H_{22} - ES_{22} & \cdots & H_{2i} - ES_{2i} & \cdots & H_{2n} - ES_{2n} \\
\vdots & & & & & \\
H_{i1} - ES_{i1} & H_{i2} - ES_{i2} & \cdots & H_{ii} - ES_{ii} & \cdots & H_{in} - ES_{in} \\
\vdots & & & & & \\
H_{n1} - ES_{n1} & H_{n2} - ES_{n2} & \cdots & H_{ni} - ES_{ni} & \cdots & H_{nn} - ES_{nn}
\end{vmatrix} = 0
$$

in which the symbols H_{ij} and S_{ij} have the following definitions: *

$$
H_{ij} = \int \psi_i \mathcal{H} \psi_j \, d\tau
$$

$$
S_{ij} = \int \psi_i \psi_j \, d\tau
$$

This is called the secular equation. A derivation may be found in most elementary texts dealing with quantum mechanics. When the determinant is expanded it gives an nth order polynomial in E, and if n is a number greater than four, the solution of the equation constitutes a rather formidable problem in applied mathematics.

The great importance of group theory in problems of this nature is due to the fact that it can show us how to choose wave functions so that the secular equation may be greatly simplified if the molecule possesses some symmetry.

Before utilizing symmetry considerations, we may effect some simplification by choosing our wave functions so that they form an orthonormal set. This means that each one is normalized to unity and is orthogonal to all others. This immediately disposes of all of the S_{ij} since all those on

---

* It is assumed here and subsequently that all wave functions are real rather than complex or imaginary.

the diagonal, $S_{11}, S_{22} \ldots S_{ii} \ldots S_{nn}$, are equal to 1 and all others are equal to zero. The secular equation now has the somewhat simpler appearance:

$$
\begin{vmatrix}
H_{11} - E & H_{12} & \cdots & H_{1i} & \cdots & H_{1n} \\
H_{21} & H_{22} - E & \cdots & H_{2i} & \cdots & H_{2n} \\
& \vdots & & & & \\
H_{i1} & H_{i2} & \cdots & H_{ii} - E & \cdots & H_{in} \\
& \vdots & & & & \\
H_{n1} & H_{n2} & \cdots & H_{ni} & \cdots & H_{nn} - E
\end{vmatrix} = 0
$$

This simplification somewhat lessens the labor of solving the equation, but, clearly, a major saving of labor could be effected by eliminating as many as possible of the off-diagonal elements. If all of them could be eliminated we would have the trivially easy case of a completely diagonal determinant, and the values of the energies would be $H_{11}, H_{22} \ldots H_{ii} \ldots H_{nn}$. This can sometimes be done. More generally, however, it is possible to eliminate nondiagonal elements in such a way as to give a "blocked out" or factored determinant of the type:

$$
\begin{vmatrix}
H_{11} - E & H_{12} & 0 & 0 & 0 & 0 & 0 & 0 \\
H_{21} & H_{22} - E & 0 & 0 & 0 & 0 & 0 & 0 \\
0 & 0 & H_{33} - E & 0 & 0 & 0 & 0 & 0 \\
0 & 0 & 0 & H_{44} - E & H_{45} & H_{46} & 0 & 0 \\
0 & 0 & 0 & H_{54} & H_{55} - E & H_{56} & 0 & 0 \\
0 & 0 & 0 & H_{64} & H_{65} & H_{66} - E & 0 & 0 \\
0 & 0 & 0 & 0 & 0 & 0 & H_{77} - E & H_{78} \\
0 & 0 & 0 & 0 & 0 & 0 & H_{87} & H_{88} - E
\end{vmatrix} = 0
$$

In this example, the entire determinant is of order 8×8 and would in general require the solution of an eighth-order equation in E to obtain the energies. But it is easy to show that because of the way in which the above determinant is blocked out, each of the small determinants lying along the diagonal may be solved separately to obtain the eight energy values. Thus, instead of solving one 8×8 determinantal equation—a very laborious undertaking—we need only solve one cubic equation, two quadratics, and a first-order equation. It will be noted that complete diagonalization is only a special case of this form of blocking out or factorization.

We come now to the main point of this section, namely, the explanation of how group theory provides a straightforward way to write down the secular equation so that it is factored to the maximum possible extent. We examine an integral, often called a resonance integral, of the form

$$H_{ij} = \int \psi_i \mathcal{H} \psi_j \, d\tau$$

It has been shown in Section 5.2 that this integral will vanish unless ψ_i and ψ_j belong to the same representation of the symmetry group of the molecule. Thus, in order to be quite certain that the secular determinant for any molecule will be factored to the maximum possible extent, we must choose our wave functions so that they are explicitly bases for irreducible representations of the group, and then number them so that all those belonging to the same representation occur consecutively. In the example of the factored 8 × 8 determinant cited above, this would mean that we had chosen our ψ_i's in such a way that ψ_1 and ψ_2 belong to a representation Γ_1; ψ_3 is the only wave function belonging to a representation Γ_2; ψ_4, ψ_5, and ψ_6 all belong to another representation, Γ_3; and ψ_7 and ψ_8 belong to still another representation, Γ_4.

When doubly degenerate representations are involved there will be two blocks, differing in the expressions for the elements but having the same roots. For triply degenerate representations there will be three blocks all having the same roots.

The Hückel Approximation

In the following sections of this chapter we will discuss the application of molecular orbital theory to various types of molecules, mostly to the π electron systems of organic molecules. We shall discuss actual computational methods only in the simple approximation commonly called the Hückel approximation. This is rather crude but experience shows that certain properties at least can be estimated with a useful degree of accuracy. It has, at any rate, been widely used, and the literature contains many examples in which results obtained by this method have prompted experiments or have been invoked to explain experiments. Thus familiarity with it is valuable if only to make possible intelligent reading of the more recent literature in certain areas of organic| and organometallic chemistry. For our purposes, the advantage of this simple approximation is that it will enable us to carry the treatments of the various molecules through all of the stages in which symmetry considerations are helpful without getting bogged down in algebra and in questions of physics which do not in themselves contribute to our understanding of the symmetry considerations.

In the Hückel approximation we express a π molecular orbital, ψ_i, as a linear combination of atomic $p\pi$ orbitals. In this book we shall use ϕ_i to represent the $p\pi$ orbital on the ith atom. We further assume that each of the ϕ's is normalized and that its overlap with neighboring ϕ's is negligible. This last assumption would seem to be a particularly self-defeating one since, qualitatively, we think of a molecular orbital as resulting from the fusing together of individual atomic orbitals. Actually, it is not as damaging as we might suppose since it is partly compensated by other approximations in the Hückel approach. The most obvious result of this assumption is the effect that it has on the normalization constants, but this is easily taken care of as will be shown presently. With the above mentioned rules, we write a molecular orbital as a *linear combination of atomic orbitals*, an LCAO-MO, as follows:

$$\psi_i = N_i \sum_j a_{ij}\phi_j$$

The normalizing factor is obtained, assuming that we want ψ_i to be normalized to unity, as follows:

$$\frac{1}{N_i{}^2} = \int\left(\sum_j a_{ij}\phi_j\right)^2 d\tau$$

$$= \sum_j a_{ij}^2 \int \phi_j\phi_j \, d\tau + \sum_{\substack{j,\,k \\ (j\neq k)}} a_{ij}a_{ik}\int\phi_j\phi_k \, d\tau$$

The second sum is equal to zero because overlap is assumed to be zero. The first sum is just equal to $\sum_j a_{ij}^2$ since the ϕ_j's are assumed to be normalized. Thus

$$\frac{1}{N_i{}^2} = \sum_i a_{ij}^2$$

or

$$N_i = \frac{1}{\sqrt{\sum_j a_{ij}^2}}$$

For the special but not uncommon case in which all a_{ij}'s are ± 1, N is just $1/\sqrt{n}$ where n is the number of atomic orbitals in the linear combination.

The remaining assumptions of the Hückel approximation pertain to the evaluation of the energies of these LCAO-MO's. The energy of any orbital is given by the quantum mechanical expression

$$E_i = \int \psi_i \mathcal{H} \psi_i \, d\tau$$

where we assume that all wave functions are real.

If ψ_i is an LCAO-MO, we write

$$E_i = N_i^2 \left\{ \sum_j (a_{ij}^2 \int \phi_j \mathcal{H} \phi_j \, d\tau) + \sum_{\substack{j,\,k \\ (j \neq k)}} (a_{ij} a_{ik} \int \phi_j \mathcal{H} \phi_k \, d\tau) \right\}$$

The integrals in the first sum, $\int \phi_j \mathcal{H} \phi_j \, d\tau$, represent the energy of the individual ϕ_j's. If these are all identical, say all $p\pi$ orbitals of carbon atoms, we can represent this energy by α and write

$$E_i = \alpha + N_i^2 \sum_{\substack{j,\,k \\ (j \neq k)}} (a_{ij} a_{ik} \int \phi_j \mathcal{H} \phi_k \, d\tau)$$

In the remaining sum of integrals of the type $\int \phi_i \mathcal{H} \phi_j \, d\tau$ it is assumed that if ϕ_i and ϕ_j are on adjacent atoms, the integral will have a finite value—that is, there will be a significant interaction—while for all other cases in which the two orbitals are more widely separated the integral is assumed to be of negligible importance and is set equal to zero. If all the ϕ_j's are equivalent, we may write

$$\int \phi_i \mathcal{H} \phi_j \, d\tau = \int \phi_j \mathcal{H} \phi_i \, d\tau = \beta$$

and we get the following simplified general expression for the molecular orbital energies in the Hückel approximation:

$$E_i = \alpha + (2N_i^2 \sum_{\substack{j,\,k \\ (j = k+1)}} a_{ij} a_{ik})\beta$$

The normalization constants can be corrected for the finite overlap between adjacent orbitals. The value of the overlap integral, S, given by

$$S_{ij} = \int \phi_i \phi_j \, d\tau$$

can be estimated using tabulations to be found in the literature. If we use as an example the following MO in which the ϕ's are taken to be carbon $p\pi$ orbitals

$$\psi = N(\phi_1 + \phi_2 + \phi_3)$$

the value of N neglecting overlap is $1/\sqrt{3}$. If this MO applies to an open chain of three carbon atoms so that $S_{12} = S_{23} = S$ and $S_{13} = 0$, we can calculate a new normalization constant, as follows:

$$\frac{1}{N^2}$$

$$= \int (\phi_1 + \phi_2 + \phi_3)(\phi_1 + \phi_2 + \phi_3) \, d\tau$$

$$= \int \phi_1 \phi_1 \, d\tau + \int \phi_2 \phi_2 \, d\tau + \int \phi_3 \phi_3 \, d\tau + 2 \int \phi_1 \phi_2 \, d\tau + 2 \int \phi_2 \phi_3 \, d\tau + 2 \int \phi_1 \phi_3 \, d\tau$$

$$= \quad 1 \quad + \quad 1 \quad + \quad 1 \quad + \quad 2S \quad + \quad 2S \quad + \quad 0$$

Thus

$$N = \frac{1}{\sqrt{3 + 4S}}$$

Using tabulated values of overlap integrals it would be found that the $p\pi - p\pi$ overlap for carbon atoms at an internuclear distance of ~ 1.4 Å is about 0.2. Thus with neglect of overlap we get $N = 0.578$, while inclusion of nearest neighbor overlap gives $N = 0.513$. Thus no serious error is introduced and considerable time is saved by neglecting S. However, when desirable, it can be included without any basic change in the overall computational procedure.

In the following sections of this chapter we shall describe the use of symmetry considerations in setting up the "blocked out" or factored secular equations for molecular orbital treatment of various kinds of molecules, and we shall carry through the calculation of certain properties of the molecules such as molecular orbital energies, resonance stabilization energies, electron density distributions, and bond orders using the simple Hückel approximation.

Before proceeding to these examples it is appropriate to define a few more terms and concepts which will recur throughout the following pages.

Energy Level Diagrams. In many instances it is helpful to plot the calculated energies of molecular orbitals in a diagram (see next page).

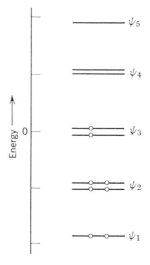

The energy scale is vertical and each orbital is represented as a short horizontal line placed at the position corresponding to the energy of the orbital. For doubly degenerate orbitals we use a pair of closely spaced lines. The occupation of the orbitals by electrons is indicated by placing small circles on the lines.

Hund's Rule and the Exclusion Principle. The order of filling of MO's for the ground state of a molecule follows the same rules as does the filling of orbitals in the ground state of an atom. Thus an electron will go into the lowest unfilled level subject to the following restrictions: Only two electrons may occupy a single level, and their spins must be of opposite sign (exclusion principle). When electrons are to be placed in a pair of degenerate orbitals, they will (as shown for ψ_3 in the above diagram) occupy each of the two degenerate orbitals singly, giving a total spin of 1 (Hund's rule).

Bonding Character of Orbitals. Normally we choose the zero of our energy scale to be that of the system in the hypothetical condition where no interaction between the separate atomic orbitals is occurring. In the actual state of the molecule then, some MO's will be of lower energy, some of higher energy, and, in certain cases, some of the same energy as this state which we take as zero. The MO's which are more stable than the separate, noninteracting atomic orbitals have energies <0 and are called *bonding* orbitals. Those with energies >0 are called *antibonding* orbitals, and any orbitals having energies of precisely 0 are called *nonbonding* orbitals. In the above example we have a strongly bonding MO, ψ_1, a less strongly bonding, doubly degenerate MO, ψ_2, a nonbonding, doubly degenerate MO, ψ_3, a moderately antibonding, doubly degenerate MO, ψ_4, and a strongly antibonding, nondegenerate MO, ψ_5.

7.2   Simple LCAO-MO Theory of Homocyclic π Systems

One of the best known applications of the LCAO-MO approach is to the treatment of the π bonding in planar, symmetric carbocyclic systems (real or hypothetical) such as cyclobutadiene, cyclopentadienyl ion and radical, benzene, tropylium ion, and so forth. The results can be used to calculate approximate values of resonance energies, as a first approximation in explaining electronic spectra, and as a starting point for treatment of the binding of such systems to metal atoms in compounds such as ferrocene, dibenzenechromium, cyclobutadiene-nickel (II) chloride, and many others.

It is assumed in these $(CH)_n$ systems that the carbon atoms use hybrids formed from an s and two p orbitals (p_x and p_y if we call the molecular plane the xy plane) to form σ bonds to two neighboring carbon atoms and to a hydrogen atom. This leaves each carbon atom with a p orbital perpendicular to the molecular plane. Our problem is now to determine how these n p orbitals may combine to form n molecular orbitals, what the relative energies of these MO's will be, and thence how they will be occupied by electrons.

The first step is to determine the representation of the symmetry group of the $(CH)_n$ molecule for which the set of n p orbitals, hereafter called $\phi_0, \phi_1, \phi_2 \ldots \phi_{n-1}$, forms a basis and to determine then the irreducible representations which it contains. The n molecular orbitals, called hereafter $\psi_1, \psi_2, \psi_3 \ldots \psi_n$, which are eigenfunctions of the molecule, must correspond to these irreducible representations. We need not use all operations in the group D_{nh}, since we only need to know the relative signs of the ϕ_i's in a given ψ. The operations of the rotation subgroup C_n can shift each ϕ to each of the other positions and thus provide this information. Let us consider the case of benzene, $(CH)_6$, where we use the rotation group C_6. The following results are obtained.

C_6	E	C_6	C_3	C_2	$C_3{}^2$	$C_6{}^5$
A	1	1	1	1	1	1
B	1	-1	1	-1	1	-1
E_1	$\begin{cases}1 \\ 1\end{cases}$	$\begin{matrix}\epsilon \\ \epsilon^*\end{matrix}$	$\begin{matrix}-\epsilon^* \\ -\epsilon\end{matrix}$	$\begin{matrix}-1 \\ -1\end{matrix}$	$\begin{matrix}-\epsilon \\ -\epsilon^*\end{matrix}$	$\begin{matrix}\epsilon^* \\ \epsilon\end{matrix}$
E_2	$\begin{cases}1 \\ 1\end{cases}$	$\begin{matrix}-\epsilon^* \\ -\epsilon\end{matrix}$	$\begin{matrix}-\epsilon \\ -\epsilon^*\end{matrix}$	$\begin{matrix}1 \\ 1\end{matrix}$	$\begin{matrix}-\epsilon^* \\ -\epsilon\end{matrix}$	$\begin{matrix}-\epsilon \\ -\epsilon^*\end{matrix}$
Γ_ϕ	6	0	0	0	0	0

$$\Gamma_\phi = A + B + E_1 + E_2$$

There are several conspicuous features of these results. First, note that in Γ_ϕ, $\chi(E) = 6 = n$ in $(CH)_n$. This must always be true regardless of the particular value of n. Second, note that all other $\chi(R)$ in Γ_ϕ are zero. This must also be true in general, for any rotation will always shift each ϕ so that all diagonal elements of the matrices must always be zero. Third, note that Γ_ϕ contains each irreducible representation once. This again will be true regardless of the particular value of n, since the sum of $\chi(R)$ for each operation over all n irreducible representations will always equal zero except for the $\chi(E)$'s which always sum to n. Thus, in all cases, we have the rule:

In a cyclic $(CH)_n$ molecule, the π molecular orbitals will always be n in number and there will be one corresponding to each irreducible representation of the group C_n.

We shall call the molecular orbital belonging to the ith irreducible representation ψ_i, and, in the LCAO approximation, we may express it as

$$\psi_i = \sum_{j=0}^{n-1} a_{ij}\phi_j \tag{7.2-1}$$

We wish to determine the values of the a_{ij}'s of which there are n in each MO, or n^2 altogether. This can be done quite straightforwardly since each irreducible representation is of dimension 1, which means that the character of the representation *is* the representation. Because ψ_i is a basis for the ith representation, we can write, for any operation R,

$$R\psi_i = \chi_i(R)\psi_i = \chi_i(R) \sum_j a_{ij}\phi_j = \sum_j a_{ij}[R\phi_j] \tag{7.2-2}$$

In a rotation group of order n the operations may all be written $C_n{}^0$, $C_n{}^1$, $C_n{}^2 \ldots C_n{}^m \ldots C_n^{n-1}$. The effect of an operation $C_n{}^m$ upon ϕ_j can always be written

$$C_n{}^m\phi_j = \phi_{j-m}$$

if we agree that

$$\phi_{j-m} = \phi_{j-m+n} \quad \text{for } j - m < 0$$

Thus, proceeding from Equation 7.2-2, we may write

$$\chi_i(C_n{}^m) \sum_j a_{ij}\phi_j = \sum_j a_{ij}[C_n{}^m\phi_j]$$

$$= \sum_j a_{ij}\phi_{j-m}$$

$$= \sum_j a_{i(j+m)}\phi_j \tag{7.2-3}$$

Specifically, 7.2-3 means that, since the coefficient of ϕ_j must be the same on both sides,

$$a_{i0} = \chi_i(C_n{}^0)a_{i0}$$

$$a_{i1} = \chi_i(C_n)a_{i0}$$

$$a_{i2} = \chi_i(C_n{}^2)a_{i0}$$

.

.

.

$$a_{i(n-1)} = \chi_i(c_n^{n-1})a_{i0}$$

Thus, if we assign to a_{i0} the value $+1$, we can write

$$\psi_i = \phi_0 + \chi_i(C_n)\phi_1 + \chi_i(C_n{}^2)\phi_2 \cdots + \chi_i(C_n{}^m)\phi_m \cdots + \chi_i(C_n^{n-1})\phi_{n-1}$$

But these coefficients, $\chi_i(C_n{}^m)$, are simply the characters of the ith representation. Thus we have obtained the solution to Equation 7.2-1. We may immediately write out the LCAO expressions for our molecular orbitals by inspection of the character table of the appropriate group, C_n.

For the sake of concreteness, let us continue to use benzene as an example and write out the ψ's.

$$A: \quad \psi_1 = \phi_0 + \phi_1 + \phi_2 + \phi_3 + \phi_4 + \phi_5$$

$$B: \quad \psi_2 = \phi_0 - \phi_1 + \phi_2 - \phi_3 + \phi_4 - \phi_5$$

$$E_1: \begin{cases} \psi_3 = \phi_0 + \epsilon\phi_1 - \epsilon^*\phi_2 - \phi_3 - \epsilon\phi_4 + \epsilon^*\phi_5 \\ \psi_4 = \phi_0 + \epsilon^*\phi_1 - \epsilon\phi_2 - \phi_3 - \epsilon^*\phi_4 + \epsilon\phi_5 \end{cases}$$

$$E_2: \begin{cases} \psi_5 = \phi_0 - \epsilon^*\phi_1 - \epsilon\phi_2 + \phi_3 - \epsilon^*\phi_4 - \epsilon\phi_5 \\ \psi_6 = \phi_0 - \epsilon\phi_1 - \epsilon^*\phi_2 + \phi_3 - \epsilon\phi_4 - \epsilon^*\phi_5 \end{cases}$$

From a practical point of view there are two disadvantages in these LCAO-MO's. First, they contain imaginary coefficients. Second, they are not normalized to unity. We shall deal with the former problem first, and leave normalization for the final step.

If energy calculations were to be made on the above wave functions, it would be found that ψ_3 and ψ_4 are degenerate as are ψ_5 and ψ_6. Hence, as proved in Section 5.1, linear combinations of ψ_3 and ψ_4 and of ψ_5 and ψ_6 are also satisfactory solutions of the wave equation. We can make linear combinations in such a way as to remove all imaginary coefficients. Adding ψ_3 and ψ_4 we get

$$\psi(E_1a)$$

$$= 2\phi_0 + (\epsilon + \epsilon^*)\phi_1 - (\epsilon^* + \epsilon)\phi_2 - 2\phi_3 - (\epsilon + \epsilon^*)\phi_4 + (\epsilon^* + \epsilon)\phi_5$$

Now each coefficient is a pure real number or the sum of a complex number and its complex conjugate, which sum is, by the definition of a complex conjugate, equal to twice the real part of the complex number. In the present case,

$$\epsilon = \cos 2\pi/6 - i \sin 2\pi/6$$

hence

$$\epsilon + \epsilon^* = 2 \cos 2\pi/6 = 1$$

so the above expression for $\psi(E_1 a)$ reduces to

$$\psi(E_1 a) = 2\phi_0 + \phi_1 - \phi_2 - 2\phi_3 - \phi_4 + \phi_5$$

The second linear combination we shall take is $(\psi_3 - \psi_4)/i$, which is, explicitly,

$$\psi(E_1 b) = [(\epsilon - \epsilon^*)\phi_1 - (\epsilon^* - \epsilon)\phi_2 - (\epsilon - \epsilon^*)\phi_4 + (\epsilon^* - \epsilon)\phi_5]/i$$
$$= -\sqrt{3}\phi_1 - \sqrt{3}\phi_2 + \sqrt{3}\phi_4 + \sqrt{3}\phi_5$$

ψ_5 and ψ_6 may be combined similarly giving

$$\psi(E_2 a) = \psi_5 + \psi_6 = 2\phi_0 - \phi_1 - \phi_2 + 2\phi_3 - \phi_4 - \phi_5$$
$$\psi(E_2 b) = (\psi_5 - \psi_6)/i = -\sqrt{3}\phi_1 + \sqrt{3}\phi_2 - \sqrt{3}\phi_4 + \sqrt{3}\phi_5$$

We now normalize these molecular orbital wave functions as described in Section 7.1, neglecting overlap, and obtain the following final expressions:

$$\psi(A) = \frac{1}{\sqrt{6}} (\phi_0 + \phi_1 + \phi_2 + \phi_3 + \phi_4 + \phi_5)$$

$$\psi(B) = \frac{1}{\sqrt{6}} (\phi_0 - \phi_1 + \phi_2 - \phi_3 + \phi_4 - \phi_5)$$

$$\psi(E_1 a) = \frac{1}{\sqrt{12}} (2\phi_0 + \phi_1 - \phi_2 - 2\phi_3 - \phi_4 + \phi_5)$$

$$\psi(E_1 b) = \frac{1}{2} (\phi_1 + \phi_2 - \phi_4 - \phi_5)$$

$$\psi(E_2 a) = \frac{1}{\sqrt{12}} (2\phi_0 - \phi_1 - \phi_2 + 2\phi_3 - \phi_4 - \phi_5)$$

$$\psi(E_2 b) = \frac{1}{2} (\phi_1 - \phi_2 + \phi_4 - \phi_5)$$

In addition to being normalized our MO's should be mutually orthogonal. It is easy to verify that those given above are so, but it follows from the procedure used to construct them that they must be.

It is instructive to examine some diagrams showing how the signs of the ψ's vary around the ring. For benzene, using the orbitals constructed above, we can make the following drawings:

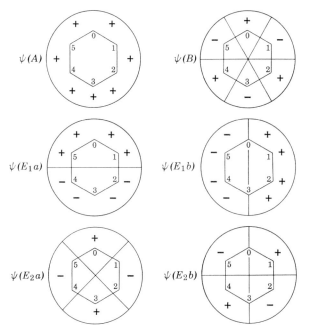

Note that the E_1 orbitals have one nodal plane and the E_2 orbitals two nodal planes.

The energies of these MO's may now be calculated using the Hückel approximation as discussed in Section 7.1. For $\psi(A)$ we obtain

$$E_A = \tfrac{1}{6}[6\alpha + 12\beta] = \alpha + 2\beta$$

Proceeding in a similar way the energies of the the other LCAO-MO's for benzene are found to be

$$E_B = \alpha - 2\beta$$
$$E_{E_1a} = E_{E_1b} = \alpha + \beta$$
$$E_{E_2a} = E_{E_2b} = \alpha - \beta$$

Since α is the energy of an electron in a pure atomic orbital, ϕ, we can conveniently take α as the zero of energy. It can be shown that β is intrinsically negative. Therefore we may express the above results in the form of an energy level diagram, viz.,

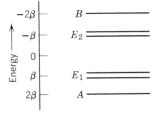

If the six π electrons in benzene each occupied a single atomic π orbital and there were no interaction, each would have an energy of α. The total energy would then be 6α which is zero if we assume, as above, that α is the zero of our energy scale. However, when the atomic orbitals interact to produce the molecular orbitals, the six electrons will now occupy these MO's according to Hund's rule and the Pauli exclusion principle. The first two will enter the A orbital and the remaining four occupy the E_1 orbitals. The total energy of the system is then

$$E_T = 2(2\beta) + 4(\beta) = 8\beta$$

Remembering that β is negative, we see that π bonding has stabilized the molecule by 8β. Energies expressed in units of β are not very informative, however, unless we can estimate the value of β. We shall next turn to the calculation of the resonance energy of benzene in units of β. Since the resonance energy may be estimated experimentally, we shall then be able to evaluate β. It is not practicable to evaluate β by computation.

Strictly speaking, the concept of resonance energy belongs in valence bond theory. It is defined there as the difference between the energy of the most stable canonical structure, which is one of the Kekulé structures, and the actual energy. The actual energy is assumed to be calculable, according to valence bond theory, by taking into account resonance between all possible canonical structures. Of these usually only five are considered to be of sufficiently low energy to be significant. These are the two equivalent Kekulé structures and the three Dewar structures:

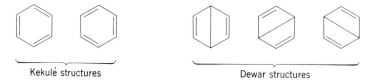

Kekulé structures   Dewar structures

However, it may be assumed that the difference between the energy of one Kekulé structure and the actual energy as calculated by molecular orbital theory will also be the resonance energy. In other words, while the ideas of resonance and resonance energy are essentially valence bond theory concepts, the "actual energy" is an observable which can, in principle, be equally well calculated by either method. The resonance energy estimated in this way is sometimes called the delocalization energy.

We have already shown that the energy of the system of six π electrons in benzene is equal to 8β. We must now calculate, in units of β, the energy of a Kekulé structure. In a Kekulé structure there are three localized π bonds. When two atomic π orbitals, say ϕ_1 and ϕ_2, interact to form a two-center bond, two molecular orbitals, ψ_1 and ψ_2, are formed. In order that these be real, normalized, and orthogonal, they must be

$$\psi_1 = \frac{1}{\sqrt{2}} (\phi_1 + \phi_2)$$

$$\psi_2 = \frac{1}{\sqrt{2}} (\phi_1 - \phi_2)$$

Their energies are readily seen to be

$$E_1 = \int \psi_1 \mathfrak{K} \psi_1 \, d\tau = \tfrac{1}{2} \Big[\int \phi_1 \mathfrak{K} \phi_1 \, d\tau + \int \phi_1 \mathfrak{K} \phi_2 \, d\tau$$

$$+ \int \phi_2 \mathfrak{K} \phi_1 \, d\tau + \int \phi_2 \mathfrak{K} \phi_2 \, d\tau \Big]$$

$$= \tfrac{1}{2}[2\alpha + 2\beta] = \beta$$

$$E_2 = -\beta$$

Since ψ_1 is the stable MO the two π electrons will occupy it and their combined energy will be 2β. Thus each of the pairs of localized π electrons in a Kekulé structure contribute 2β to the energy of the molecule, making the total π electron energy of a Kekulé structure 6β. But the actual energy is 8β; hence the resonance or delocalization energy is 2β.

Experimentally, the resonance energy of benzene is estimated in the following way. The actual enthalpy of formation of benzene can be determined by thermochemical measurements. The energy of a hypothetical molecule having a Kekulé structure can be estimated by using the energies for C—C, C=C, and C—H bonds found in other molecules such as ethane and ethylene. The difference between these energies is the "experimental" value of the resonance energy. We then evaluate $|\beta|$, since

$$|\beta| = \tfrac{1}{2}(\text{``experimental'' resonance energy})$$

The value of β obtained for benzene is 18–20 Kcal/mole, depending on choices of bond energies.* Practically the same value of β is obtained when other aromatic molecules, such as naphthalene, anthracene, and so on, are treated in the same way, which lends support to the belief that the LCAO method is at least empirically valid.

Other homocyclic systems which may be treated in a manner quite analogous to the above treatment of benzene are cyclobutadiene, the

* See Appendix IV for some important qualifications concerning the evaluation of β.

cyclopentadienyl radical and anion, benzene positive and negative ions, tropylium ion, and so on. Results for some of these systems will now be summarized. Practice in the application of the method may be had by deriving these results.

Cyclobutadiene has been an intriguing theoretical and experimental puzzle for many years. From the experimental viewpoint, the objective has been to synthesize it, or a substituted derivative. Such efforts have been only conditionally successful and it appears that the compound can have at best only a transient existence. Theoretically, the objective has been to calculate whether or not this molecule *should* be stable. A valence bond theory calculation of the resonance energy suggests stability. However, MO calculations indicate instability. Simple LCAO-MO theory gives the following results:

$$\psi(A) = \tfrac{1}{2}(\phi_0 + \phi_1 + \phi_2 + \phi_3) \qquad E = \alpha + 2\beta$$

$$\left.\begin{array}{l} \psi(Ea) = \dfrac{1}{\sqrt{2}}\,(\phi_0 - \phi_2) \\[2ex] \psi(Eb) = \dfrac{1}{\sqrt{2}}\,(\phi_1 - \phi_3) \end{array}\right\} \qquad E = \alpha$$

$$\psi(B) = \tfrac{1}{2}(\phi_0 - \phi_1 + \phi_2 - \phi_3) \qquad E = \alpha - 2\beta$$

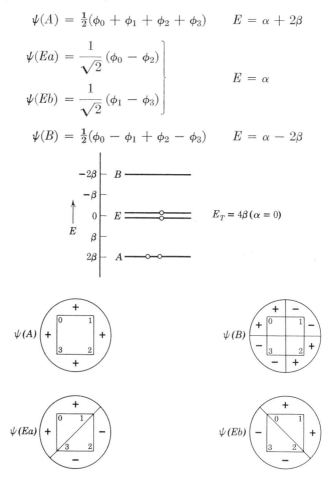

This simple treatment predicts that the molecule would be a diradical with a resonance energy of zero. Moreover, there would be a Jahn-Teller effect tending to cause distortion. More sophisticated MO treatments leave some doubt about the diradical character, but the prediction of zero resonance energy stands. Thus molecular orbital theory does not lead us to be optimistic about the existence of cyclobutadiene as a stable free molecule. It appears to be stable, however, when bound to a metal atom in the proper way. The MO basis for this increased stability will be discussed later (page 180).

The (C_5H_5) (cyclopentadienyl) radical and $(C_5H_5)^-$ (cyclopentadienyl anion) systems are of considerable interest in connection with recent studies of the cyclopentadienyl metal compounds such as ferrocene. Simple LCAO theory for the $(CH)_5$ system gives the following results: *

$$\psi(A) = \frac{1}{\sqrt{5}} (\phi_0 + \phi_1 + \phi_2 + \phi_3 + \phi_4) \quad E = \alpha + 2\beta$$

$$\left. \begin{aligned} \psi(E_1a) &= \sqrt{\frac{2}{5}} (\phi_0 + \phi_1 \cos \omega + \phi_2 \cos 2\omega \\ &\quad + \phi_3 \cos 2\omega + \phi_4 \cos \omega) \\ \psi(E_1b) &= \sqrt{\frac{2}{3}} (\phi_1 \sin \omega + \phi_2 \sin 2\omega \\ &\quad - \phi_3 \sin 2\omega - \phi_4 \sin \omega) \end{aligned} \right\} E = \alpha + (2 \cos \omega)\beta$$

$$\left. \begin{aligned} \psi(E_2a) &= \sqrt{\frac{2}{5}} (\phi_0 + \phi_1 \cos 2\omega + \phi_2 \cos \omega \\ &\quad + \phi_3 \cos \omega + \phi_4 \cos 2\omega) \\ \psi(E_2b) &= \sqrt{\frac{2}{3}} (\phi_1 \sin 2\omega - \phi_2 \sin \omega \\ &\quad + \phi_3 \sin \omega - \phi_4 \sin 2\omega) \end{aligned} \right\} E = \alpha + (2 \cos 2\omega)\beta$$

where $\omega = 2\pi/5$

* In obtaining these results and those for the $(CH)_7$ system to be discussed next, we have used the relation

$$\sum_{k=0}^{n-1} \cos^2 \frac{k2\pi}{n} = \sum_{k=0}^{n-1} \sin^2 \frac{k2\pi}{n} = \frac{n}{2}$$

along with other more familiar trigonometric identities. Although the energies of the double degenerate orbitals can be obtained using the expressions given above for them and the method described for benzene, some rather messy trigonometric algebra is encountered. A simpler method, which, however, involves some quantum theory which is not treated in this book, is available. See Eyring, Walter, and Kimball, *Quantum Chemistry*, John Wiley and Sons, Inc., 1944, pp. 254–255.

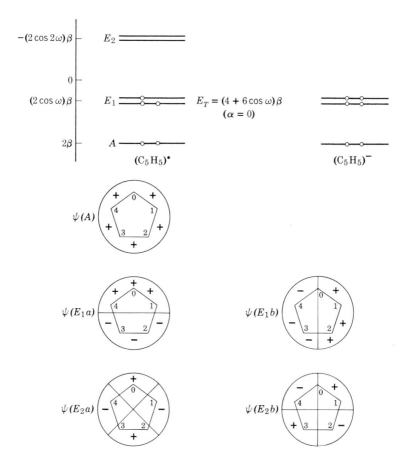

The resonance energy of $(C_5H_5)^{\bullet}$ is found to be $(6 \cos \omega)\beta = 1.854\beta$; taking β to be 18–20 Kcal/mole as in benzene, we estimate 33–37 Kcal/mole of resonance stabilization energy. It should be noted that free pentagonally symmetric $(C_5H_5)^{\bullet}$ is only hypothetical since a Jahn-Teller effect will operate to distort this symmetric configuration and thus somewhat alter the energies.

The $(C_7H_7)^{\bullet}$ (tropylium radical) and $(C_7H_7)^{+}$ (tropylium ion) systems are of interest both in their own right and in respect to their ability to form delocalized bonds to metal atoms. The simple LCAO-MO treatment gives the following results.

$$\psi(A) = \frac{1}{\sqrt{7}} (\phi_0 + \phi_1 + \phi_2 + \phi_3 + \phi_4 + \phi_5 + \phi_6) \qquad E = \alpha + 2\beta$$

$$\left. \begin{aligned} \psi(E_1 a) &= \sqrt{\frac{2}{7}} (\phi_0 + \phi_1 \cos \omega + \phi_2 \cos 2\omega + \phi_3 \cos 3\omega \\ &\quad + \phi_4 \cos 3\omega + \phi_5 \cos 2\omega + \phi_6 \cos \omega) \\ \psi(E_1 b) &= \sqrt{\frac{2}{5}} (\phi_1 \sin \omega + \phi_2 \sin 2\omega + \phi_3 \sin 3\omega \\ &\quad - \phi_4 \sin 3\omega - \phi_5 \sin 2\omega - \phi_6 \sin \omega) \end{aligned} \right\} \quad \begin{aligned} E &= \alpha + 2\beta \\ &\quad \cos \omega \end{aligned}$$

$$\left. \begin{aligned} \psi(E_2 a) &= \sqrt{\frac{2}{7}} (\phi_0 + \phi_1 \cos 2\omega + \phi_2 \cos 3\omega + \phi_3 \cos \omega \\ &\quad + \phi_4 \cos \omega + \phi_5 \cos 3\omega + \phi_6 \cos 2\omega) \\ \psi(E_2 b) &= \sqrt{\frac{2}{5}} (\phi_1 \sin 2\omega - \phi_2 \sin 3\omega - \phi_3 \sin \omega \\ &\quad + \phi_4 \sin \omega + \phi_5 \sin 3\omega - \phi_6 \sin 2\omega) \end{aligned} \right\} \quad \begin{aligned} E &= \alpha + 2\beta \\ &\quad \cos 2\omega \end{aligned}$$

$$\left. \begin{aligned} \psi(E_3 a) &= \sqrt{\frac{2}{7}} (\phi_0 + \phi_1 \cos 3\omega + \phi_2 \cos \omega + \phi_3 \cos 2\omega \\ &\quad + \phi_4 \cos 2\omega + \phi_5 \cos \omega + \phi_6 \cos 3\omega) \\ \psi(E_3 b) &= \sqrt{\frac{2}{5}} (\phi_1 \sin 3\omega - \phi_2 \sin \omega + \phi_3 \sin 2\omega \\ &\quad - \phi_4 \sin 2\omega + \phi_5 \sin \omega - \phi_6 \sin 3\omega) \end{aligned} \right\} \quad \begin{aligned} E &= \alpha + 2\beta \\ &\quad \cos 3\omega \end{aligned}$$

where $\omega = 2\pi/7$

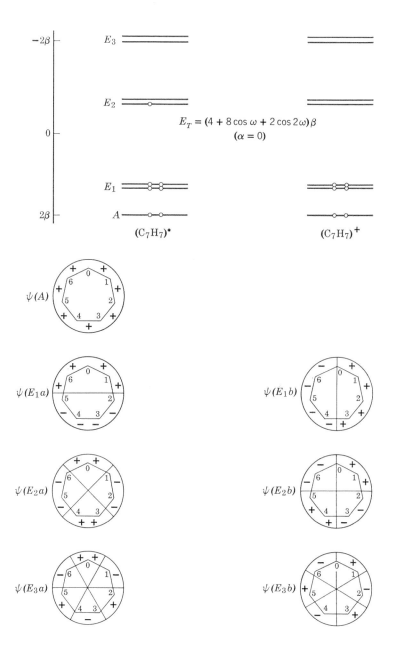

The resonance energy of $(C_7H_7)^\bullet$ is found to be $[(4 + 8 \cos \omega + 2 \cos 2\omega) - 6]\beta$; again taking β to be 18–20 Kcal/mole, as in benzene, we estimate 46–51 Kcal/mole of resonance stabilization energy. Again, it should be mentioned that because of the Jahn-Teller effect $(C_7H_7)^\bullet$ would be unstable in its most symmetrical form and would distort in some manner. The resonance energy of the tropylium ion, which is isolable in the form of salts with various anions, can be estimated as about 50–55 Kcal/mole, which must thus be of considerable importance in stabilizing this ion.

Cyclooctatetraene, $(CH)_8$, is of course well known to be nonplanar and nonaromatic. It is properly described as a conjugated but nonaromatic tetraolefin. A molecular orbital treatment of the *hypothetical* planar $(CH)_8$ is of some interest, however, in respect to the questions of the instability of this configuration for the free molecule as well as the possibility of the stabilization of this configuration by formation of the anions $C_8H_8^-$ and $C_8H_8^{2-}$. The simple LCAO-MO treatment of $(CH)_8$ gives the following results.

$$\psi(A) = \frac{1}{\sqrt{8}} (\phi_0 + \phi_1 + \phi_2 + \phi_3 + \phi_4 + \phi_5 + \phi_6 + \phi_7) \qquad E = \alpha + 2\beta$$

$$\psi(B) = \frac{1}{\sqrt{8}} (\phi_0 - \phi_1 + \phi_2 - \phi_3 + \phi_4 - \phi_5 + \phi_6 - \phi_7) \qquad E = \alpha - 2\beta$$

$$\psi(E_1 a) = \frac{1}{\sqrt{8}} (\sqrt{2}\,\phi_0 + \phi_1 - \phi_3 - \sqrt{2}\,\phi_4 - \phi_5 + \phi_7)$$
$$\psi(E_1 b) = \frac{1}{\sqrt{8}} (\phi_1 + \sqrt{2}\,\phi_2 + \phi_3 - \phi_5 - \sqrt{2}\,\phi_6 - \phi_7) \qquad E = \alpha + \sqrt{2}\beta$$

$$\psi(E_2 a) = \frac{1}{2} (\phi_0 - \phi_2 + \phi_4 - \phi_6)$$
$$\psi(E_2 b) = \frac{1}{2} (\phi_1 - \phi_3 + \phi_5 - \phi_7) \qquad E = \alpha$$

$$\psi(E_3 a) = \frac{1}{\sqrt{8}} (\sqrt{2}\,\phi_0 - \phi_1 + \phi_3 - \sqrt{2}\,\phi_4 + \phi_5 - \phi_7)$$
$$\psi(E_3 b) = \frac{1}{\sqrt{8}} (\phi_1 - \sqrt{2}\,\phi_2 + \phi_3 - \phi_5 + \sqrt{2}\,\phi_6 - \phi_7) \qquad E = \alpha - \sqrt{2}\beta$$

It is seen that the treatment leads us to expect the planar C_8H_8 to be a diradical, as in the case of butadiene. In this case, however, there is resonance stabilization energy equal to $[4(1 + \sqrt{2}) - 8]\beta = 1.66\beta$, which comes to about 30–33 Kcal/mole.

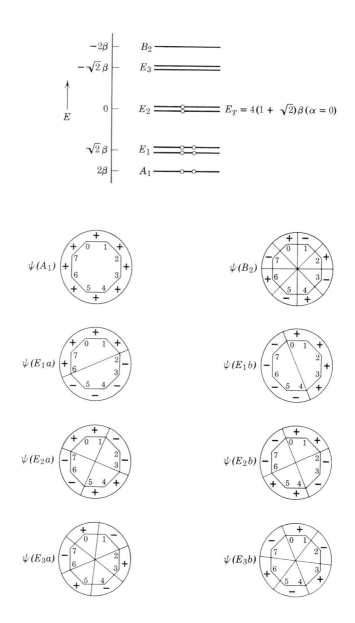

The 4n + 2 Rule

From the results we have obtained for the systems C_4H_4, C_6H_6, and C_8H_8 we can infer a rule, first discovered by Hückel and now rather well known, concerning the aromaticity of planar, carbocyclic systems of the type $(CH)_n$.

According to valence bond theory, any such system in which the number of carbon atoms is even would be expected to have resonance stabilization because of the existence of canonical forms of the type illustrated below for the first three members of the homologous series:

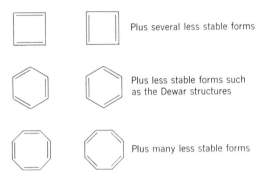

Plus several less stable forms

Plus less stable forms such as the Dewar structures

Plus many less stable forms

Since a calculation of the resonance energy of benzene by the VB method shows that the greater part of it is due to resonance between the two Kekulé structures shown, we might suppose that its homologs would also have significant resonance stabilization energies, and explicit calculations confirm this. However, such conclusions seemingly are at variance with experimental fact since cyclobutadiene appears to be too unstable to have any permanent existence, and cyclooctatetraene exists as a nonplanar tetraolefin incapable of having resonance stabilization of the sort considered.

Simple LCAO-MO theory provides a direct and natural explanation for the facts. It may be seen that for C_4H_4, C_6H_6, and C_8H_8 the energy level diagrams have the same general arrangement of energy levels, namely a symmetrical distribution of a strongly bonding, nondegenerate A level, a strongly antibonding, nondegenerate B level with a set of E levels between them. It can be shown that such a pattern will always develop in such a system. Now in order to fill the lowest nondegenerate A level and then to fill completely the first x pairs of degenerate levels above it, to give a closed configuration (that is, one with all electrons paired) of the general type $(\psi_A)^2(\psi_{E_1})^4 \ldots (\psi_{E_x})^4$, $4x + 2$ electrons will be required. It therefore follows that only for systems in which n, which is both the number of pi electrons and the ring size of $(CH)_n$, is a number expressible as $4x + 2$ ($x = 1, 2, 3 \ldots$) can we obtain a closed configuration. The numbers, n, meeting this requirement are 6, 10, 14 .... For the other even integers, namely 4, 8, 12 ..., we shall always have an electron configuration of the sort $(\psi_A)^2(\psi_{E_1})^4 \ldots (\psi_{E_x})^2$.

We have seen that in the case of cyclobutadiene the LCAO-MO calculation shows that besides the diradical character there is zero resonance stabilization energy, whereas for C_8H_8 appreciable resonance energy is expected. In general the systems not satisfying the $4n + 2$ rule will have some resonance energy in the planar form, but it is assumed that a distortion, required by the Jahn-Teller theorem and abetted by the fact that twisting into a nonplanar conformation will relieve hydrogen-hydrogen repulsion (which increases for the planar conformation as ring size increases) will, as in C_8H_8, cause a nonplanar, nonaromatic conformation to be the most stable one.

7.3   More General Cases of LCAO-MO Pi Bonding

The homocyclic systems treated in the preceding section have the simplifying feature that there is only one MO belonging to each irreducible representation of the rotation group (and also of the true point group) of the molecule. In the more general case there will be two or more MO's belonging to at least one or several of the irreducible representations of the point group of the molecule. When this happens the treatment becomes a little more complicated.

Let us suppose that we have two normalized, orthogonal LCAO-MO's, ψ_1 and ψ_2, of the same symmetry. One of the factors or blocks in the secular equation will then be

$$\begin{vmatrix} H_{11} - E & H_{12} \\ H_{21} & H_{22} - E \end{vmatrix} = 0$$

where

$$H_{11} = \int \psi_1 \mathcal{3C} \psi_1 \, d\tau$$

$$H_{22} = \int \psi_2 \mathcal{3C} \psi_2 \, d\tau$$

$$H_{12} = H_{21} = \int \psi_1 \mathcal{3C} \psi_2 \, d\tau = \int \psi_2 \mathcal{3C} \psi_1 \, d\tau$$

We can then obtain the energies by solving this quadratic determinantal equation. If we want nothing further we have no need to do more, but if we wish to obtain any further results which depend on the correct expressions for the true LCAO-MO's, then we must first obtain such expressions. ψ_1 and ψ_2 are not themselves the actual MO's unless by chance $H_{12} = 0$; the actual MO's are orbitals which have the calculated energies. These can be expressed as linear combinations of ψ_1 and ψ_2, adjusting the mixing coefficients so that the correct energies are obtained. Thus, if the two energies are E_1 and E_2 we would write

$$\psi_1' = \frac{1}{\sqrt{1 + x^2}} \, (\psi_1 + x\psi_2)$$

$$\psi_2' = \frac{1}{\sqrt{1 + x^2}} \, (x\psi_1 - \psi_2)$$

We would then set up expressions for the energies of these new MO's and find the value of the mixing coefficient, x, required to make their energies equal to E_1 and E_2. The two orbitals ψ_1' and ψ_2' are then also orthogonal to one another, viz.,

$$\int \psi_1' \psi_2' \, d\tau = \frac{1}{1 + x^2} \int (\psi_1 + x\psi_2)(x\psi_1 - \psi_2) \, d\tau$$

$$= \frac{1}{1 + x^2} \left[x \int \psi_1^2 \, d\tau - \int \psi_1 \psi_2 \, d\tau + x^2 \int \psi_1 \psi_2 \, d\tau - x \int \psi_2^2 \, d\tau \right]$$

$$= \frac{1}{1 + x^2} \left[x(1) - 0 + x^2(0) - x(1) \right] = 0$$

and they can be used to write a new, completely diagonal, secular determinant since the correct choice of x makes

$$\int \psi_1' \mathcal{H} \psi_2' \, d\tau$$

equal to zero.

Rather than attempt any more discussion of this situation in the abstract, we shall proceed to discuss two examples of its occurrence in real molecules. Both of these are molecules which were predicted by simple

LCAO-MO theory to have closed configurations and have recently (1960 and 1962) been isolated.

Tetramethylenecyclobutane

This molecule was predicted to have about 30 Kcal/mole of resonance stabilization energy * in 1952 and the inference drawn that it would be stable once made. In 1962 its synthesis was reported by Griffin.† It is assumed to be planar and the drawing below shows the numbering system which will be used in the following LCAO-MO treatment.

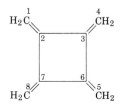

The molecule belongs to the point group D_{4h}. By using the set of eight carbon $p\pi$ orbitals as a basis we can obtain a reducible representation which will contain the irreducible representations to which the π-MO's must belong. This is shown below:

D_{4h}	E	$2C_4$	C_2	$2C_2'$	$2C_2''$	i	$2S_4$	σ_h	$2\sigma_v$	$2\sigma_d$
Γ_π	8	0	0	0	-4	0	0	-8	0	4

$$\Gamma_\pi = 2A_{2u} + 2B_{1u} + 2E_g$$

There is a very important feature of this situation which we can turn to advantage. It will be observed that the set of four methylene carbon atoms, numbers 1, 4, 5, and 8, possess D_{4h} symmetry by themselves and that the set of four carbon atoms in the ring, numbers 2, 3, 6, and 7, also by themselves constitute a set having D_{4h} symmetry. Furthermore, the atoms in one set are not equivalent symmetrically to any of those in the

* See J. D. Roberts, A. Streitwieser, Jr., and C. M. Regan, *J. Am. Chem. Soc.*, **74**, 4579 (1952), who also give the results of an LCAO-MO treatment in the Hückel approximation for numerous other small unsaturated molecules. Many of the other molecules treated by them provide excellent examples which the reader may use for practice.
† G. W. Griffin and L. I. Peterson, *J. Am. Chem. Soc.*, **84**, 3398 (1962).

other. None of the outer atoms is ever interchanged with any of the inner atoms by any symmetry operation. Thus each of these sets can be used separately as the basis for a representation of the group and if this is done we obtain from each set a representation, Γ'_π, which reduces as follows

$$\Gamma'_\pi = A_{2u} + B_{1u} + E_g$$

This means that if we write an expression for an A_{2u} MO as a combination of all eight orbitals, viz.,

$$\psi_{A_{2u}} = N(a_1\phi_1 + a_2\phi_2 + a_3\phi_3 + a_4\phi_4 + a_5\phi_5 + a_6\phi_6 + a_7\phi_7 + a_8\phi_8)$$

we can separate it into two components, one made up only of orbitals of the inner set and one made up only of orbitals of the outer set, viz.,

$$\psi_{A_{2u}} = \underset{\text{inner set}}{N(a_2\phi_2 + a_3\phi_3 + a_6\phi_6 + a_7\phi_7)} + \underset{\text{outer set}}{N(a_1\phi_1 + a_4\phi_4 + a_5\phi_5 + a_8\phi_8)}$$

Since the symmetry operations cannot interchange orbitals of the two sets, each of the subsets in the expression for the A_{2u} MO must itself have A_{2u} symmetry. Thus, in order to construct an orbital of A_{2u} symmetry for the entire molecule, we can first construct partial orbitals from the atomic orbitals in each of the subsets and then combine them into a complete MO. A similar line of reasoning applies to MO's of any other symmetry.

Our immediate problem then is to combine the four outer orbitals into linear combinations having A_{2u}, B_{1u}, and E_g symmetry and also to combine the four inner orbitals into linear combinations having these same symmetries. As in the case of the carbocyclic rings, this process can be simplified by using only the corresponding rotation group C_4 instead of D_{4h} since the former can discriminate between the orbitals. That is, if we construct an orbital of A symmetry in the group C_4 it will automatically turn out to have A_{2u} symmetry in D_{4h} because of the inherent symmetry of the $p\pi$ orbitals themselves, namely their antisymmetric character with respect to reflection in the molecular plane.

With these considerations in mind, the process of constructing the correct linear combinations of the subsets proceeds exactly as in the case of the carbocyclic systems: The correct coefficients of the atomic orbitals are simply the characters of the representations. For the E orbitals we will obtain some imaginary coefficients, but these may be eliminated by taking the appropriate linear combinations. We can thus write, almost by direct inspection of the character table of the C_4 group:

$$\psi_A{}^i = \frac{1}{2}(\phi_2 + \phi_3 + \phi_6 + \phi_7)$$

$$\psi_A{}^o = \frac{1}{2}(\phi_1 + \phi_4 + \phi_5 + \phi_8)$$

$$\psi_B{}^i = \frac{1}{2}(\phi_2 - \phi_3 + \phi_6 - \phi_7)$$

$$\psi_B{}^o = \frac{1}{2}(\phi_1 - \phi_4 + \phi_5 - \phi_8)$$

$$\psi_{Ea}^i = \frac{1}{\sqrt{2}}(\phi_2 - \phi_6)$$

$$\psi_{Eb}^i = \frac{1}{\sqrt{2}}(\phi_3 - \phi_7)$$

$$\psi_{Ea}^o = \frac{1}{\sqrt{2}}(\phi_1 - \phi_5)$$

$$\psi_{Eb}^o = \frac{1}{\sqrt{2}}(\phi_4 - \phi_8)$$

where we use the superscripts i and o to indicate that the combination is made up of inner or outer orbitals.

We may now solve the secular equation using these symmetry-correct MO's and obtain the MO energies. Thus, for the A orbitals we have the equation

$$\begin{vmatrix} H_{A^iA^i} - E & H_{A^iA^o} \\ H_{A^oA^i} & H_{A^oA^o} - E \end{vmatrix} = 0$$

The elements of this determinant are easily evaluated using the Hückel approximation:

$$H_{A^iA^i} = \int \psi_A{}^i \mathcal{H} \psi_A{}^i \, d\tau = \frac{1}{4}\int (\phi_2 + \phi_3 + \phi_6 + \phi_7)\mathcal{H}(\phi_2 + \phi_3 + \phi_6 + \phi_7)\, d\tau$$

$$= \frac{1}{4}\left[\int \phi_2 \mathcal{H}\phi_2 \, d\tau + \int \phi_2 \mathcal{H}\phi_3 \, d\tau + \int \phi_2 \mathcal{H}\phi_6 \, d\tau + \cdots + \int \phi_7 \mathcal{H}\phi_7 \, d\tau\right]$$

$$= \frac{1}{4}[\alpha + \beta + 0 + \cdots + \alpha]$$

$$= \frac{1}{4}[4\alpha + 8\beta] = \alpha + 2\beta$$

$$H_{A^o A^o} = \int \psi_A{}^o \mathfrak{IC} \psi_A{}^o \, d\tau = \tfrac{1}{4} \int (\phi_1 + \phi_4 + \phi_5 + \phi_8) \mathfrak{IC} (\phi_1 + \phi_4 + \phi_5 + \phi_8) \, d\tau$$

$$= \tfrac{1}{4}[4\alpha] = \alpha$$

$$H_{A^t A^o} = H_{A^o A^t} = \int \psi_A{}^o \mathfrak{IC} \psi_A{}^i \, d\tau$$

$$= \tfrac{1}{4} \int (\phi_1 + \phi_4 + \phi_5 + \phi_8) \mathfrak{IC} (\phi_2 + \phi_3 + \phi_6 + \phi_7) \, d\tau$$

$$= \tfrac{1}{4}[4\beta] = \beta$$

As before it is convenient to choose the energy of an isolated ϕ as zero; thus, setting $\alpha = 0$ and substituting into the secular determinant, we obtain

$$\begin{vmatrix} 2\beta - E & \beta \\ \beta & -E \end{vmatrix} = 0$$

which is expanded into the quadratic equation

$$E^2 - 2\beta E - \beta^2 = 0$$

The solutions are easily found and turn out to be

$$E_A = (1 + \sqrt{2})\beta, \; (1 - \sqrt{2})\beta$$

Following precisely the same procedure for the two orbitals of B symmetry, we obtain

$$\begin{vmatrix} H_{B^t B^t} - E & H_{B^t B^o} \\ H_{B^o B^t} & H_{B^o B^o} - E \end{vmatrix} = \begin{vmatrix} -2\beta - E & \beta \\ \beta & -E \end{vmatrix} = 0$$

The solutions are

$$E_B = (\sqrt{2} - 1)\beta, \; (-\sqrt{2} - 1)\beta$$

For the E orbitals we will obtain two 2×2 determinants, one involving the Ea orbitals and another involving the Eb orbitals. It is only necessary to solve one of them. Choosing the Ea determinant we have

$$\begin{vmatrix} H_{E^t E^t} - E & H_{E^t E^o} \\ H_{E^o E} & H_{E^o E^o} - E \end{vmatrix} = \begin{vmatrix} -E & \beta \\ \beta & -E \end{vmatrix} = 0$$

The solutions here are

$$E_E = \pm\beta$$

Remembering that β is intrinsically negative, we may use these results to construct the following energy level diagram, in which the eight electrons have been added to the lower four orbitals:

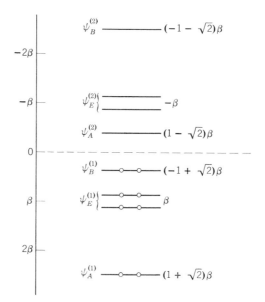

It can be seen that the order of the levels is such that all of the bonding levels (those with energies <0) are just filled, and all electrons must have their spins paired.

The resonance stabilization energy can be easily calculated. The most stable arrangement of the four electron pairs in localized double bonds would undoubtedly be the one labeled (*a*) below, all other arrangements, such as (*b*) or (*c*), containing fewer than four short, strong double bonds.

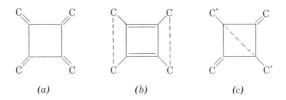

(*a*)   (*b*)   (*c*)

The energy of this arrangement, taking $\alpha = 0$, can easily be seen, by the argument used in Section 7.2 for benzene in a Kekulé structure, to be 8β. The total energy of the eight electrons occupying the molecular orbitals as shown in the energy level diagram above is

$$[2(1 + \sqrt{2}) + 4(1) + 2(\sqrt{2} - 1)]\beta = 9.656\beta$$

Hence the resonance or delocalization energy is 1.66β which, taking $|\beta| = 20$ Kcal/mole comes to about 33 Kcal/mole.

Our next problem is to determine the correct expressions for the true molecular orbitals, that is, for MO's which have the energies we have calculated. As indicated earlier, these must be appropriate combinations of the symmetry orbitals we have used in the secular equation.

To find the A orbital having the energy $(1 + \sqrt{2})\beta$, that is, $\psi_A^{(1)}$ as it has been labeled in the energy level diagram, we write

$$\psi_A^{(1)} = \frac{1}{\sqrt{1 + x^2}} (\psi_A{}^o + x\psi_A{}^i)$$

set up the equation requiring this to have the energy $(1 + \sqrt{2})\beta$ and solve it for the required value of x; thus

$$E_A^{(1)} = (1 + \sqrt{2})\beta = \int \psi_A^{(1)} \mathcal{H}\psi_A^{(1)} \, d\tau$$

$$= \frac{1}{1 + x^2} \int (\psi_A{}^o + x\psi_A{}^i)\mathcal{H}(\psi_A{}^o + x\psi_A{}^i) \, d\tau$$

$$= \frac{1}{1 + x^2} \left[\int \psi_A{}^o\mathcal{H}\psi_A{}^o \, d\tau + 2x \int \psi_A{}^i\mathcal{H}\psi_A{}^o \, d\tau \right.$$

$$\left. + x^2 \int \psi_A{}^i\mathcal{H}\psi_A{}^i \, d\tau \right]$$

$$= \frac{1}{1 + x^2} [H_{A^oA^o} + 2xH_{A^iA^o} + x^2H_{A^iA^i}]$$

$$= \frac{1}{1 + x^2} [\alpha + 2x\beta + x^2(\alpha + 2\beta)]$$

Setting α equal to zero, collecting terms in x^2 and x, and dividing out β, we obtain the following quadratic equation in x:

$$(\sqrt{2} - 1)x^2 - 2x + (1 + \sqrt{2}) = 0$$

which has the unique solution $\sqrt{2} + 1$.

Proceeding in exactly the same manner for the $\psi_B^{(1)}$ orbital, expressed as

$$\psi_B^{(1)} = \frac{1}{\sqrt{1 + y^2}} (\psi_B{}^o + y\psi_B{}^i)$$

we obtain

$$y = \sqrt{2} - 1$$

For the Ea orbitals we write

$$\psi_{Ea}^{(1)} = \frac{1}{\sqrt{1 + z^2}} (\psi_{Ea}^o + z\psi_{Ea}^i)$$

and obtain

$$z = 1$$

Thus the true bonding MO's, that is, MO's which have exactly the energies previously calculated, are:

$$\psi_A^{(1)} = (8\sqrt{2} + 16)^{-\frac{1}{2}}[(\phi_1 + \phi_4 + \phi_5 + \phi_8)$$
$$+ (\sqrt{2} + 1)(\phi_2 + \phi_3 + \phi_6 + \phi_7)]$$

$$\psi_B^{(1)} = (16 - 8\sqrt{2})^{-\frac{1}{2}}[(\phi_1 - \phi_4 + \phi_5 - \phi_8)$$
$$+ (\sqrt{2} - 1)(\phi_2 - \phi_3 + \phi_6 - \phi_7)]$$

$$\psi_{Ea}^{(1)} = \tfrac{1}{2}(\phi_1 + \phi_2 - \phi_5 - \phi_6)$$

$$\psi_{Eb}^{(1)} = \tfrac{1}{2}(\phi_3 + \phi_4 - \phi_7 - \phi_8)$$

For convenience in the following numerical computations we will now rewrite these expressions using numerical values for the coefficients.

$$\psi_A^{(1)} = 0.191(\phi_1 + \phi_4 + \phi_5 + \phi_8)$$
$$+ 0.462(\phi_2 + \phi_3 + \phi_6 + \phi_7)$$

$$\psi_B^{(1)} = 0.462(\phi_1 - \phi_4 + \phi_5 - \phi_8)$$
$$+ 0.191(\phi_2 - \phi_3 + \phi_6 - \phi_7)$$

$$\psi_{Ea}^{(1)} = 0.500(\phi_1 + \phi_2 - \phi_5 - \phi_6)$$

$$\psi_{Ea}^{(2)} = 0.500(\phi_3 + \phi_4 - \phi_7 - \phi_8)$$

As examples of the use of such LCAO-MO's, let us calculate the bond orders in tetramethylenecyclobutane. The order of the bond between two atoms is defined as the sum of the products of the coefficients of the atomic orbitals of the two atoms in each of the occupied MO's, each product being weighted with the number of electrons occupying the MO. Thus we have for one of the equivalent ring bonds, say the one between C_2 and C_3:

$$
\begin{array}{llll}
\psi_A^{(1)}: & 2 \times (0.462)(0.462) & = & 0.428 \\
\psi_B^{(1)}: & 2 \times (0.191)(-0.191) & = & -0.074 \\
\psi_{Ea}^{(1)}: & 2 \times (0.500)(0) & = & 0.000 \\
\psi_{Eb}^{(1)}: & 2 \times (0.500)(0) & = & 0.000 \\
\hline
& & & 0.354
\end{array}
$$

For one of the exo bonds, say the one between C_1 and C_2:

$$\psi_A^{(1)}: \quad 2 \times (0.191)(0.462) = 0.176$$
$$\psi_B^{(1)}: \quad 2 \times (0.462)(0.191) = 0.176$$
$$\psi_{Ea}^{(1)}: \quad 2 \times (0.500)(0.500) = 0.500$$
$$\psi_{Eb}^{(1)}: \quad 2 \times (0)(0) \qquad\quad = 0.000$$

$$\overline{0.852}$$

From these numbers we can see that the pi electrons are much more heavily localized in the exo bonds than in the ring bonds.

Bicyclooctatriene

The presumed structure of this compound, which was first reported in 1960 * is shown in Figure 7.1a. It belongs to the point group D_{3h}. An LCAO-MO treatment of it has been described † but not in as much detail as we shall explain it here.

Figure 7.1b shows a numbered set of six $p\pi$ atomic orbitals which will be used to construct the π MO's. Using these atomic orbitals as a basis for a representation of the group D_{3h}, we obtain the following results:

D_{3h}	E	$2C_3$	$3C_2$	σ_h	$2S_3$	$3\sigma_v$
Γ_π	6	0	0	0	0	-2

$$\Gamma_\pi = A_2' + A_1'' + E' + E''$$

It is to be noted that in this molecule all of the $p\pi$ orbitals are members of one equivalent set; there is some symmetry operation which will exchange any two of them. Thus we must consider all six in making up MO's of the appropriate symmetries; it will in fact be entirely impossible to make up orbitals of the correct symmetry using any fewer than the entire six. We now show how this can easily be done.

We first note that all types of A orbitals (in D_{3h}) have the same symmetry properties with respect to the rotations constituting the subgroup C_3; also, both E' and E'' orbitals have the same properties with respect to these rotations. Thus we can use the group C_3 to set up some linear com-

---

* H. E. Zimmerman and R. M. Paufler, *J. Am. Chem. Soc.*, **82**, 1514 (1960).
† C. F. Wilcox, Jr., S. Winstein, and W. G. McMillan, *J. Am. Chem. Soc.*, **82**, 5450 (1960).

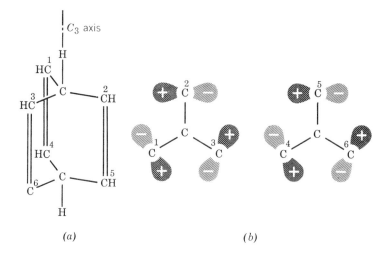

(a)   (b)

Figure 7.1   (a) The molecular structure and the numbering of the carbon atoms for bicyclooctatriene. (b) A sketch showing the orientation of the $p\pi$ orbitals (ϕ_i's) used in the MO treatment.

binations which will be correct to this extent. Since these rotations about the C_3 axis do not interchange any of the orbitals ϕ_1, ϕ_2, ϕ_3 with those of the set ϕ_4, ϕ_5, ϕ_6, we can, *temporarily*, treat the two sets separately. We thus first write down linear combinations corresponding to the A and E representations of C_3. As shown in Section 7.2 for such cyclic systems, the characters are the correct coefficients, and we can thus write, by inspection of the character table for the group C_3:

$$A:\quad \phi_1 + \phi_2 + \phi_3 \qquad \text{and} \qquad \phi_4 + \phi_5 + \phi_6$$

$$E:\begin{Bmatrix} \phi_1 + \epsilon\phi_2 + \epsilon^*\phi_3 \\ \phi_1 + \epsilon^*\phi_2 + \epsilon\phi_3 \end{Bmatrix} \quad \text{and} \quad \begin{Bmatrix} \phi_4 + \epsilon\phi_5 + \epsilon^*\phi_6 \\ \phi_4 + \epsilon^*\phi_5 + \epsilon\phi_6 \end{Bmatrix}$$

Again using the procedure explained in Section 7.2 we take linear combinations of the above expressions for the E orbitals so as to obtain real coefficients, obtaining

$$E:\begin{Bmatrix} 2\phi_1 - \phi_2 - \phi_3 \\ \phi_2 - \phi_3 \end{Bmatrix} \quad \text{and} \quad \begin{Bmatrix} 2\phi_4 - \phi_5 - \phi_6 \\ \phi_5 - \phi_6 \end{Bmatrix}$$

We have not bothered to normalize these since they are not yet actually wave functions.

We now turn back to the character table for D_{3h} and note that an A_2' orbital must go into itself on reflection through the horizontal symmetry plane. The effect of this symmetry operation on the individual atomic orbitals is as follows:

$$\sigma_h(\phi_1) \rightarrow \phi_4 \qquad \sigma_h(\phi_4) \rightarrow \phi_1$$

$$\sigma_h(\phi_2) \rightarrow \phi_5 \qquad \sigma_h(\phi_5) \rightarrow \phi_2$$

$$\sigma_h(\phi_3) \rightarrow \phi_6 \qquad \sigma_h(\phi_6) \rightarrow \phi_3$$

Thus we must combine the two sums which have A symmetry with respect to the threefold rotations into one which goes into itself on re-flection through σ_h, making use of the above transformation properties of the individual atomic orbitals. It is obvious that the correct result must be

$$\psi_{A'} = \phi_1 + \phi_2 + \phi_3 + \phi_4 + \phi_5 + \phi_6$$

We can see from the character table that an A_1' orbital would also have the same symmetry properties as those which we have so far consciously built into this LCAO. However, A_1' and A_2' orbitals differ in their be-havior upon rotation about a twofold axis or upon reflection in σ_v. The inherent symmetry of the p orbitals is responsible for the fact that the type of orbital we require is A_2' and not A_1' without our having explicitly looked after this. We can easily confirm this. If we reflect through the σ_v which passes through carbons 1 and 4, the atomic orbitals transform as follows:

$$\sigma_v(\phi_1) \rightarrow -\phi_1 \qquad \sigma_v(\phi_4) \rightarrow -\phi_4$$

$$\sigma_v(\phi_2) \rightarrow -\phi_3 \qquad \sigma_v(\phi_5) \rightarrow -\phi_6$$

$$\sigma_v(\phi_3) \rightarrow -\phi_2 \qquad \sigma_v(\phi_6) \rightarrow -\phi_5$$

Therefore

$$\sigma_v(\psi_{A'}) = \sigma_v(\phi_1 + \phi_2 + \phi_3 + \phi_4 + \phi_5 + \phi_6)$$

$$= (-\phi_1 - \phi_3 - \phi_2 - \phi_4 - \phi_6 - \phi_5)$$

$$= -(\phi_1 + \phi_2 + \phi_3 + \phi_4 + \phi_5 + \phi_6)$$

$$= -\psi_{A'}$$

Thus, as stated, this orbital is an A_2' orbital. The correct normalization constant in the Hückel approximation is $1/\sqrt{6}$.

The A_1'' orbital, which must change sign on reflection through σ_h and also on reflection through σ_v obviously has the form

$$\psi_{A_1''} = \frac{1}{\sqrt{6}} (\phi_1 + \phi_2 + \phi_3 - \phi_4 - \phi_5 - \phi_6)$$

Similarly, the characters of the E' and E'' representations under σ_h are 2 and -2 respectively, meaning that each member of an E' pair will go into itself on reflection through σ_h while each member of an E'' set will go into the negative of itself on reflection in σ_h. These requirements are satisfied by combining the above expressions which have E symmetry with respect to the threefold rotations as follows:

$$\psi_{E'a} = 2\phi_1 - \phi_2 - \phi_3 + 2\phi_4 - \phi_5 - \phi_6$$

$$\psi_{E'b} = \phi_2 - \phi_3 + \phi_5 - \phi_6$$

$$\psi_{E''a} = 2\phi_1 - \phi_2 - \phi_3 - 2\phi_4 + \phi_5 + \phi_6$$

$$\psi_{E''b} = \phi_2 - \phi_3 - \phi_5 + \phi_6$$

Now, collecting together all of the above results and normalizing each one, we write the following final list of the LCAO-MO's for bicyclo-octatriene:

$$\psi_{A_2'} = \frac{1}{\sqrt{6}} (\phi_1 + \phi_2 + \phi_3 + \phi_4 + \phi_5 + \phi_6)$$

$$\psi_{A_1''} = \frac{1}{\sqrt{6}} (\phi_1 + \phi_2 + \phi_3 - \phi_4 - \phi_5 - \phi_6)$$

$$\psi_{E'a} = \frac{1}{\sqrt{12}} (2\phi_1 - \phi_2 - \phi_3 + 2\phi_4 - \phi_5 - \phi_6)$$

$$\psi_{E'b} = \tfrac{1}{2} (\phi_2 - \phi_3 + \phi_5 - \phi_6)$$

$$\psi_{E''a} = \frac{1}{\sqrt{12}} (2\phi_1 - \phi_2 - \phi_3 - 2\phi_4 + \phi_5 + \phi_6)$$

$$\psi_{E''b} = \tfrac{1}{2} (\phi_2 - \phi_3 - \phi_5 + \phi_6)$$

We now consider the energies of these MO's. If we calculate these using the Hückel approximation, we set all resonance integrals other than

$H_{14} = H_{41}$, $H_{25} = H_{52}$, and $H_{36} = H_{63}$ equal to zero. We then obtain the following results:

ORBITAL	ENERGY	ORBITAL	ENERGY
A_1''	$\alpha - \beta$	A_2'	$\alpha + \beta$
E''	$\alpha - \beta$	E'	$\alpha + \beta$

Thus, in this approximation, the A_1'' orbital is accidentally degenerate with the E'' orbitals and the A_2' orbital is accidentally degenerate with the E' orbitals.

To use the Hückel approximation in this case, however, is to make the entire process of using a molecular orbital treatment pointless, for we then obtain exactly the same answer as we would obtain by assuming the molecule to contain three isolated double bonds. Each double bond can be regarded as resulting from the formation of two two-center MO's, one of energy $\alpha + \beta$ (bonding) and one of energy $\alpha - \beta$ (antibonding). In the Hückel approximation, therefore, we find that bicyclooctatriene has no resonance stabilization energy.

The advantage of the MO treatment is that we can rather easily extend it to take account of interaction between the double bonds. To do this we recognize that the energy of interaction between two orbitals such as ϕ_1 and ϕ_2, viz., the integral $\int \phi_1 \mathcal{H} \phi_2 \, d\tau$, will not be exactly zero but will have some finite value, say β'. Also, there will be some finite value for the integrals such as $\int \phi_1 \mathcal{H} \phi_5 \, d\tau$ which we may call β''. If we recalculate the energies including these quantities we will get somewhat different results. Thus for $\psi_{A_1''}$ we obtain

$$E_{A_1''} = \tfrac{1}{6} \int (\phi_1 + \phi_2 + \phi_3 - \phi_4 - \phi_5 - \phi_6) \mathcal{H} (\phi_1$$

$$+ \phi_2 + \phi_3 - \phi_4 - \phi_5 - \phi_6) \, d\tau$$

$$= \tfrac{1}{6} [\int \phi_1 \mathcal{H} \phi_1 \, d\tau + \int \phi_1 \mathcal{H} \phi_2 \, d\tau + \int \phi_1 \mathcal{H} \phi_3 \, d\tau - \int \phi_1 \mathcal{H} \phi_4 \, d\tau$$

$$- \int \phi_1 \mathcal{H} \phi_5 \, d\tau - \int \phi_1 \mathcal{H} \phi_6 \, d\tau + \int \phi_2 \mathcal{H} \phi_1 \, d\tau + \cdots]$$

$$= \tfrac{1}{6} [\alpha + \beta' + \beta' - \beta - \beta'' - \beta'' + \beta' + \cdots]$$

$$= \alpha - \beta + 2\beta' - 2\beta''$$

Similarly, for $\psi_{E''b}$, we obtain

$$E_{E''b} = \tfrac{1}{4}\int (\phi_2 - \phi_3 - \phi_5 + \phi_6)\mathcal{H}(\phi_2 - \phi_3 - \phi_5 + \phi_6)\, d\tau$$

$$= \tfrac{1}{4}[\int \phi_2\mathcal{H}\phi_2\, d\tau - \int \phi_2\mathcal{H}\phi_3\, d\tau - \int \phi_2\mathcal{H}\phi_5\, d\tau$$

$$+ \int \phi_2\mathcal{H}\phi_6\, d\tau - \int \phi_3\mathcal{H}\phi_2\, d\tau + \cdots]$$

$$= \tfrac{1}{4}[\alpha - \beta' - \beta + \beta'' - \beta' + \cdots]$$

$$= \alpha - \beta - \beta' + \beta''$$

Thus, when allowance is made for these additional interactions we find that the accidental degeneracies are removed. In the same way, we find that the energies of the A_2' and E' orbitals are

$$E_{A_2'} = \alpha + \beta + 2\beta' + 2\beta''$$

$$E_{E'} = \alpha + \beta - \beta' - \beta''$$

Let us now see what effect this allowance for interaction between the double bonds has on the calculated resonance energy.

The quantity β is intrinsically negative since it is a measure of the interaction between adjacent $p\pi$ orbitals so oriented (Figure 7.2a) as to give a bonding interaction. The integral β' measures the interaction between p orbitals oriented as in Figure 7.2b. It can be seen that this interaction will be antibonding so that β' is positive, and also that it should be smaller in absolute magnitude than β since the orbitals concerned are

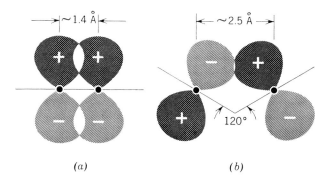

(a)   (b)

Figure 7.2   (a) The relative orientation of $p\pi$ orbitals on adjacent, bonded carbon atoms of bicyclooctatriene. (b) The relative orientation of $p\pi$ orbitals on two non-adjacent carbon atoms of bicyclooctatriene.

much farther apart and overlap less. The ratio $-\beta'/\beta$ can be roughly estimated using overlap integrals and it is ~ 0.1. Also using overlap integrals, it may be shown that β'' is still smaller and for the present we shall neglect it entirely. With these considerations in mind we can draw the following energy level diagram, in which, as usual, we take α as the zero of energy:

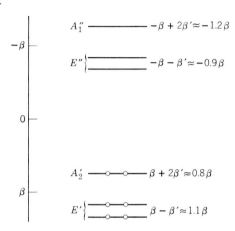

The energy of the six electrons occupying these orbitals as shown is given by

$$4(\beta - \beta') + 2(\beta + 2\beta') = 6\beta$$

The same answer is obtained even when the complete expressions using β'' are used. Thus the conclusion is that while interaction between the double bonds causes certain displacements of the energy levels, it does not result in any increased stabilization of the molecule. The delocalization energy remains zero.

7.4   Three-Center Bonding

It is now recognized that there are many molecules in which bonding must be treated with three-atom units as the smallest ones considered. In other words, the three atoms must be regarded as one indivisible entity instead of as a pair of two-center systems with an atom in common. We will thus assume that electrons may be delocalized over the framework of three atoms instead of localized between only two of them. If our three-atom framework constitutes a complete molecule or ion in itself, then our treatment will be a molecular orbital one in the strict sense of the word. If the three-atom entity is instead only a portion of a larger molecule, then our analysis will not be a molecular orbital one in the strict sense of considering the possibility of delocalization of electrons over the entire molecule, but its principles and results as they apply to the selected group of three atoms will not of course differ in any essential way from those obtained when the three atoms are the entire molecule.

As examples of three-center bonding, we will take the following:

(i) Open three-center bonding as found for example in the pi system of the allyl ion, $[H_2CCHCH_2]^-$, and in the bridge bonding in the trimethyl aluminum dimer and diborane.

(ii) Closed three-center bonding as found for example in one of the types of B—B—B bonding occurring in certain boron hydrides.

Open Three-Center Bonding

The nuclear framework, $p\pi$ atomic orbitals and a set of reference axes for the allyl ion are shown below:

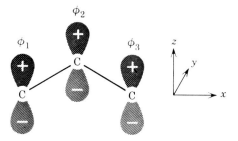

The ion belongs to the C_{2v} point group, and the set of three $p\pi$ orbitals forms a basis for the following representation:

C_{2v}	E	C_2	σ_{yz}	σ_{xy}
Γ_π	3	-1	1	-3

$$\Gamma_\pi = A_2 + 2B_1$$

We must now devise linear combinations of the atomic orbitals which belong to these representations. For the A_2 orbital we write the following general expression:

$$\psi_{A_2} = a_1\phi_1 + a_2\phi_2 + a_3\phi_3$$

According to the character table for the group C_{2v}, an orbital of A_2 symmetry must be symmetric (that is, go into itself) when the operation C_2 is applied, and be antisymmetric when either of the σ_v's is applied.

Because our orbital is to be constructed of p_z orbitals it will automatically be antisymmetric to σ_{xy}. The requirement that it be symmetric to twofold rotation, which has the following effects on the individual ϕ's:

$$C_2(\phi_1) \rightarrow -\phi_3$$

$$C_2(\phi_2) \rightarrow -\phi_2$$

$$C_2(\phi_3) \rightarrow -\phi_1$$

means that

$$C_2(\psi_{A_2}) = C_2(a_1\phi_1 + a_2\phi_2 + a_3\phi_3) = -a_1\phi_3 - a_2\phi_2 - a_3\phi_1$$

$$= -a_3\phi_1 - a_2\phi_2 - a_1\phi_3 = a_1\phi_1 + a_2\phi_2 + a_3\phi_3$$

This can only be true if

$$a_1 = -a_3$$

$$a_2 = -a_2 = 0$$

$$a_3 = -a_1$$

Thus the relative values of all of the coefficients are fixed; their absolute values will be chosen so as to make ψ_{A_2} normalized, and we thus obtain

$$\psi_{A_2} = \frac{1}{\sqrt{2}}(\phi_1 - \phi_3)$$

It can easily be seen that this orbital is antisymmetric to reflection in σ_{yz}. Its energy in the Hückel approximation turns out to be just α since there are no adjacent atomic orbitals occurring in it.

The orbital ϕ_2 by itself has B_1 symmetry. ϕ_1 and ϕ_3 must be combined to make a second B_1 orbital. The combination must change sign when the operation C_2 is applied. The correct, normalized expressions must therefore be

$$\psi'_{B_1} = \phi_2$$

$$\psi''_{B_1} = \frac{1}{\sqrt{2}}(\phi_1 + \phi_3)$$

The secular equation to be solved is then

$$\begin{vmatrix} H_{B'B'} - E & H_{B'B''} \\ H_{B''B'} & H_{B''B''} - E \end{vmatrix} = 0$$

The elements of the determinant are evaluated as follows:

$$H_{B'B'} = \int \phi_2 \mathcal{H} \phi_2 \, d\tau = \alpha$$

$$H_{B'B''} = H_{B''B'} = \frac{1}{\sqrt{2}} \int (\phi_2) \mathcal{H} (\phi_1 + \phi_3) \, d\tau$$

$$= \frac{1}{\sqrt{2}} \left[\int \phi_2 \mathcal{H} \phi_1 \, d\tau + \int \phi_2 \mathcal{H} \phi_3 \, d\tau \right]$$

$$= \frac{1}{\sqrt{2}} [\beta + \beta] = \sqrt{2}\beta$$

$$H_{B''B''} = \tfrac{1}{2} \int (\phi_1 + \phi_3) \mathcal{H} (\phi_1 + \phi_3) \, d\tau$$

$$= \tfrac{1}{2} \left[\int \phi_1 \mathcal{H} \phi_1 \, d\tau + \int \phi_1 \mathcal{H} \phi_3 \, d\tau \right.$$

$$\left. + \int \phi_3 \mathcal{H} \phi_1 \, d\tau + \int \phi_3 \mathcal{H} \phi_3 \, d\tau \right]$$

$$= \tfrac{1}{2}[\alpha + 0 + 0 + \alpha] = \alpha$$

Taking $\alpha = 0$, as usual, and inserting into the determinant, we obtain

$$\begin{vmatrix} -E & \sqrt{2}\beta \\ \sqrt{2}\beta & -E \end{vmatrix} = 0$$

which has the roots $\pm\sqrt{2}\beta$.

To find the B_1 MO with energy $\sqrt{2}\beta$ we need to find the correct value of x in the equation

$$\frac{1}{1 + x^2} \int (\psi'_{B_1} + x\psi''_{B_1}) \mathcal{H} (\psi'_{B_1} + x\psi''_{B_1}) \, d\tau = \sqrt{2}\beta$$

which we do as follows:

$$\frac{1}{1 + x^2} \left[\int \psi'_{B_1} \mathcal{H} \psi'_{B_1} \, d\tau + 2x \int \psi''_{B_1} \mathcal{H} \psi'_{B_1} \, d\tau + x^2 \int \psi''_{B_1} \mathcal{H} \psi''_{B_1} \, d\tau \right]$$

$$= \frac{1}{1 + x^2} [H_{B'B'} + 2xH_{B'B''} + x^2 H_{B''B''}]$$

$$= \frac{1}{1 + x^2} [\;\;0\;\; + 2x\sqrt{2}\beta + \;\;\;0\;\;\;] = \sqrt{2}\beta$$

Eliminating β and collecting terms in x and x^2, we obtain the quadratic equation

$$x^2 - 2x + 1 = 0$$

which has the unique solution

$$x = 1$$

Thus the desired MO has the form

$$\psi_{B_1}^{(1)} = \frac{1}{\sqrt{2}} (\psi'_{B_1} + \psi''_{B_1})$$

$$= \frac{1}{\sqrt{2}} [\phi_2 + \frac{1}{\sqrt{2}} (\phi_1 + \phi_3)]$$

$$= \tfrac{1}{2}(\phi_1 + \sqrt{2} \, \phi_2 + \phi_3)$$

By the same procedure we find that the B_1 MO with the energy $-\sqrt{2}\beta$ has the form

$$\psi_{B_1}^{(2)} = \tfrac{1}{2}(\phi_1 - \sqrt{2} \, \phi_2 + \phi_3)$$

We can thus draw the following energy level diagram for the allyl anion:

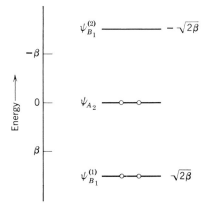

The energy of the allyl ion in the canonical form $H_2\ddot{C}$—CH=CH$_2$ would be $2\alpha + (2\alpha + 2\beta)$, or, with α taken as our zero of energy, 2β. The energy of the electron distribution shown above is $2\sqrt{2}\beta$. Hence the resonance energy is calculated to be $(2\sqrt{2} - 2)\beta = 0.828\beta \approx 16$ Kcal/mole.

Generalization of the Results

We have so far treated only the specific case of pi bonding in a three-center system of identical atoms using identical pi orbitals. It is easy to make a semiquantitative generalization of these results. A few examples should suffice to show how this is done.

Suppose that we have a system of three atoms each with a pi orbital but with the center atom different from the end atoms as in NO_2 or NO_2^-. The symmetry is still C_{2v} and so we still expect MO's belonging to the representations A_2 and $2B_1$ of C_{2v}. The expression for our A_2 orbital will still be, for reasons of symmetry alone

$$\psi_{A_2} = \frac{1}{\sqrt{2}} (\phi_1 - \phi_3)$$

and its energy will be α_O where the subscript shows that this is the energy of an oxygen p orbital. We can again set up the same two linear combinations of orbitals having B_1 symmetry. The elements of the secular determinant will have the values shown below:

$$\begin{vmatrix} \alpha_N - E & \sqrt{2}\beta \\ \sqrt{2}\beta & \alpha_O - E \end{vmatrix} = 0$$

Because we now have two different α's, we cannot obtain the extremely simple result we previously did, but qualitatively the results will be very similar as indicated on the following energy level diagram:

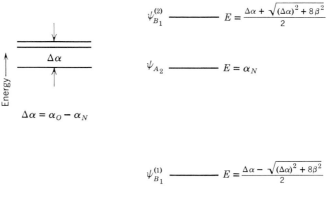

$$\psi_{B_1}^{(2)} \quad\underline{\hspace{2cm}}\quad E = \frac{\Delta\alpha + \sqrt{(\Delta\alpha)^2 + 8\beta^2}}{2}$$

$$\psi_{A_2} \quad\underline{\hspace{2cm}}\quad E = \alpha_N$$

$$\psi_{B_1}^{(1)} \quad\underline{\hspace{2cm}}\quad E = \frac{\Delta\alpha - \sqrt{(\Delta\alpha)^2 + 8\beta^2}}{2}$$

Atomic orbitals   Molecular orbitals

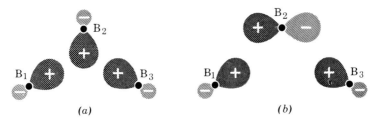

Figure 7.3　Two sets of atomic orbitals which may be used to form three-center bonds in certain boron hydrides.

The two B_1 orbitals are not now symmetrically placed with respect to the A_2 orbital, but so long as $|\beta| \gg \Delta\alpha$, which is likely to be true for NO_2, the deviation from the symmetrical arrangement will not be too great. The qualitative pattern of levels is still essentially the same, viz., one strongly bonding MO, one approximately nonbonding MO, and one strongly antibonding MO.

Let us now look at some systems involving sigma bonding instead of pi bonding. Examples of these are the B—B—B groups in certain boron hydrides and the B—H—B, Al—C—Al, Be—C—Be groups in boron hydrides and the dimeric aluminum and beryllium alkyls. For a system of three atoms, each providing a sigma orbital as shown in Figure 7.3a, we find that these orbitals form a basis for the following representation of the group C_{2v}.

C_{2v}	E	C_2	σ_1	σ_2	(σ_1 = molecular plane)
Γ_σ	3	1	3	1	

$$\Gamma_\sigma = 2A_1 + B_1$$

The correct expression for the B_1 orbital can be written down immediately from the character table:

$$\psi_{B_1} = \frac{1}{\sqrt{2}} (\phi_1 - \phi_3)$$

The energy of this orbital is calculated as follows:

$$E_{B_1} = \int \psi_{B_1} \mathcal{H} \psi_{B_1} \, d\tau = \frac{1}{2} \left[\int \phi_1 \mathcal{H} \phi_1 \, d\tau - 2 \int \phi_1 \mathcal{H} \phi_3 \, d\tau + \int \phi_3 \mathcal{H} \phi_3 \, d\tau \right]$$

$$= \alpha_1 - \beta_{13}$$

where the meaning of α_1 and β_{13} should be obvious

For the A_1 orbitals we first write the following linear combinations which have A_1 symmetry:

$$\psi'_{A_1} = \phi_2$$

$$\psi''_{A_1} = \frac{1}{\sqrt{2}} (\phi_1 + \phi_3)$$

These may be used to solve the appropriate secular equation which will then take the form

$$\begin{vmatrix} \alpha_2 - E & \sqrt{2}\beta_{12} \\ \sqrt{2}\beta_{12} & \alpha_1 + \beta_{13} - E \end{vmatrix} = 0$$

Left in this general form the solutions to the equation will be somewhat complicated. In general we may expect that the following two approximations will be reasonable ones. First, we assume that the energy of the orbital on the center boron atom, α_2, is the same as that of the orbitals on the outer borons, α_1. This would be strictly correct if all the boron atoms used exactly the same atomic or hybrid orbital; in general, the orbital used by the center boron atom will differ to some extent in its hybridization from those used by the outer boron atoms, but moderate differences in hybridization will make only relatively small differences in energies. Second, we shall assume that the direct interaction between the two outer atoms, represented by β_{13}, is negligible in comparison to the interaction between adjacent boron atoms, represented by β_{12}. This assumption is analogous to that made in the Hückel approximation for pi systems.

With these approximations, and taking $\alpha_1 = \alpha_2 = 0$, we get exactly the same energy level diagram as we obtained for the allyl ion. For systems such as B—H—B, Be—C—Be, and Al—C—Al, the assumption that $\alpha_1 = \alpha_2$ will be a rather poorer approximation. If we drop this assumption our energy level diagram will be altered in the same way as was the diagram for a pi system on going from the allyl ion to NO_2^-. There will still be a bonding, a nonbonding, and an antibonding orbital.

In the B—H—B, Be—C—Be, and Al—C—Al systems as they occur in the boron hydrides and the beryllium and aluminum methyls, there are two electrons to be accommodated in these three-center bonding systems. These will occupy the bonding MO. Thus we see that two electrons can be used to bond three atoms together just as they can be used to bond two atoms together. The nature of the bonding MO can be visualized by inspecting the LCAO expression for it as it was derived in the case of the allyl ion. It is a weighted sum of the atomic orbitals of the three atoms and it thus has a banana-like shape and extends over all

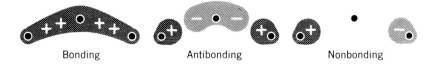

Bonding   Antibonding   Nonbonding

Figure 7.4   Rough sketches showing the wave functions of the three MO's in a three-center bonding situation arising from the three atomic orbitals shown in Figure 7.3*a*.

three nuclei as shown in Figure 7.4, where we also give similar rough sketches of the other two MO's.

In certain boron hydrides the possibility of three-center bonding in which the center boron atom uses a p orbital oriented as shown in Figure 7.3*b* has been considered. In this case the three atomic orbitals form a basis for a representation of the group C_{2v} which reduces to $A_1 + 2B_1$. The A_1 orbital can be written down immediately as

$$\psi_{A_1} = \frac{1}{\sqrt{2}} (\phi_1 + \phi_3)$$

and linear combinations of the atomic orbitals having B_1 symmetry are

$$\psi'_{B_1} = \phi_2$$

$$\psi''_{B_1} = \frac{1}{\sqrt{2}} (\phi_1 - \phi_3)$$

If we neglect interaction between ϕ_1 and ϕ_3 and assume that the energies of ϕ_1, ϕ_2, and ϕ_3 are all equal, the secular equation for the energies of the B_1 orbitals takes the simple form

$$\begin{vmatrix} \alpha - E & \sqrt{2}\beta \\ \sqrt{2}\beta & \alpha - E \end{vmatrix} = 0$$

which is identical with the one obtained in previous cases in which the same assumptions were made. Taking $\alpha = 0$ it has the roots $\pm\sqrt{2}\beta$ and we have the same symmetrical energy level diagram as for the allyl ion. These energies can be used to obtain the correct expressions for the B_1 MO's and they turn out to be

$$\psi_{B_1}^{(1)} = \tfrac{1}{2}(\phi_1 + \sqrt{2}\,\phi_2 - \phi_3) \quad \text{(bonding)}$$

$$\psi_{B_1}^{(2)} = \tfrac{1}{2}(\phi_1 - \sqrt{2}\,\phi_2 - \phi_3) \quad \text{(antibonding)}$$

Bonding   Antibonding   Nonbonding

Figure 7.5   Rough sketches showing the wave functions of the three MO's in a three-center bonding situation arising from the three atomic orbitals shown in Figure 7.3b.

In Figure 7.5 are rough sketches of these and the A_1 MO. It can be seen that although their symmetries are different the results with regard to bonding character are the same. Orbitals which have nodes between the nuclei are antibonding in both cases. It should be remembered that the electron density is proportional to the square of the wave function so that it is only the placement of the nodes and not the sign of a wave function which is important in determining its bonding character.

Closed Three-Center Bonding

In the examples treated so far we have assumed that the outer atoms are so far apart that direct interaction between them as represented by β_{13} can be ignored. We shall now consider what happens as this restriction is relaxed, that is, as we allow the magnitude of β_{13} to increase from zero and become, eventually, equal to β_{12}. This is most easily done by considering first the extreme in which $\beta_{13} = \beta_{12}$. In order to calculate the energies of the B_1 orbitals in this case we return to our secular equation on page 157 and re-evaluate the elements of the determinant with $\beta_{13} = \beta_{12}$. We thus have

$$H_{B'B'} = \int \phi_2 \mathcal{H} \phi_2 \, d\tau = \alpha$$

$$H_{B'B''} = \frac{1}{\sqrt{2}} \int \phi_2 \mathcal{H} (\phi_1 + \phi_3) \, d\tau = \sqrt{2}\beta$$

$$H_{B''B''} = \frac{1}{2} \int (\phi_1 + \phi_3) \mathcal{H} (\phi_1 + \phi_3) \, d\tau$$

$$= \alpha + \beta$$

With $\alpha = 0$, the secular equation now takes the form

$$\begin{vmatrix} -E & \sqrt{2}\beta \\ \sqrt{2}\beta & \beta - E \end{vmatrix} = 0$$

and has the roots

$$E_{B_1} = -\beta, 2\beta$$

When the energy of the A_2 orbital is also recalculated assuming $\beta_{13} = \beta_{12}$, we obtain

$$E_{A_2} = -\beta \qquad (\alpha = 0)$$

Since there must be a continuous change in the energies of the MO's as the magnitude of β_{13} increases, we can draw the following energy level diagram:

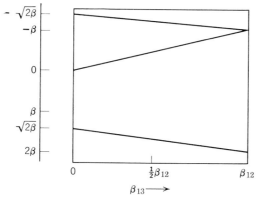

It may be noted that the results we obtain when $\beta_{13} = \beta_{12}$ are the same as we should obtain by making the calculation for the cyclopropenyl, $(CH)_3$, group. This can be done by the method described in Section 7.2 for other carbocyclic systems. The symmetry of the $(CH)_3$ system is D_{3h}, and thus at the extreme right of the above energy level diagram the two MO's with energy $-\beta$ form a doubly degenerate pair belonging to the E'' representation of D_{3h}, and the level at 2β belongs to the representation A_2''.

It is easy to show that if the three orbitals used in the closed three-center bonding system are equivalent σ orbitals, as in the B_3 groups occurring in some boron hydrides, the pattern of energy levels will be exactly the same as the one obtained for the system of three π orbitals.

7.5 Open-Chain Pi Systems: Butadiene

For open-chain olefins the use of group theory also immensely simplifies the calculation of the energies and other properties by permitting rapid and efficient factoring of the secular equation. In these compounds there cannot be any degenerate levels since none will possess symmetry axes of order greater than 2. Thus the procedure for setting up a fully factored secular equation is quite simple.

As an example we treat butadiene in its *trans* form as shown below with the carbon atoms numbered.

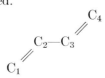

The symmetry is C_{2h}. We note that there are two nonequivalent sets of carbon atoms, namely, 1 and 4, 2 and 3. Using these as bases for representations of the group, we obtain the results

C_{2h}	E	C_2	i	σ_h
Γ_{14}	2	0	0	-2
Γ_{23}	2	0	0	-2

$$\Gamma_{14} = \Gamma_{23} = B_g + A_u$$

Thus two of the MO's will be of B_g symmetry and two of A_u symmetry.

We now proceed to set up linear combinations of the two orbitals of each set having these symmetries, solve the appropriate secular equations for the energies, and then combine these linear combinations of the two sets into complete MO's having the correct energies. As all of this procedure has been explained in great detail in several previous examples, we will summarize this process briefly, leaving out all of the intermediate algebra.

B_g orbitals must be antisymmetric to C_2 rotation. Hence we can write

$$\psi_{B_g}^o = \frac{1}{\sqrt{2}} (\phi_1 - \phi_4) \qquad \psi_{B_g}^i = \frac{1}{\sqrt{2}} (\phi_2 - \phi_3)$$

The secular determinant will be

$$\begin{vmatrix} H_{oo} - E & H_{oi} \\ H_{io} & H_{ii} - E \end{vmatrix} = 0$$

and its elements have the following values:

$$H_{oo} = \alpha \qquad H_{oi} = H_{io} = \beta \qquad H_{ii} = \alpha - \beta$$

Taking α as zero we obtain

$$\begin{vmatrix} -E & \beta \\ \beta & -\beta - E \end{vmatrix} = 0$$

$$E^2 + E\beta - \beta^2 = 0$$

$$E = \frac{-\beta \pm \sqrt{5}\beta}{2} = \frac{-1 \pm \sqrt{5}}{2}\beta = \begin{cases} -1.62\beta \\ 0.62\beta \end{cases}$$

Similarly, for the A_u orbitals we note that they must be symmetric to C_2 rotation and write

$$\psi_{A_u}^o = \frac{1}{\sqrt{2}}(\phi_1 + \phi_4) \qquad \psi_{A_u}^o = \frac{1}{\sqrt{2}}(\phi_2 + \phi_3)$$

The elements of the secular determinant have the values

$$H_{oo} = \alpha \qquad H_{oi} = H_{io} = \beta \qquad H_{ii} = \alpha + \beta$$

and the roots of the secular equation are

$$E = \frac{\beta \pm \sqrt{5}\beta}{2} = \frac{1 \pm \sqrt{5}}{2}\beta = \begin{cases} +1.62\beta \\ -0.62\beta \end{cases}$$

We thus have the following energy level diagram for the pi system of butadiene:

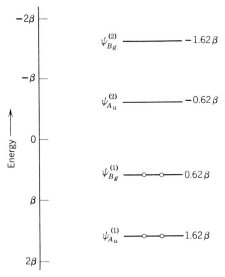

The total energy of this electron distribution is

$$[2(1.62) + 2(0.62)]\beta = 4.48\beta$$

For two noninteracting double bonds as shown in the sketch the energy (taking $\alpha = 0$) would be 4β. Hence the resonance or delocalization energy is $0.48\beta \approx 9$ Kcal/mole.

It is also of interest to determine the bond orders in butadiene. To do this we find the correct combinations of $\psi^i_{A_u}$ and $\psi^o_{A_u}$ to give $\psi^{(1)}_{A_u}$, and of $\psi^i_{B_g}$ and $\psi^o_{B_g}$ to give $\psi^{(1)}_{B_g}$. Writing

$$\psi^{(1)}_{A_u} = \frac{1}{\sqrt{1 + x^2}} \, (\psi^i_{A_u} + x\psi^o_{A_u})$$

and solving for x in the energy equation, we obtain $x = 1$ so that the correct MO is

$$\psi^{(1)}_{A_u} = 0.37\phi_1 + 0.61\phi_2 + 0.61\phi_3 + 0.37\phi_4$$

By the same procedure we obtain for $\psi^{(1)}_{B_g}$:

$$\psi^{(1)}_{B_g} = 0.61\phi_1 + 0.37\phi_2 - 0.37\phi_3 - 0.61\phi_4$$

Using these coefficients the bond orders are determined in the manner described earlier (page 148). For the C_2—C_3 bond we have

$$
\begin{array}{lrr}
A^{(1)}_u: & 2(0.61)(0.61) = & 0.724 \\
B^{(1)}_g: & 2(0.37)(-0.37) = & -0.273 \\
\hline
& & 0.451
\end{array}
$$

and for one of the outer bonds, say the C_1—C_2 bond:

$$
\begin{array}{lrr}
A^{(1)}_u: & 2(0.37)(0.61) = & 0.451 \\
B^{(1)}_g: & 2(0.61)(0.37) = & 0.451 \\
\hline
& & 0.902
\end{array}
$$

These results mean that while there is substantial pi character in the center bond, the outer bonds have twice as much.

Higher polyolefins can be treated by a similar procedure. The algebra required to obtain the true MO wave functions increases, however, because of an increase in the number of sets of equivalent atoms.

7.6   Molecular Orbitals for the Metal Sandwich Compounds

The term "metal sandwich compounds" applies strictly to compounds of the type $(C_nH_n)_2M$, such as $(C_5H_5)_2Fe$ and $(C_6H_6)_2Cr$, in which a metal atom is "sandwiched" symmetrically between two parallel carbocyclic ring systems, but the term is commonly used in a broader sense to include in addition all those compounds in which at least one carbocyclic ring, C_nH_n, such as C_4H_4, C_5H_5, C_6H_6, C_7H_7, is bound to a metal atom in such a way that the metal atom lies along the n-fold symmetry axis of the ring and is thus equivalently bonded to all of the carbon atoms in the ring. Thus, in addition to the highly symmetrical molecules mentioned above, the term refers also to such mono-ring compounds as C_5H_5NiNO, $C_6H_6Cr(CO)_3$, $[C_7H_7Mo(CO)_3]^+$, and $C_5H_5Fe(CO)_2C_2H_5$, and mixed ring systems such as $(C_5H_5)(C_7H_7)V$ and $(C_5H_5)(C_6H_6)Mn$. It should be noted that there are also compounds such as $(C_5H_5)_2ReH$ and $(C_5H_5)_2TaH_3$ in which the rings are not exactly parallel although it is believed that the metal-ring bonding is still symmetrical about the symmetry axes of the rings. The bonding in such cases will have essentially the same features as in the more symmetrical cases but cannot of course be treated with the same degree of rigor with regard to symmetry.

Some references to molecular orbital treatments of the true sandwich systems and to the more approximate MO treatments of the less symmetrical systems are given below.* It may also be noted that Pauling has pointed out that the resonating valence bond method can, in principle, be applied to sandwich compounds.† However, the molecular orbital method is conceptually just as simple and affords a basis for computations; it has been and seems likely to remain the preferred one for these molecules.

Using ferrocene, $(C_5H_5)_2Fe$, as an example, we can exhibit all of the basic ideas in the molecular orbital treatment for the whole class of molecules. Accordingly, we will first treat ferrocene in detail and then briefly outline the application of the method to a few other selected cases, viz., $(C_6H_6)_2Cr$, $(C_5H_5)Ni(NO)$, $(C_5H_5)Mn(CO)_3$, and $[(CCH_3)_4NiCl_2]_2$.

Ferrocene

The basic strategy is to construct linear combinations of all of the $p\pi$ orbitals of the two C_5H_5 rings belonging to the irreducible representations of the molecular point group D_{5d} (see page 43), to classify the orbitals in the valence shell of the metal atom according to their symmetry in the point group, and then to combine metal and ring orbitals into molecular orbitals of the entire molecule.

In order to construct the proper linear combinations of $p\pi$ orbitals, we can make use of the results we have already obtained for a single C_5H_5

---

* J. D. Dunitz and L. E. Orgel, *J. Chem. Phys.*, **23**, 954 (1955). E. M. Shustorovich and M. E. Dyatkina, *Doklady Akad. Nauk.*, SSSR, **128**, 1234 (1959). J. P. Dahl and C. J. Ballhausen, *Kong. Danske Vidensk. Selsk.*, Mat. Fys. Medd., **33**, No. 5 (1961). L. E. Orgel, *J. Inorg. Nucl. Chem.*, **2**, 315 (1956). D. A. Brown, *ibid.*, **10**, 39 (1959).

† L. Pauling, *The Nature of the Chemical Bond*, 3rd ed., Cornell University Press, 1960, pp. 385–392.

ring. For such a ring we have constructed LCAO-MO's transforming correctly under the rotations belonging to the group C_5 (see page 133). These are of A, E_1, and E_2 symmetry. The set of ten $p\pi$ orbitals provided by two such rings oriented as they are in the ferrocene molecule spans the following representations of D_{5d}:

D_{5d}	E	$2C_5$	$2C_5^2$	$5C_2$	i	$2S_{10}$	$2S_{10}^3$	$5\sigma_d$
Γ_π	10	0	0	0	0	0	0	2

$$\Gamma_\pi = A_{1g} + A_{2u} + E_{1g} + E_{1u} + E_{2g} + E_{2u}$$

Thus we see that for the system of two rings we require two A orbitals, one symmetric and the other antisymmetric to inversion in the center, two E_1 orbitals, one symmetric and the other antisymmetric, and finally, two E_2 orbitals, one symmetric and one antisymmetric to inversion in the center. It is rather easy to write down expressions for these by making appropriate combinations of the orbitals we already have for the individual rings. In doing this we will refer to the rings and orbitals as they are shown and labeled in Figure 7.6. It is very important here to note that we have chosen the directions of the $p\pi$ orbitals such that their positive lobes all point in toward the metal atom. Thus the $+z$ axis for ring A is in the opposite direction to the $+z$ axis for ring B.

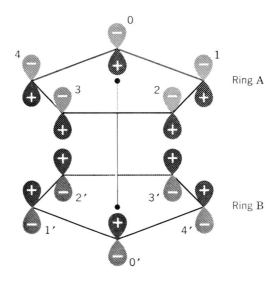

Figure 7.6   Sketch showing the $p\pi$ orbitals on the two rings used to construct molecular orbitals for a bis(cyclopentadienyl)metal molecule.

Referring to the character table for group D_{5d} we see that an A_{1g} orbital must be symmetric to inversion in the center of symmetry. This requirement will be satisfied by the following combination of the A orbitals of the two rings:

$$\psi(A_{1g}) = \frac{1}{\sqrt{2}}[\psi_A(A) + \psi_B(A)]$$

where we use subscripts A and B to refer to the rings. It can also easily be seen that the $\psi(A_{1g})$ so obtained satisfies all other symmetry requirements. To obtain an orbital of the system of two rings which is antisymmetric to inversion we take the linear combination

$$\psi(A_{2u}) = \frac{1}{\sqrt{2}}[\psi_A(A) - \psi_B(A)]$$

Again, a simple check will show that this orbital, $\psi(A_{2u})$, satisfies all the symmetry requirements of the A_{2u} representation.

For the E_1 and E_2 orbitals we proceed in exactly the same way, choosing normalized combinations of the E_1 and E_2 orbitals of the individual rings so as to obtain functions which are symmetric and antisymmetric to inversion, namely,

$$\left[\begin{array}{l} \psi(E_{1g}a) = \dfrac{1}{\sqrt{2}}[\psi_A(E_1a) + \psi_B(E_1a)] \\[2mm] \psi(E_{1g}b) = \dfrac{1}{\sqrt{2}}[\psi_A(E_1b) + \psi_B(E_1b)] \end{array}\right.$$

$$\left[\begin{array}{l} \psi(E_{1u}a) = \dfrac{1}{\sqrt{2}}[\psi_A(E_1a) - \psi_B(E_1a)] \\[2mm] \psi(E_{1u}b) = \dfrac{1}{\sqrt{2}}[\psi_A(E_1b) - \psi_B(E_1b)] \end{array}\right.$$

$$\left[\begin{array}{l} \psi(E_{2g}a) = \dfrac{1}{\sqrt{2}}[\psi_A(E_2a) + \psi_B(E_2a)] \\[2mm] \psi(E_{2g}b) = \dfrac{1}{\sqrt{2}}[\psi_A(E_2b) + \psi_B(E_2b)] \end{array}\right.$$

$$\left[\begin{array}{l} \psi(E_{2u}a) = \dfrac{1}{\sqrt{2}}[\psi_A(E_2a) - \psi_B(E_2a)] \\[2mm] \psi(E_{2u}b) = \dfrac{1}{\sqrt{2}}[\psi_A(E_2b) - \psi_B(E_2b)] \end{array}\right.$$

For the metal atom, Fe, the valence shell orbitals are the five $3d$ orbitals, the $4s$ orbital, and the three $4p$ orbitals. The transformation properties of these orbitals may be ascertained immediately by inspection of the character table for D_{5d}, the results being

$$A_{1g}: \quad 4s; 3d_{z^2}$$
$$E_{1g}: \quad (3d_{xz}, 3d_{yz})$$
$$E_{2g}: \quad (3d_{xy}, 3d_{x^2-y^2})$$
$$A_{2u}: \quad 4p_z$$
$$E_{1u}: \quad (4p_x, 4p_y)$$

Thus we have a total, counting the degeneracies, of nineteen orbitals, but because of their symmetry properties, as shown in Section 7.1, we do not have to solve a 19×19 secular determinant. Instead we have only the following small determinants:

One 3×3 for the A_{1g} MO's

Two 2×2 for the E_{1g} MO's (same roots for both)

Two 2×2 for the E_{2g} MO's (same roots for both)

One 2×2 for the A_{2u} MO's

Two 2×2 for the E_{1u} MO's (same roots for both)

The E_{2u} MO's on the rings are in themselves E_{2u} MO's for the whole molecule since there are no E_{2u} metal orbitals with which they might interact.

In order to solve these small secular determinants it is necessary to evaluate the various elements occurring in them. We must know the values of integrals such as

$$\int \psi(A_{2u}) \mathcal{H} p_z \, d\tau$$

At this point, symmetry arguments have done all that they can for us— though that is a great deal indeed—and the problem becomes one of quantum mechanical computation. The published attempts to evaluate these integrals have mostly involved the assumption that their values are proportional to the corresponding overlap integrals, the proportionality constant being ~ 2 electron volts. That is, for example,

$$\int \psi(A_{2u}) \mathcal{H} p_z \, d\tau \approx 2 \int \psi(A_{2u}) p_z \, d\tau$$

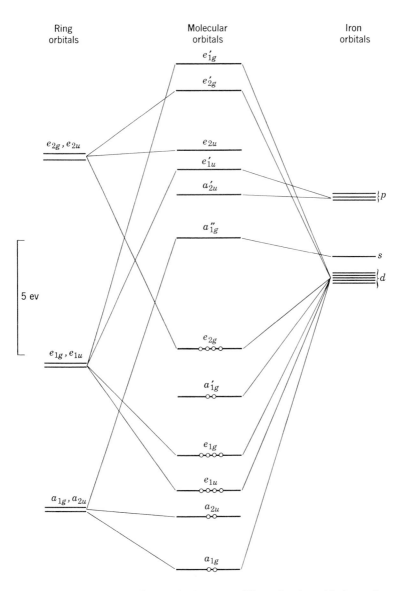

Figure 7.7   An energy level diagram for ferrocene. The molecular orbital energies are those calculated by Schustorovich and Dyatkina (*loc. cit.*) using a self-consistent field procedure. The positions of the ring and Fe orbitals on this diagram are only approximate.

The overlap integrals are relatively easy to compute either using published tables of overlap integrals for Slater (pure nodeless) orbitals, or, more accurately, using self-consistent field orbitals for the metal atom expressed as linear combinations of Slater orbitals. We shall not discuss the details of these computations here but they may be found in several of the papers cited earlier.

The results of a computation of this sort can be most conveniently embodied in an energy level diagram such as that shown in Figure 7.7. The energies of the ring orbitals relative to one another have already been estimated in the Hückel approximation in units of β (page 133); as explained in Appendix IV, we choose here the "spectroscopic" value of β, $\sim$60 Kcal/mole, for use in constructing the energy level diagram. Moreover, since the rings are about 4Å apart in the molecule the reasonable assumption is made that there is no significant direct interaction between them; the g and u orbitals of the same rotational symmetry are thus taken to have the same energy. The energy differences between the orbitals of the metal atom can be deduced from the spectrum of the atom. The energies of the ring orbitals relative to the energies of the metal orbitals must be estimated from the ionization potentials for the ring and the metal atom.

In Figure 7.7 the electron distribution is shown for ferrocene. It will be seen that there are nine more or less bonding orbitals which are just filled by the eighteen electrons originating in the pi systems of the rings and in the valence shell orbitals of the metal atoms. For other $(C_5H_5)_2M$ compounds, energy level diagrams having the same qualitative features would be anticipated, but the relative order of the least stable bonding MO's is subject to variation due both to variation in the relative energies of metal and ligand orbitals and variations in the relative magnitudes of the different interaction energies. Consequently, there must be some caution exercised in attempting to predict from a diagram constructed specifically for one $(C_5H_5)_2M$ compound the electronic structure of another containing a different metal.

Dibenzenechromium

Assuming that this molecule consists of two benzene rings placed on either side of the chromium atom so that their planes are parallel and their C_6 axes colinear, the molecular symmetry may be D_{6d} or D_{6h} depending on whether the rings are staggered or eclipsed. X-ray study of the crystalline compound shows that the chromium atom is at a center of inversion so that in the crystalline state at least the molecular point group is D_{6h}.* There is evidence from infrared and Raman spectra that the molecule has D_{6h} symmetry in solution.

Assuming D_{6h} symmetry, a molecular orbital bonding scheme similar to that given above for ferrocene can easily be developed. Again we begin with the LCAO-MO pi orbitals of a single ring and combine them to obtain symmetry orbitals appropriate to the entire molecule. Using the twelve carbon $p\pi$ orbitals as the basis for a representation of the group D_{6h}, and breaking this down into the irreducible representations, we find that the symmetry orbitals must belong to the following irreducible representations:

$$A_{1g},\ A_{2u},\ B_{2g},\ B_{1u},\ E_{1g},\ E_{2g},\ E_{1u},\ E_{2u}$$

By combining the A, B, E_1, and E_2 orbitals for the individual rings into combinations which are symmetric and antisymmetric to inversion, we readily obtain expressions for symmetry orbitals of the required types. The relative energies of these symmetry orbitals in units of β (again using the spectroscopic value) are those already calculated (page 129) for benzene.

For the metal atom we find from the character table for the group D_{6h} that its valence shell orbitals belong to irreducible representations as follows:

$$A_{1g}: \quad s;\ d_{z^2}$$
$$E_{1g}: \quad (d_{xz},\ d_{yz})$$
$$E_{2g}: \quad (d_{xy},\ d_{x^2-y^2})$$
$$A_{2u}: \quad p_z$$
$$E_{1u}: \quad (p_x,\ p_y)$$

Figure 7.8 shows an energy level diagram for dibenzenechromium. In the center are the molecular orbitals (at energies given by Schustorovich and Dyatkina, *loc. cit.*, who made a self-consistent field calculation). The energies of the ring orbitals and metal orbitals as shown on this diagram are only approximate and are included as a guide in qualitative interpretation of the diagram. It will be noted how similar the MO scheme is to that in ferrocene. This is not too surprising in view of the fact that the only qualitative difference in the two systems is in the presence here of high energy orbitals of B symmetry in C_6H_6 which, however, do not participate in the ring-metal interaction since the metal has no valence shell orbitals of B symmetry.

* It has recently been claimed that on exhaustive refinement of the structural parameters obtained by x-ray study an alternation in the C—C bond lengths is disclosed, the molecular symmetry in the crystal being thus only D_{3d} [cf. Jellinek, *Nature*, **187**, 871 (1960)].

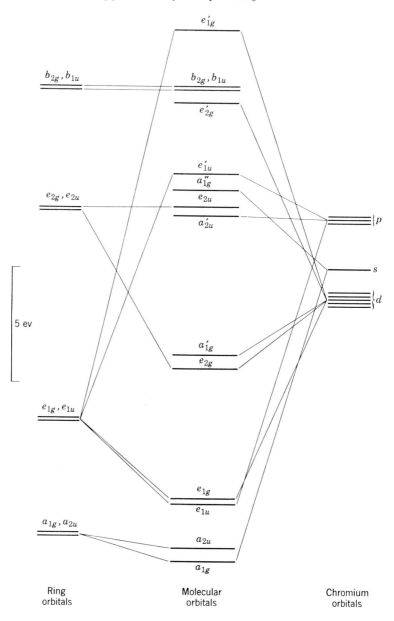

Figure 7.8   An energy level diagram for dibenzenechromium. The molecular orbital energies are those calculated by Schustorovich and Dyatkina (*loc. cit.*) using a self-consistent field procedure. The positions of the ring and Cr orbitals on this diagram are only approximate.

Cyclopentadienylnickel Nitrosyl

This molecule, $(C_5H_5)NiNO$, has been shown by microwave spectroscopy to be a symmetric top and hence to have C_{5v} symmetry. It represents probably the most symmetrical known type of mono-ring compound of a transition metal. In order to construct a molecular orbital diagram for this molecule we must first determine the transformation properties of the π orbitals of C_5H_5, the valence shell orbitals of Ni, and the σ and π orbitals of NO in the group C_{5v}. By comparison of the expressions previously obtained for the π MO's of the C_5H_5 system (page 133) with the character table for C_{5v}, it is evident that these belong to the A_1, E_1, and E_2 representations. The C_{5v} character table tells us explicitly that the metal atom valence shell orbitals are assigned to the irreducible representations of C_{5v} as follows:

$$A_1: \quad s,\ p_z,\ d_{z^2}$$
$$E_1: \quad (p_x,\ p_y),\ (d_{xz},\ d_{yz})$$
$$E_2: \quad (d_{xy},\ d_{x^2-y^2})$$

Finally, for the NO molecule, it is easily seen that the σ orbitals belong to the A_1 representation, and the pairs of π orbitals must belong to the E_1 representation. In considering the bonding of NO to Ni we will consider only the filled, nonbonding σ orbital on the nitrogen atom and the pair of π orbitals containing the odd electron of the NO molecule. There are then a total of five A_1 orbitals, four pairs of E_1 orbitals, and two pairs of E_2 orbitals so that a computation of the MO energies would require the solution of one 5×5, one 4×4, and one 2×2 secular determinants. While this is considerably easier than solving an 11×11 determinant, as we would have to do if no use had been made of symmetry properties to factor this secular equation, it still amounts to a considerable task— one which has not in fact been attempted numerically. These results serve to illustrate the point that even when maximum advantage is taken of symmetry properties, molecules having many atoms but only moderately high symmetry still present rather arduous computational challenges if complete numerical solutions, even in a low order of approximation, are desired.

We shall give here an energy level diagram based on what are frankly "guesstimates" of the relative energies of the molecular orbitals. This diagram is shown in Figure 7.9 and it is to be emphasized that it is schematic and not to be interpreted quantitatively. Some reasons for believing that an essentially similar diagram is qualitatively correct have

C$_5$H$_5$ Ni   NO

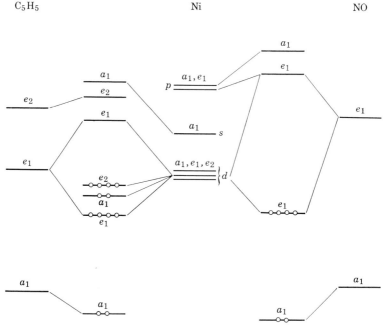

Figure 7.9   A schematic MO energy level diagram for (C$_5$H$_5$)NiNO.

been given by Orgel (*loc. cit.*). The manner in which Figure 7.9 is drawn is intended to emphasize which metal orbitals appear likely to interact more with the NO than with C$_5$H$_5$ and vice versa, but it should be kept in mind that all of the MO's of a given symmetry type owe their energy positions to more extensive interactions. For example, the σ bond from N to Ni is doubtless due to the interaction of the a_1 orbital on N with all of the a_1 orbitals on Ni (s, p_z, d_{z^2}), although the diagram suggests that the p_z orbital predominates. For the e_1 interactions it does seem reasonable to suppose that the de_1 orbitals will overlap more effectively with the ring e_1 orbitals than with the e_1 orbitals of NO.

Cyclopentadienylmanganese Tricarbonyl

This molecule provides a significant example of the type in which the true or overall molecular symmetry is very low but in which the bonding in parts of the molecule may be treated, at least qualitatively, in terms of relatively high *local* symmetries. In this case the (C_5H_5)Mn part of the molecule may be considered to have C_{5v} symmetry and the Mn(CO)$_3$ part taken as having C_{3v} symmetry, although the molecule in its entirety can have no more than C_s symmetry, and that only for two particular orientations of the C_5H_5 ring relative to the Mn(CO)$_3$ grouping. In treating the (C_5H_5)Mn and Mn(CO)$_3$ bonding separately, each in terms of its own ideal local symmetry, we make the assumption, *inter alia*, that degeneracies permitted in C_{5v} symmetry will not be greatly split by the presence of C_{3v} symmetry in the other part of the molecule and vice versa. Because of the particular shapes of the d orbitals such an assumption probably has some validity in this case, but it cannot be assumed that this will always be so. Figure 7.10 shows a schematic energy level diagram for (C_5H_5)Mn(CO)$_3$. In the center the valence shell orbitals of Mn are shown. They are labeled on the right with their symmetries in C_3 and on the left with their symmetries in C_5. At the extreme left are the π MO's of the C_5H_5 ring labeled with their symmetries in C_5 and with the energy of the e_1 orbitals placed at about the same level as

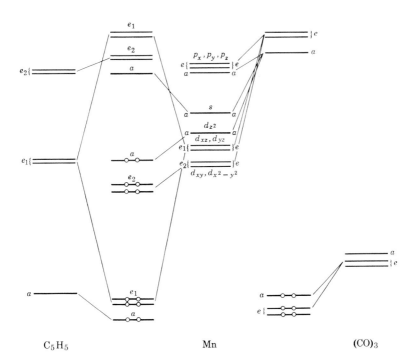

Figure 7.10   A schematic MO energy level diagram for (C_5H_5)Mn(CO)$_3$.

the d orbitals of Mn. On the extreme right are shown the energy levels of the σ orbitals for the three CO groups, with symmetry designations appropriate to C_3. These designations were obtained by taking the set of three σ orbitals on the carbon atoms as a basis for a representation of the group C_3 and decomposing that representation into its component irreducible representations. The energy of these symmetry orbitals constructed from the carbon σ orbitals has been assumed to be about the same as the energy of the a orbital of C_5H_5. No account has been taken of the interaction of the metal with the π orbitals of the CO groups. This could be done by finding the representations spanned by the six π orbitals and then permitting them to interact with metal orbitals of the same symmetry types. Although it is certain from the vibrational frequencies of the CO groups in this molecule that the M—C π interactions are substantial, we have chosen to omit them here since they can only be crudely estimated and their inclusion in the energy level diagram would make it extremely unwieldy.

The only real justification for drawing an entirely schematic diagram such as this one is that it helps with the "bookkeeping." It makes it somewhat easier to see how the orbitals of different components of the molecule may interact in order to produce a satisfactory set of bonding MO's than could be done by merely inspecting a list of these components. For example, the shapes of the metal e_1 orbitals, d_{xz} and d_{yz}, are such that their overlap with the ring e_1 orbitals should be fairly substantial and the diagram accordingly shows a sizable interaction of these orbitals. On the other hand, the metal e_2 orbitals are not strongly directed toward the ring e_2 orbitals and the energy difference is initially greater so that a much weaker interaction would be expected, as indicated.

Cyclobutadiene Sandwich Compounds

As shown on page 132, MO treatment in the Hückel approximation of cyclobutadiene leads to the conclusion that the molecule will be a diradical with no resonance stabilization. In agreement with this, neither cyclobutadiene nor any simply substituted derivative thereof (dibenzcyclobutadiene, y-clept biphenylene, not being considered a valid case) has been isolated. However, by direct x-ray structural work it is definitely established that two compounds contain substituted cyclobutadiene derivatives bound to metal atoms by sandwich bonds. These are tetraphenylcyclobutadieneiron tricarbonyl, $(C_6H_5C)_4Fe(CO)_3$, and the dimer of tetramethylcyclobutadienenickel dichloride, $[(CH_3C)_4NiCl_2]_2$, the structures of which are shown in Figure 7.11. Examination of

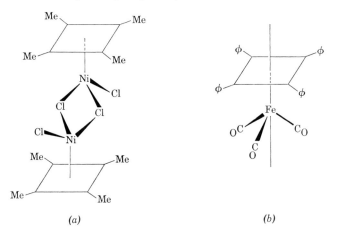

Figure 7.11   The structures of (a) tetramethylcyclobutadienenickel(II) chloride dimer and (b) tetraphenylcyclobutadieneiron tricarbonyl.

the details of the sandwich bonding in these compounds by molecular orbital theory provides a very satisfying explanation for the stability of the rings when bound to the metal atoms and in fact considerations of the sort outlined below led to the prediction * that such compounds would be stable before any were known to exist.

The important feature in the bonding in these compounds is that the metal makes available a pair of electrons in e orbitals which can be paired in bond formation with the two electrons occupying the e orbitals of the cyclobutadiene ring. This simultaneously neutralizes the diradical character of the ring, which otherwise makes it subject to Jahn-Teller distortion and chemical attack, and provides extra stabilization as a result of bond formation which is needed to compensate for the lack of resonance energy in the unbound ring system.

In the case of the nickel compound each nickel atom is bound to two chlorine atoms which bridge the two nickel atoms and also to a third chlorine atom which is nonbridging. These three chlorine atoms form a roughly triangular array and the structure can be idealized by thinking of the nickel atom as sandwiched between the parallel planes of the C_4 ring and the Cl_3 triangle, the ring and the triangle having colinear four- and threefold axes passing through the nickel atom. Similarly, in the iron compound, the $Fe(CO)_3$ moiety is at least approximately a triangular

* H. C. Longuet-Higgins and L. E. Orgel, *J. Chem. Soc.*, 1969 (1956).

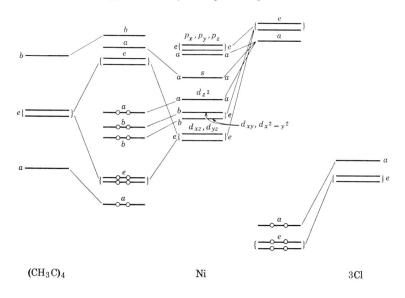

(CH₃C)₄   **Ni**   **3Cl**

Figure 7.12   Schematic MO energy level diagram for the bonding to one nickel atom in tetramethylcyclobutadienenickel dichloride dimer, $[(CH_3C)_4NiCl_2]_2$.

pyramid with its threefold axis colinear with the fourfold axis of the cyclobutadiene ring.

Thus, as in the $(C_5H_5)Mn(CO)_3$ molecule, there are no true symmetry axes in these molecules in their entirety but as an approximation we may think in terms of the local symmetry of the two halves. In Figure 7.12 we show in the center the orbitals of the metal atom, giving on the right their symmetries in C_3 and on the left their symmetries in C_4. It is seen that metal orbitals are available to form σ bonds to the three chlorine atoms or CO groups, leaving e orbitals which may interact with the e orbitals of the cyclobutadiene ring to create strong metal-ring bonding and leave no unshared electrons.

8

Ligand Field Theory

8.1   Introductory Remarks

For conciseness, the title of this chapter is simply "Ligand Field Theory." However, many of the principles which will be developed are as much a part of crystal field theory and the molecular orbital theory of transition metal complexes as they are of ligand field theory. Indeed these three theories are very closely related. Since the reader has probably heard of all three, it seems advisable to begin this chapter with a very brief, historically oriented discussion of the nature of these three theories. After we have developed the basic principles we can give a more technical discussion of their similarities and differences.

The beginning of all three theories can be traced to the year 1929 when H. Bethe published his classic paper entitled "Splitting of Terms in Crystals." * There are really two completely separate parts to Bethe's paper. The first is the part concerned purely with the *qualitative consequences of the symmetry* of the surroundings of a cation in a crystal lattice. In this part, Bethe showed that, in general, the states arising from a particular electronic configuration of an ion which are degenerate when the ion is free of perturbing influences must break up into two or more nonequivalent states when the ion is introduced into a lattice. He showed how it is possible, using the methods of group theory, to determine just what states will result when an ion of any given electronic configuration is introduced into a crystalline environment of definite symmetry.

The second part of Bethe's paper describes a method by which the magnitudes of the splittings of the free-ion states may be calculated

---

* *Annalen der Physik*, **3**, 133–206 (1929). An English translation of this paper is available for $3.00 from Consultants Bureau, Inc., 227 W. 17th Street, New York 11, N. Y.

assuming that the surroundings effect these splittings by purely electrostatic forces. It is this assumption that all interactions between the ion and its surroundings may be treated as *purely* electrostatic interactions between point charges that is the defining feature of the crystal field theory. It has the consequence that all electrons which are in metal-ion orbitals in the free ion are treated as though they remain in orbitals which are 100 per cent metal-ion orbitals.

It was first pointed out by Van Vleck that the first part of Bethe's approach, the symmetry part, will remain entirely valid if we change the computational part from a purely electrostatic approach to one which admits the existence of some chemical bonding between the metal ion and its neighbors. If we do so, the orbitals with which we must deal will no longer be pure metal orbitals, but only partly metal orbitals. This means that in principle we cannot write down the same fairly simple expressions for energies, because the orbitals involved are no longer simple. In practice, however, if the covalence of the metal ligand bonds is relatively small, energies will be given by equations identical in form to the equations which come out of the crystal field theory. This modified crystal field theory, which admits that there is some covalent as well as electrostatic interaction between the ion and its neighbors is called ligand field theory.

Van Vleck also pointed out that even in the case of very highly covalent bonding (as in, for example, $Ni(CO)_4$ or $Fe(CN)_6^{4-}$), which is best treated using a molecular orbital theory, the symmetry properties and requirements remain exactly the same as for the crystal field model and the ligand field model.

Thus, in order to gain an understanding of any one of these theories, the same symmetry considerations are required at the outset.

8.2   Electronic Structures of Free Atoms and Ions

We intend in this chapter to consider the manner in which the symmetry of the chemical surroundings of an ion determines the effect of that environment on the energy levels of the ion. In the crystal field and ligand field theories we often wish to regard the effect of the environment as a small perturbation on the states of the free ion. For the benefit of readers not acquainted with certain general features of the electronic structures of free atoms and ions, a brief résumé of that subject is given in this section.

Wave Functions and Quantum Numbers for a Single Electron

The wave function Ψ for a single electron, in a hydrogen atom for example, may be written as a product of four factors. These are the radial function $R(r)$, which is dependent only on the radial distance r from the nucleus, two angular functions $\Theta(\theta)$ and $\Phi(\phi)$, which depend only on the angles θ and ϕ (cf. Figure 6.1), and a spin function ψ_s, which is independent of the spatial coordinates r, θ, and ϕ. Thus we write

$$\Psi = R(r) \cdot \Theta(\theta) \cdot \Phi(\phi) \cdot \psi_s \qquad (8.2\text{-}1)$$

This overall wave function and each of its factors separately have a parametric dependence on certain quantities called quantum numbers, of which there are four: n, l, m, s.

n is the principal quantum number, taking all integral values from 1 to infinity. It determines the nature of the radial part, $R(r)$, of the wave function only.

The quantum number l occurs in the $\Theta(\theta)$ factor of the wave function. It may be thought of as representing the angular momentum of the electron, in units of $h/2\pi$, due to its orbital motion, and we shall call it the orbital momentum quantum number.* It may take all values 0, 1, 2 ... $(n - 1)$ where n is the principal quantum number. Thus, in the first principal shell, there exist only wave functions with $l = 0$; in the second shell there are wave functions with $l = 0$ and 1, and so on. For historical reasons, letter symbols are given to orbitals according to the value of l, as shown in the following scheme:

$$l = 0 \quad 1 \quad 2 \quad 3 \quad 4 \quad 5 \quad 6 \quad \ldots$$

$$\text{Letter symbol:} \quad s \quad p \quad d \quad f \quad g \quad h \quad i \quad \ldots$$

If we continue to take the classical view of an electron as a discrete charged particle having angular momentum due to its orbital motion, we must also conclude that because of its charge its orbital motion will generate a magnetic dipole. The vector representing this magnetic dipole will be colinear with the vector representing its angular momentum (both are perpendicular to the plane of the orbit), and the value of this orbital magnetic dipole, μ_l, is directly proportional to the angular momentum.

The quantum number m occurs in both the $\Theta(\theta)$ and $\Phi(\phi)$ parts of the wave function. It indicates the tilt of the plane of orbital motion with respect to some reference direction. It can take all integral values from l to

---

* To be precise, the total orbital angular momentum is not $l(h/2\pi)$ but $\sqrt{l(l + 1)}(h/2\pi)$, but this point need not concern us here.

$-l$ or $2l + 1$ values in all. Its relation to the tilt of the orbital plane may be stated more explicitly as follows. If the plane is perpendicular to the reference direction, the length of the projection of the vector representing l on the reference line is numerically equal to l. The next largest angle of tilt permitted by quantum mechanics is such that the length of the projection equals $l - 1$, the next such that the length of the projection is $l - 2$, and so on, until the value of $-l$ is reached. m is simply the length of the projection of l on the reference line. The situation is illustrated for the case of $l = 2$ in the sketch below.

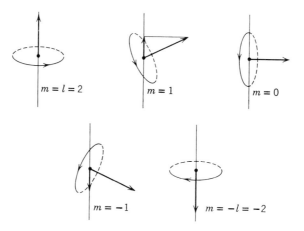

For given n and $l = 0$ there is only one possible orbital, namely, one with $m = 0$. Thus there is only one s orbital of each principal quantum shell. For given n and $l = 1$ there are three possible m values. Hence each principal shell has three different p orbitals. Similarly, d orbitals come in sets of five, f orbitals in sets of seven, and so on. In the absence of any external forces, the energy of an orbital is independent of its m value. Hence all three np orbitals, all five nd orbitals, and so on, are of the same energy.

The electron spin quantum number s is the number on which ψ_s depends and it may take only the values $+\frac{1}{2}$ and $-\frac{1}{2}$. It may be interpreted, classically, as a measure of the spin angular momentum of the electron, that is, as a measure of angular momentum due to the rotation of the electron about its own axis. We may think of the electron as intrinsically having spin angular momentum equal to $\frac{1}{2}(h/2\pi)$ * and consider that this may be oriented with respect to a reference direction so as to produce components of $+\frac{1}{2}$ or $-\frac{1}{2}$ along the reference direction. Again, however, in the framework of this classical picture, we must also expect that if a

---

* Again, strictly $\sqrt{\frac{1}{2}(\frac{1}{2} + 1)}(h/2\pi)$.

charged body is rotating, a magnetic dipole is generated. Thus every electron has associated with it a spin magnetic dipole, μ_s, the direction of which depends on s.

While these four quantum numbers are always sufficient to specify completely the state of an electron, there is another quantum number, j, which is useful in accounting for the energy of the state. In units of $h/2\pi$, j gives the total angular momentum of the electron, which is a vector sum of the orbital angular momentum and the spin angular momentum. Quantum mechanics requires that the vector sum can only be made in certain ways, however. The value of j may be either $l + \frac{1}{2}$ or $l - \frac{1}{2}$. So long as we regard the spin wave function, ψ_s, as entirely independent of the orbital wave function, $R(r)\Theta(\theta)\Phi(\phi)$, these two j states have the same energy.

Actually, spin and orbital magnetic moments do interact, so that the state with $j = l - \frac{1}{2}$ is of lower energy than the state with $j = l + \frac{1}{2}$. This would be expected classically since in the $j = l - \frac{1}{2}$ state the orbital and spin moments are opposed. In the hydrogen atom, in all hydrogen-like ions, and in all atoms and ions having one electron outside of a closed core, the splittings due to this phenomenon of spin-orbit coupling are very small compared to the energy differences between orbitals differing in their l values. Thus the effect of spin-orbit coupling in such cases is justifiably regarded as a small perturbation on an energy level pattern which is basically determined only by the values of n and l.

Quantum Numbers for Many-Electron Atoms

There are various general cases which come under this heading, but we need consider only one. This is the case where most of the electrons in the atom or ion are in closed shells and the others are in the *same* partly filled shell. The closed shells are spherically symmetric, and the only effect they have on the other electrons is to diminish the strength of the nuclear attraction for the other electrons. This means that the wave function for the one electron in a partly filled shell containing only one electron will have the same angular functions, $\Theta(\theta)$ and $\Phi(\phi)$, as it would if this were the only electron in the atom, but its radial function will be different according to the "effective" nuclear charge which it feels.

To a first approximation each of several electrons in such a partly filled shell may be assigned its own private set of one-electron quantum numbers, n, l, m, and s. However, there are always fairly strong inter-actions between these electrons which make this approximation un-realistic. In general the nature of these interactions is not easy to describe, but the behavior of real atoms often approximates closely to a limiting situation which is called the L-S or Russell-Saunders coupling scheme.

In L-S or Russell-Saunders coupling, a quantum number L, which gives the total orbital angular momentum of all the electrons, and a quantum number S, which gives the total spin angular momentum of all the electrons, are used. Note the use of capital letters for quantum numbers characteristic of the entire configuration in contrast to the use of lower-case letters for quantum numbers of individual electrons. This practice is carried further in assigning letter symbols to states of different L. We have the following scheme, which is completely analogous to the scheme for single electrons:

$$L = 0 \quad 1 \quad 2 \quad 3 \quad 4 \quad 5 \quad 6 \quad 7 \quad \ldots$$

$$\text{Letter symbol: } S \quad P \quad D \quad F \quad G \quad H \quad I \quad J \quad \ldots$$

In the Russell-Saunders coupling scheme it is assumed that the angular momenta of the individual electrons are coupled to one another and the spins of the individual electrons are coupled to one another to give, respectively, the L and S values for the configuration. Suppose, for example, that we have an atom which has, outside of closed shells, a $3d$ electron and a $4d$ electron. Each of these has an l value of 2 and an s value of $\frac{1}{2}$. Now the two l vectors may combine to give integral vector sums as shown in Figure 8.1, where l_1 refers to the $3d$ electron and l_2 to

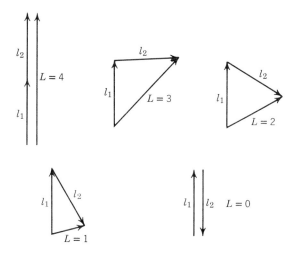

Figure 8.1   Integral vector sums, L, of two vectors, l_1 and l_2, each of length 2.

the $4d$ electron, or vice versa. Thus L values of 0, 1, 2, 3, 4 are possible and hence states symbolized S, P, D, F, and G may arise from two non-equivalent d electrons. By nonequivalent we mean differing in the principal shell to which they belong. Similarly, the s vectors may combine to give S values of 1 or 0. Since the electrons differ in their principal quantum number, any L value may be combined with any S value without violating the exclusion principle. Thus there are altogether ten states or, as they are called, *terms*, which may arise when there are two d electrons present but in different principal shells.

With a single electron the total angular momentum, j, is the vector sum of l and s. Here there are only two possibilities, namely, $j = l + s = l + \frac{1}{2}$ and $j = l - s = l - \frac{1}{2}$. More generally, the total angular momentum, denoted J for a multielectron configuration, may take all of the values $L + S$, $L + S - 1$, $L + S - 2 \ldots |L - S|$, or altogether $2S + 1$ different values. This number $2S + 1$ is called the multiplicity of a term, and it is placed as a left superscript to the term symbol. Just as with one electron, states with the same value of L and S but different values of J will differ somewhat in energy. If these differences in J value are important and must be specified, this is done by putting the J value as a right subscript to the term symbol. Thus all of the different terms, including those differing in their J values, for an $ndmd$ configuration are:

$$^1S_0 \quad ^1P_1 \quad ^1D_2 \quad ^1F_3 \quad ^1G_4$$
$$^3S_1 \quad ^3P_0 \quad ^3D_1 \quad ^3F_2 \quad ^3G_3$$
$$^3P_1 \quad ^3D_2 \quad ^3F_3 \quad ^3G_4$$
$$^3P_2 \quad ^3D_3 \quad ^3F_4 \quad ^3G_5$$

For the ^3S state the triplet character is not actually realized because when $L = 0$, J can only equal S. There is no finite value of L with which S may combine vectorially.

Now that we have seen how two d electrons in different principal shells couple to give terms in the Russell-Saunders or L-S coupling scheme, let us turn to the more directly interesting problem of what terms may arise when the two d electrons belong to the *same* principal shell. Straightforward but lengthy procedures for making certain that we do not violate the exclusion principle are necessary since now we cannot count on a difference in n values to prevent this.* It is found that for a d^2 configuration only the following states may arise:

$$^1S_0 \quad ^3P_{0,1,2} \quad ^1D_2 \quad ^3F_{2,3,4} \quad ^1G_4$$

* These considerations are treated in many books on atomic structure. See, for example, H. E. White's *Introduction to Atomic Spectra*, McGraw-Hill, New York, 1934, Sections 12.1 and 13.11.

Table 8.1   States for d^n Systems in Russell-Saunders Coupling

d^1		$^2(D)$					
d^2	$^1(S, D, G)$		$^3(P, F)$				
d^3		$^2(D)$		$^2(P, D, F, G, H)$	$^4(P, F)$		
d^4	$^1(S, D, G)$		$^3(P, F)$	$^1(S, D, F, G, I)$	$^3(P, D, F, G, H)$	$^5(D)$	
d^5		$^2(D)$		$^2(P, D, F, G, H)$	$^4(P, F)^2(S, D, F, G, I)$	$^4(D, G)$	$^6(S)$
d^6	Same as d^4						
d^7	Same as d^3						
d^8	Same as d^2						
d^9	Same as d^1						
d^{10}	$^1(S)$						

This L-S coupling scheme may be considered a useful approximation when the components of a given multiplet term, that is, states with the same S and L values but different J values, differ in energy by amounts which are small compared to the differences between one multiplet term as a whole and another. Among the transition elements, to which we wish to apply ligand field theory, the L-S coupling scheme works well enough for many purposes in the ions of elements in the first and second transition series. In the third transition series it is not a very good approximation, although it can serve as a starting point for more elaborate treatments. In general, the adequacy of the L-S coupling approximation diminishes steadily as the atomic number increases. In the actinide elements it is too poor to be of any use at all.

For convenience, the states which may arise by Russell-Saunders coupling from all d^n configurations are listed in Table 8.1. For quantitative applications of ligand field theory we must know not only the nature of the states but their relative energies in a particular ion. For a great number of the ions of practical interest these energies are known from experimental measurements. The standard tabulation of such data is C. E. Moore's "Atomic Energy Levels." *

8.3   Splitting of Levels and Terms in a Chemical Environment

We may use the set of five d wave functions as a basis for a representation of the point group of a particular environment and thus determine the manner in which the set of d orbitals is split by that environment. Let us choose an octahedral environment for our first illustration. In order to

* Circular 467, National Bureau of Standards, for sale by the Superintendent of Documents, U. S. Government Printing Office, Washington 25, D. C., Volume I, Hydrogen-Vanadium; Volume II, Chromium-Niobium; Volume III, Molybdenum-Lanthanum and Hafnium-Actinium.

determine the representation for which the set of d wave functions forms a basis, we must determine the elements of the matrices which express the effect upon the set of wave functions of each of the symmetry operations in the group; the characters of these matrices will then be the characters of the representation we are seeking.

The octahedral point group, O_h, is related to the group O. The latter contains only rotations, viz., E, $6C_4$, $3C_2$, $6C'_2$, $8C_3$. Since the group O is a subgroup of O_h, the character table for O is contained within the table for O_h. The O_h table in Appendix II is so arranged that the rotations constituting the group O are collected to the left. The g and u subscripts are to be dropped in O and, for example, (R_x, R_y, R_z) and (x, y, z) both belong to the same representation in O, namely the T_1 representation. If to this set of rotations we add the inversion operation, i, and include all of its products with the rotations, we obtain the elements of O_h. Since we already know that all d wave functions are symmetric to inversion, this being determined by $\Theta(\theta)$, we need not bother to consider the effects of any of the operations in O_h which arise from the inversion. These results would not tell us anything in addition to what we will learn from the effects of the rotations. Thus we shall actually deal only with the group O instead of O_h. So the question we must answer is simply: What does the matrix representing the effect of an n-fold rotation on the set of d orbitals look like, and, then, what is its character?

We assume that the wave functions of a set of d orbitals are each of the general form specified by equation 8.2-1. We shall further assume that the spin function, ψ_s, is entirely independent of the orbital functions and pay no further attention to it for the present. Since the radial function, $R(r)$, involves no directional variables it is invariant to all operations in a point group and need concern us no further. The function $\Theta(\theta)$ depends only upon the angle θ. Therefore, if all rotations are carried out about the axis from which θ is measured (the z axis in Figure 6.1), $\Theta(\theta)$ will also be invariant. Thus, by always choosing the axes of rotation in this way (or, in other words, always quantizing the orbitals about the axis of rotation), only the function $\Phi(\phi)$ will be altered by rotations. The explicit form of the $\Phi(\phi)$ function, aside from a normalizing constant, is

$$\Phi(\phi) = \exp\,(im\phi) \tag{8.3-1}$$

and the five d orbitals are those in which m takes the values l, $(l - 1)$ $\ldots 0 \ldots (1 - l)$, $-l$, namely, $2, 1, 0, -1, -2$.

If we take the function $e^{im\phi}$ and rotate by an angle α, the function becomes $e^{im(\phi+\alpha)}$. Thus we can easily see that the set of $\Phi(\phi)$ wave functions, I,

$$\begin{bmatrix} e^{2i\phi} \\ e^{i\phi} \\ e^{0} \\ e^{-i\phi} \\ e^{-2i\phi} \end{bmatrix} \xrightarrow[\text{by } \alpha]{\text{rotation}} \begin{bmatrix} e^{2i(\phi+\alpha)} \\ e^{i(\phi+\alpha)} \\ e^{0} \\ e^{-i(\phi+\alpha)} \\ e^{-2i(\phi+\alpha)} \end{bmatrix}$$

$$\text{I} \qquad\qquad\qquad \text{II}$$

becomes II on rotation by α. It should be easy to see by inspection that the matrix necessary to produce this transformation is

$$\begin{bmatrix} e^{2i\alpha} & 0 & 0 & 0 & 0 \\ 0 & e^{i\alpha} & 0 & 0 & 0 \\ 0 & 0 & e^{0} & 0 & 0 \\ 0 & 0 & 0 & e^{-i\alpha} & 0 \\ 0 & 0 & 0 & 0 & e^{-2i\alpha} \end{bmatrix}$$

This five-dimensional matrix is only a special case for a set of d functions, and clearly in the $2l + 1$ fold set of functions ($l = 0$ for an s level, 1 for a p level, 3 for an f level, and so on) we shall have

$$\begin{bmatrix} e^{li\alpha} & 0 & \cdots & & 0 \\ \cdot & e^{(l-1)i\alpha} & \cdots & \cdot & \cdot \\ \cdot & \cdot & \cdots & \cdot & \cdot \\ \cdot & \cdot & \cdots & \cdot & \cdot \\ \cdot & \cdot & \cdots & \cdot & \cdot \\ \cdot & \cdot & \cdots & e^{(1-l)i\alpha} & 0 \\ 0 & 0 & \cdots & \cdot & e^{-li\alpha} \end{bmatrix}$$

The sum of the diagonal elements, $\chi(\alpha)$, can be shown to be *

$$\chi(\alpha) = \frac{\sin (l + \frac{1}{2})\alpha}{\sin (\alpha/2)} \qquad (\alpha \neq 0) \qquad\qquad (8.3\text{-}2)$$

We now have the necessary formula to determine the characters of the representation we seek. Let us proceed to work them out.

For a twofold rotation, $\alpha = \pi$ and hence

$$\chi(C_2) = \frac{\sin (5\pi/2)}{\sin (\pi/2)} = \frac{1}{1} = 1$$

* The proof of this will not be given here, but is suggested as a useful exercise. Hint: The quantities being summed form a geometric progression.

Similarly for the threefold and fourfold rotations:

$$\chi(C_3) = \frac{\sin (5\pi/3)}{\sin (\pi/3)} = \frac{-\sin (\pi/3)}{\sin (\pi/3)} = -1$$

$$\chi(C_4) = \frac{\sin (5\pi/4)}{\sin (\pi/4)} = -1$$

The general formula above is inapplicable if $\alpha = 0$; however, it is obvious that in this case each diagonal element is equal to 1 and the character is equal, in the general case, to $2l + 1$; in the present instance, $\chi(E) = 5$. Referring to the character table for the group O and using the methods developed in Chapter 4, we easily see that the representation we have derived is reducible to $E + T_2$. In the group O_h we will have, since the d wave functions are inherently g in their inversion property:

$$\Gamma_d = E_g + T_{2g}$$

Thus we have shown that the set of five d wave functions, degenerate in the free atom or ion (or more precisely, under conditions of spherical symmetry), do not remain degenerate when the atom or ion is placed in an environment with O_h symmetry. They are split into a triply degenerate set, T_{2g}, and a doubly degenerate set, E_g.

It is easy to apply the same treatment to electrons in other types of orbitals than d orbitals. The results obtained are collected in Table 8.2. It will be seen that an s orbital is totally symmetric in the O_h environment. The set of p orbitals remains unsplit, transforming as t_{1u}; this same conclusion could have been obtained directly from the O_h character table where it is seen that (x, y, z) form a basis for the t_{1u} representation of O_h. All orbitals with higher values of the quantum number l, however, are split into two or more sets; this must be so since the group O_h cannot allow any state to be more than threefold degenerate.

In a similar manner, we could determine the splitting of various sets of orbitals in environments of other symmetries which we may encounter in complexes, such as T_d, D_{4h}, D_{2d}, C_{2v}, and so on, and indeed for any sort of symmetry we may encounter. An alternative and simpler way of obtaining this information is to use the results we have obtained for the octahedral case in conjunction with the correlation table given in Appendix II. In Table 8.3 are the results for a few point groups of particular interest.

The results we have obtained so far for single electrons in various types of orbitals also apply to the behavior of terms arising from groups of electrons. For example, just as a single d electron in a free atom has a wave function which belongs to a fivefold degenerate set corresponding

Table 8.2   Splitting of One-Electron Levels in an Octahedral Environment

TYPE OF LEVEL	l	$\chi(E)$	$\chi(C_2)$	$\chi(C_3)$	$\chi(C_4)$	IRREDUCIBLE REPRESENTATIONS SPANNED
s	0	1	1	1	1	A_{1g}
p	1	3	-1	0	1	T_{1u}
d	2	5	1	-1	-1	$E_g + T_{2g}$
f	3	7	-1	1	-1	$A_{2u} + T_{1u} + T_{2u}$
g	4	9	1	0	1	$A_{1g} + E_g + T_{1g} + T_{2g}$
h	5	11	-1	-1	1	$E_u + 2T_{1u} + T_{2u}$
i	6	13	1	1	-1	$A_{1g} + A_{2g} + E_g + T_{1g} + 2T_{2g}$

to the five values which m may take in the $\Phi(\phi)$ factor of the wave function, so a D state arising from any group of electrons has a completely analogous fivefold degeneracy because of the five values which the quantum number M may take. Moreover, the splitting of a D term will be just the same as the splitting of the set of one-electron d orbitals. This is so because the $\Phi(\phi)$ factor of the wave function for a D term is $\exp(iM\phi)$ in exact analogy to the $\Phi(\phi)$ factor, $\exp(im\phi)$, in the wave function for a single d electron. Exactly the same relationship exists between f orbitals and F states, p orbitals and P states, and so on. Thus all of the results given in Table 8.2 for the splitting of various sets of one-electron orbitals apply to the splitting of analogous Russell-Saunders terms. In

Table 8.3   Splitting of One-Electron

TYPE OF LEVEL	SYMMETRY OF	
	O_h	T_d
s	a_{1g}	a_1
p	t_{1u}	t_2
d	$e_g + t_{2g}$	$e + t_2$
f	$a_{2u} + t_{1u} + t_{2u}$	$a_2 + t_1 + t_2$
g	$a_{1g} + e_g + t_{1g} + t_{2g}$	$a_1 + e + t_1 + t_2$
h	$e_u + 2t_{1u} + t_{2u}$	$e + t_1 + 2t_2$
i	$a_{1g} + a_{2g} + e_g + t_{1g} + 2t_{2g}$	$a_1 + a_2 + e + t_1 + 2t_2$

Table 8.3 we have used small letters to represent the states for a single electron in the environments of various symmetries corresponding with the use of the small letters s, p, d, f ... to represent their states in the free atom. Similarly, we shall use capital letters to represent the states into which the environment splits terms of the free ion. Thus, for example, an F state of a free ion will be split into the states A_2, T_1, and T_2 when the ion is placed in the center of a tetrahedral environment.

In Table 8.3 the use of subscripts g and u is governed by the following rules. If the point group of the environment has no center of symmetry then no subscripts are used since they cannot have any meaning. When the environment does have a center of symmetry the subscripts are determined by the type of orbital, all atomic orbitals for which the quantum number l is even (s, d, g ...) being centrosymmetric and hence of g character, and all atomic orbitals for which l is odd (p, f, h ...) being antisymmetric to inversion and thus being of u character. In using Table 8.3 for term splittings the following rules apply. Again, if the environment does not have a center of symmetry the g and u subscripts are inapplicable. For those point groups in which there is a center to which the inversion operation may be referred, the g or u character will be determined by the nature of the one-electron wave functions of the individual electrons making up the configuration from which the term is derived. We shall be interested only in terms derived from d^n configurations, and all of these will give g states in point groups possessing a center of symmetry.

One other point needs to be mentioned regarding the splitting of terms of the free ion in chemical environments, and this concerns the spin multiplicity. The chemical environment does not interact directly with

Levels in Various Symmetries

ENVIRONMENT

D_{4h}	D_3	D_{2d}
a_{1g}	a_1	a_1
$a_{2u} + e_u$	$a_2 + e$	$b_2 + e$
$a_{1g} + b_{1g} + b_{2g} + e_g$	$a_1 + 2e$	$a_1 + b_1 + b_2 + e$
$a_{2u} + b_{1u} + b_{2u} + 2e_u$	$a_1 + 2a_2 + 2e$	$a_1 + a_2 + b_2 + 2e$
$2a_{1g} + a_{2g} + b_{1g} + b_{2g} + 2e_g$	$2a_1 + a_2 + 3e$	$2a_1 + a_2 + b_1 + b_2 + 2e$
$a_{1u} + 2a_{2u} + b_{1u} + b_{2u} + 3e_u$	$a_1 + 2a_2 + 4e$	$a_1 + a_2 + b_1 + 2b_2 + 3e$
$2a_{1g} + a_{2g} + 2b_{1g} + 2b_{2g} + 3e_g$	$3a_1 + 2a_2 + 4e$	$2a_1 + a_2 + 2b_1 + 2b_2 + 3e$

the electron spins and thus all of the states into which a particular term is split have the same spin multiplicity as the parent term.

In order to illustrate the splitting of terms of a d^n configuration, the states for a d^2 ion in several point groups are shown below. The free-ion terms have been given on page 189.

FREE ION TERMS	STATES IN POINT GROUPS		
	O_h	T_d	D_{4h}
^1S	$^1A_{1g}$	$^1A_1$	$^1A_{1g}$
^1G	$^1A_{1g}$ $^1T_{2g}$ ^1E_g $^1T_{1g}$	$^1A_1$ $^1T_2$ ^1E $^1T_1$	2^1A_{1g} $^1B_{2g}$ $^1A_{2g}$ 2^1E_g $^1B_{1g}$
^3P	$^3T_{1g}$	$^3T_1$	$^3A_{2g}$ ^3E_g
^1D	^1E_g $^1T_{2g}$	^1E $^1T_2$	$^1A_{1g}$ ^1E_g $^1B_{1g}$ $^1B_{2g}$
^3F	$^3A_{2g}$ $^3T_{1g}$ $^3T_{2g}$	$^3A_2$ $^3T_1$ $^3T_2$	$^3A_{2g}$ 2^3E_g $^3B_{1g}$ $^3B_{2g}$

8.4   Construction of Energy Level Diagrams

We have seen in the preceding section that all free-ion terms having $L > 1$ are split by chemical environments of symmetry O_h, T_d, or lower symmetries into two or more states which we label according to the representation of the point group which describes their transformation properties. We now turn to the question of the relative energies of these states and how these energies depend on the strength of the chemical interaction of the ion with its surroundings. Obviously, these energies can be straightforwardly calculated by setting up and solving the requisite secular equations, but it is also possible to obtain a great deal of information about the energies, especially the relative energies, *almost* entirely by use of arguments based on the symmetry properties of the states, and this is the subject of this section.

Of course, from symmetry arguments *alone*, information on energies cannot be obtained. The procedures we are about to describe do require one piece of quantitative information obtainable only by a calculation. In Section 8.5 we shall show how this piece of information is obtained, but for the present we will accept it without proof and proceed to the construction of energy level diagrams.

It will be demonstrated in Section 8.5 that the relative energies of the doubly and triply degenerate sets of d orbitals into which the set of five d orbitals is split in a tetrahedral or octahedral environment are as shown in Figure 8.2. Thus, when there is a single d electron in an ion in an octahedral environment, it will occupy one of the t_{2g} orbitals and the energy required to promote it to an e_g orbital is Δ_0, while for the same ion in a tetrahedral environment, the electron will occupy an e orbital and the energy required to promote it to a t_2 orbital will be Δ_t.

The energy level diagram we wish to construct will show how the energies of the various states into which the free-ion terms are split depend on the strength of the interaction of the ion with its environment. The separation of the two sets of orbitals into which the group of five d orbitals is split can be taken as our measure of this interaction. Thus our diagram will have the magnitude of Δ_0 or Δ_t as abscissa and energy as ordinate. At the extreme left where Δ_0 or Δ_t is zero we shall have the free-ion term energies. At the right side of the diagram we will have the energies of states which will exist when the interaction produces such a

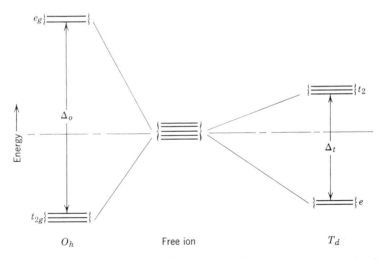

Figure 8.2   Diagram showing the relative energies of e and t_2 orbitals resulting from the splitting of the set of d orbitals by octahedral and tetrahedral environments.

great separation of the e and t_2 orbitals that the energies due to inter-electronic interactions become negligible by comparison.

We will now explain the method of constructing an energy level diagram by treating the particular case of a d^2 ion in an octahedral environment. For this system the free-ion terms, in order of increasing energy, are

$$^3F \quad ^1D \quad ^3P \quad ^1G \quad ^1S$$

In the limit of an extremely large splitting of the d orbitals, the following three configurations, in order of increasing energy, will be possible:

$$t_{2g}^2 \quad t_{2g}e_g \quad e_g^2$$

The usage of the symbols here is the same as that for showing free-atom configurations. Thus these are configurations in which (1) both electrons are in t_{2g} orbitals, t_{2g}^2; (2) one electron is in a t_{2g} orbital while the other is in an e_g orbital, $t_{2g}e_g$; and (3) the highest energy configuration, e_g^2, in which both electrons are in e_g orbitals. The energy increase from one of these to the next highest is Δ_0.

Now let us consider what will happen as we begin to relax the strong interaction of the environment with the ion so that the electrons begin to feel one another's presence. They will begin to couple in certain ways giving rise to a set of states of the entire configuration. The symmetry properties of these states can be determined by taking the direct products of the representations of the single electrons. Thus for the configuration t_{2g}^2 we take the direct product $t_{2g} \times t_{2g}$ and then decompose it into $A_{1g} + E_g + T_{1g} + T_{2g}$. Similarly the direct product $t_{2g} \times e_g$ gives $T_{1g} + T_{2g}$ and the direct product e_g^2 gives $A_{1g} + A_{2g} + E_g$. These are the symmetries of the orbital states produced by the interaction of the electrons. However, we have yet to determine the spin multiplicities of these states. Clearly, with two electrons involved, they must be either singlets or triplets, and we must be careful to observe any restrictions placed on the multiplicities by the exclusion principle.

Later in this section we shall describe a rigorous and completely general method of determining the multiplicities of the strong-field states but for the present we shall work out the d^2 case using a less elegant but instructive method. Consider first the configuration t_{2g}^2. We may regard the t_{2g} levels as a set of six boxes as shown below:

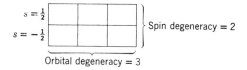

The number of ways in which two electrons may occupy these six boxes is given by $(6 \cdot 5)/2$ where the 2 in the denominator takes account of the indistinguishability of the electrons. Thus the total degeneracy of the t_{2g}^2 configuration is 15. Now as the field is decreased giving rise to the separate orbital states A_{1g}, E_g, T_{1g}, and T_{2g}, the total degeneracy must remain 15. Thus, if we write

$$t_{2g} \times t_{2g} \rightarrow {}^aA_{1g} + {}^bE_g + {}^cT_{1g} + {}^dT_{2g}$$

we may say that the total degeneracy equals 15 by writing

$$1 \cdot a + 2 \cdot b + 3 \cdot c + 3 \cdot d = 15$$

where a, b, c, and d must each be either 1 or 3. It is not difficult to see that with this restriction the equation has only three solutions, viz.,

	a	b	c	d
I	1	1	1	3
II	1	1	3	1
III	3	3	1	1

Similarly for the e_g^2 configuration we have two electrons to place in four equivalent boxes and this may be done in $(4 \cdot 3)/2 = 6$ distinguishable ways. Thus we may write

$$e_g \times e_g \rightarrow {}^aA_{1g} + {}^bA_{2g} + {}^cE_g$$

and the equation

$$1 \cdot a + 1 \cdot b + 2 \cdot c = 6$$

which admits of only two solutions, viz.,

	a	b	c
I	1	3	1
II	3	1	1

Now for the $t_{2g}e_g$ configuration we may place one electron in any of six boxes while we *independently* place the second electron in any of four boxes, giving a total of twenty-four possible arrangements. We also note that there is no possibility of two electrons being in the same box, so that for all arrangements their spins may be either paired or unpaired. Thus both the T_{1g} and T_{2g} states derived from the $t_{2g}e_g$ configuration may be both triplet and singlet. We thus get the unique answer that the configuration $t_{2g}e_g$ gives ${}^1T_{1g}$, ${}^3T_{1g}$, ${}^1T_{2g}$, and ${}^3T_{2g}$. The total degeneracy of these four states is 24, in agreement with our count of the number of arrangements in the boxes.

Now we can determine which of the possible assignments of the multiplicities in the t_{2g}^2 and e_g^2 configurations are correct by proceeding to correlate the states on the two sides of the diagram. To do this we shall use two principles, neither of which will be proved, but both of which are important and rather easily remembered. As we go from the weak to the strong interaction with the environment, we do not in any way change the symmetry properties of the system. Thus there must be the same number of each kind of state throughout, and we may accept, almost as an axiom, the principle:

There must exist a one-to-one correspondence between the states at the two extremes of the abscissa.

The second principle, which we shall not attempt to justify, is known as the noncrossing rule:

As the strength of the interaction changes, states of the same spin degeneracy and symmetry cannot cross.

In Figure 8.3 we have shown on the extreme left the states of the free ion. Immediately to the right we have shown the states into which these free-ion states split under the influence of the octahedral environment. Here we know the spin multiplicities of all states. Now at the extreme right are the states in the (hypothetical) case of an infinitely strong interaction with the environment, and immediately to the left of them are the distinct states which we have just shown to exist in the case of a very strong, but not infinitely strong, interaction. In order that each state on the left go over into a state of the same kind on the right without violation of the noncrossing rule, the connecting lines can only be drawn in the manner shown. The manner in which this was done may be briefly recapitulated.

We note that there are two $^1A_{1g}$ states on the left and no $^3A_{1g}$ states. Thus both A_{1g} states on the right must be singlets. This immediately settles the multiplicities of the states coming from the e_g^2 configuration and rules out possibility III for the t_{2g}^2 configuration. Now we note that there are two $^3T_{1g}$ states at the left. The higher one must connect to the $^3T_{1g}$ state coming from the $t_{2g}e_g$ configuration. There is only one T_{1g} state below this, namely that from t_{2g}^2, so this must be a triplet, and this settles the assignment of spin multiplicities of the states coming from the t_{2g}^2 configuration. The remaining connections are now drawn in accord with the noncrossing rule.

The complete diagram is often called a *correlation diagram*. It shows how the energy levels of the ion behave as a function of the strength of the chemical interaction with an octahedrally symmetric environment.

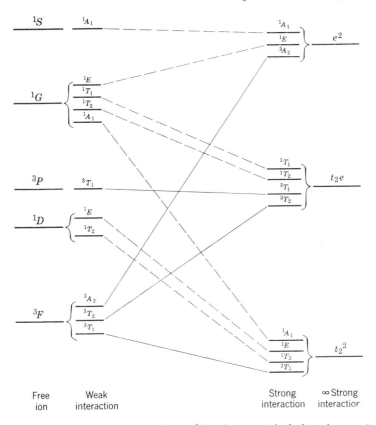

Figure 8.3 A correlation diagram for a d^2 ion in an octahedral environment. All states and orbitals are of g type and this subscript has therefore been omitted.

The Method of Descending Symmetry

In the foregoing pages we have constructed the complete correlation diagram for a d^2 ion in O_h symmetry. In the course of doing so we ran into the problem of determining the spin multiplicities of the orbital states as they arise from interelectronic interactions in the configurations e_g^2 and t_{2g}^2, but we were able to obtain a solution by the somewhat oblique procedure of requiring the states to be just those necessary to correlate with the set of weak-field states. Such a procedure would be rather impractical in more complicated cases, but there is a straightforward and general method, due to Bethe and known as the Method of Descending Symmetry, which can always give us the required information. We shall explain this method by showing its application in the d^2 case, and it should then be obvious how it can be applied in any case.

Let us begin with the $e_g{}^2$ configuration. We have shown that this must go over into the states A_{1g}, A_{2g}, and E_g as the electron interactions take effect. Suppose now we take the environment of the ion, which has O_h symmetry, and lower that symmetry to D_{4h}, say by taking a *trans* pair of ligands in an octahedral MX_6 complex and moving them out to a greater distance than the other four. The degeneracy of the one-electron e_g orbitals is now lifted and, as may be seen from the correlation table in Appendix II, we get two nondegenerate levels of symmetries a_{1g} and b_{1g}:

$$e_g \{ = \!\!= \quad \rightarrow \quad \begin{array}{c} \underline{} \ a_{1g} \\ \\ \underline{} \ b_{1g} \end{array}$$

$$O_h \qquad\qquad D_{4h}$$

Now the number of ways in which we can place the two electrons in the two levels, a_{1g} and b_{1g}, are the following:

	DIRECT PRODUCT	POSSIBLE SPIN MULTIPLICITIES
a_{1g}^2	A_{1g}	$^1A_{1g}$
$a_{1g}b_{1g}$	B_{1g}	$^1B_{1g}, ^3B_{1g}$
b_{1g}^2	A_{1g}	$^1A_{1g}$

Clearly the exclusion principle requires that the A_{1g} states resulting from the configurations a_{1g}^2 and b_{1g}^2 must be singlets, that is, the spins of the electrons must be different, whereas for the configuration $a_{1g}b_{1g}$, since the two electrons have different orbital states, there is no restriction on their spins, and the resulting states $^1B_{1g}$ and $^3B_{1g}$ are both permitted. It should be noted that the total number of arrangements of electrons in the four e_g type boxes was six and the total is still six in D_{4h} symmetry as it must be.

Now just as the one-electron level, e_g, in O_h symmetry goes over into the levels a_{1g} and b_{1g} when the symmetry is lowered to D_{4h}, so the states deriving from the $e_g{}^2$ configuration in O_h symmetry, namely A_{1g}, A_{2g}, and E_g, must go over into states appropriate to D_{4h} symmetry. Inspection of the correlation table shows that the relationship is

$$\begin{array}{cc} O_h & D_{4h} \\ A_{1g} & \rightarrow \quad A_{1g} \\ A_{2g} & \rightarrow \quad B_{1g} \\ E_g & \rightarrow \quad \begin{cases} A_{1g} \\ B_{1g} \end{cases} \end{array}$$

Lowering the symmetry cannot change the spin degeneracies, so that if the A_{1g} state in O_h is a singlet then the corresponding A_{1g} state in D_{4h} must also be a singlet and so on. Moreover, whatever is the multiplicity of the E_g state in O_h, both the A_{1g} and B_{1g} states which arise from it on lowering the symmetry to D_{4h} must have that same spin multiplicity. Since the only A_{1g} states available in D_{4h} are $^1A_{1g}$, it immediately follows that the correlation between the O_h states and the D_{4h} states must be with the spin multiplicities as shown below:

$$O_h \qquad\qquad D_{4h}$$

$$^1A_{1g} \rightarrow \quad ^1A_{1g}$$

$$^3A_{2g} \rightarrow \quad ^3B_{1g}$$

$$^1E_g \quad \rightarrow \quad \begin{cases} ^1A_{1g} \\ ^1B_{1g} \end{cases}$$

This fixes the multiplicities of the states in O_h and, of course, gives the same assignments of spin multiplicities we previously deduced.

Let us now proceed to the states arising from the t_{2g}^2 configuration, namely, $A_{1g} + E_g + T_{1g} + T_{2g}$. It should be recalled that we found previously that only three assignments of multiplicities were possible consistent with the total degeneracy (15) of the t_{2g}^2 which must be conserved. These are enumerated again in the chart below for convenient reference.

$t_{2g} \times t_{2g} =$	A_{1g}	E_g	T_{1g}	T_{2g}
Possible spin multiplicity assignments	$\begin{cases} 1 \\ 1 \\ 3 \end{cases}$	$\begin{matrix} 1 \\ 1 \\ 3 \end{matrix}$	$\begin{matrix} 1 \\ 3 \\ 1 \end{matrix}$	$\begin{matrix} 3 \\ 1 \\ 1 \end{matrix}$
Corresponding representations in C_{2h}	A_g	A_g B_g	A_g B_g B_g	A_g A_g B_g

It is now necessary to look for a subgroup of O_h such that each of the representations A_{1g}, E_g, T_{1g}, T_{2g} of O_h goes over into a *different* one-dimensional representation or sum of one-dimensional representations of the subgroup. Unless they are all different it will not be possible to obtain a complete and unambiguous result. Inspection of the correlation table for O_h in Appendix II shows that the subgroups C_{2h} and C_{2v} will be satisfactory. We shall use C_{2h} here; the reader may obtain practice in applying the method by verifying the results using C_{2v}. In the chart above we have listed under each of the O_h representations the C_{2h} representations which correspond to it as obtained from the correlation table.

Since t_{2g} in O_h goes over to $a_g + a_g + b_g$ in C_{2h}, the direct product $t_{2g} \times t_{2g}$ goes over into the sum of the six direct products of $a_g + a_g + b_g$, namely,

$$a_g \times a_g = A_g$$

$$a_g \times a_g = A_g$$

$$a_g \times b_g = B_g$$

$$a_g \times a_g = A_g$$

$$a_g \times b_g = B_g$$

$$b_g \times b_g = A_g$$

The first of these represents the occupation of one a_g orbital by both electrons and so must be a singlet, ^1A_g. The second corresponds to the placement of each electron in a different a_g orbital and can therefore give rise to both singlet and triplet states, $^1A_g + ^3A_g$. The third one as well as the fifth also correspond to placing the electrons in different orbitals and these too give rise to both triplet and singlet states, viz., $2^1B_g + 2^3B_g$. The fourth and sixth correspond to placing the two electrons in the same orbital and thus give rise only to singlet states, 2^1A_g. In summary then, the direct product $t_{2g} \times t_{2g}$ which goes over into $(a_g + a_g + b_g) \times (a_g + a_g + b_g)$ in C_{2h} gives rise to the following states in C_{2h}:

$$4^1A_g + ^3A_g + 2^1B_g + 2^3B_g$$

It may be noted that the sum of all the degeneracies, $4(1 \times 1) + (3 \times 1) + 2(1 \times 1) + 2(3 \times 1)$, equals 15 as it must if no errors have been made.

We can now obtain the result we desire. We can immediately make a unique assignment of multiplicities to the states listed in the lower part of our chart by noting that there is only one ^3A_g state and two ^3B_g states. These must therefore be assigned to the A_g and two B_g states arising from T_{1g} which establishes that the T_{1g} state is a spin triplet and, hence, that the A_{1g}, E_g, and T_{2g} states are all spin singlets. If the reader is not yet so persuaded, he can easily convince himself by trial and error that no other permutation will work.

Energy Level Diagrams in Tetrahedral Environments

Energy level diagrams for ions in tetrahedral environments can be constructed by the same procedures as those described in the preceding pages for the octahedral case. We shall briefly outline here the procedure for d^2.

To obtain the left (weak interaction) side we look up each of the free-ion terms in Table 8.3 and find that these terms split as follows:

$$^3F \rightarrow {}^3A_2 + {}^3T_1 + {}^3T_2$$

$$^1D \rightarrow {}^1E + {}^1T_2$$

$$^3P \rightarrow {}^3T_1$$

$$^1G \rightarrow {}^1A_1 + {}^1E + {}^1T_1 + {}^1T_2$$

$$^1S \rightarrow {}^1A_1$$

Turning our attention now to the right (strong interaction) side of the diagram we observe in Figure 8.2 that the one-electron e orbitals are more stable (by Δ_t) than the one-electron t_2 orbitals. Hence the three configurations under the influence of a strong interaction with the tetrahedral environment will be, in increasing order of energy: e^2, et_2, t_2^2. Taking the direct product representations of these and obtaining their constituent irreducible representations we see that interelectronic coupling will cause the following states to arise:

$$e^2 \rightarrow A_1 + A_2 + E$$

$$et_2 \rightarrow T_1 + T_2$$

$$t_2^2 \rightarrow A_1 + E + T_1 + T_2$$

We can now assign the correct spin multiplicities, 1 or 3, to these states by the same methods described in detail for the octahedral case and then correlate the states on the two sides of the diagram to obtain the complete correlation diagram shown in Figure 8.4.

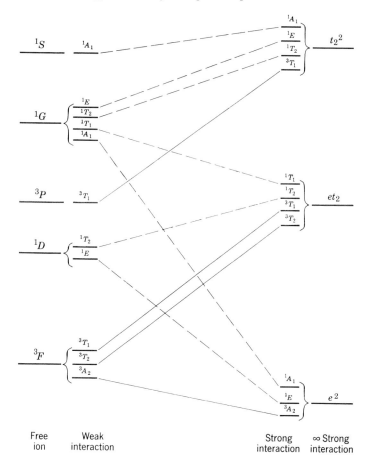

Figure 8.4 A correlation diagram for a d^2 ion in a tetrahedral environment.

The Hole Formalism

The methods illustrated above for working out the correlation diagrams of d^2 ions in octahedral and tetrahedral environments can be applied to all d^n configurations for $2 \leq n \leq 9$. However, the labor involved increases extraordinarily fast as the number of electrons increases. Fortunately there are several kinds of relationships which make it possible to obtain certain diagrams from certain others which are more readily constructed. One of these kinds of relationship is the hole formalism. According to this principle, which is thoroughly rigorous, a

d^{10-n} configuration will behave, at all points along the abscissa of the energy level diagram, in the same way as the corresponding d^n configuration, *except* that all energies of interaction with the environment will have the opposite sign. A physical way of looking at the problem is to say that n holes in the d shell may be treated as n positrons. In their interactions with one another n positrons will behave the same as n electrons. However, where the environment tends to repel an electron it will with the same force attract a positron and vice versa.

The consequences of this are most easily seen by considering the right side of the correlation diagrams. For n electrons in an octahedral environment the configuration containing as many electrons as possible in the t_2 orbitals is the most stable whereas for n positrons such a configuration is the least stable one. It should be easy indeed to see that quite generally the states at the extreme right of the diagram for a d^n configuration (in either octahedral or tetrahedral environments) will be inverted for the corresponding d^{10-n} configuration. Since the energy order of the states which arise from the free-ion terms of a d^n configuration is dictated by the energy order in which they go into the various $e^p t_2^q$ configurations on the right, it follows that the splitting patterns of the free-ion terms of a d^n system will be just inverted for the corresponding d^{10-n} system.

Thus, for example, the correlation diagram for a d^8 system in an octahedral field is obtainable from Figure 8.3 simply by inverting the vertical arrangement of the configurations $t_2{}^2$, et_2, e^2 and redrawing the connecting lines.

More General Relations

The prescription given in the preceding paragraph for obtaining the correlation diagram of a d^8 configuration in an octahedral environment from that for a d^2 configuration in an octahedral environment is exactly the same as one for obtaining the diagram of the d^2 ion in a tetrahedral environment from that for the d^2 ion in an octahedral environment. Changing the environment from octahedral to tetrahedral inverts the energies of e and t_2 orbitals and so also does the change of n electrons to n positrons while keeping the symmetry of the environment the same.

We may thus state the following very general rule, where we use the symbol $d^n(\text{oct})$ to mean the energy level order for a d^n system in an octahedral field, with the other symbols having analogous meanings:

$$d^n(\text{oct}) \equiv d^{10-n}(\text{tetr}) \text{ are inverse to } d^n(\text{tetr}) \equiv d^{10-n}(\text{oct}).$$

Thus for the eighteen possible cases, that is, $d^1 - d^9$ each in tetrahedral and octahedral environments, correlation diagrams can be obtained by explicitly working out only those for the following cases, which are the simplest:

$$d^1(\text{oct}) \quad d^2(\text{oct}) \quad d^3(\text{oct}) \quad d^4(\text{oct}) \quad d^5(\text{oct})$$

The d^5 case is special in that all of the four related diagrams here are identical. The d^n and d^{10-n} are of course the same configurations when $n = 5$ and $d^5(\text{oct}) \equiv d^5(\text{tetr})$.

In Figure 8.5 are shown energy level diagrams for all of the d^n configurations in octahedral environments. These diagrams are plotted in a manner requiring some comment. Instead of using absolute units for the ordinate and abscissa scales which would restrict each diagram to use with just the one case in which the separations of the free-ion terms matched those used in the diagram, the energy unit is the interelectronic repulsion parameter B. On each diagram are given the values of B for the common free ions of the corresponding d^n and d^{10-n} configurations. In addition it should be noted that the diagrams are so drawn that the energy of the ground state is taken as the zero of energy for all values of Δ_0. Thus, in those cases where the ground state changes there are sharp changes in the slopes of all lines. It is to be emphasized that these "kinks" are artifacts of the diagrams and do not represent real discontinuities in the energies of the states.

Energy Level Diagrams for Lower Symmetries

We have so far considered only the most highly symmetrical situations of common occurrence. We have seen that for octahedral and tetrahedral symmetry the d orbitals split into only two sets and thus only one parameter, Δ_0 or Δ_t is required to describe the energy pattern. In cases where the symmetry is high and the number of free parameters is small, symmetry considerations are, as we have seen, highly informative. When the symmetry is lower there are more splittings, more parameters and, hence, less which may be learned from symmetry considerations alone regarding the relative order of the levels. Symmetry considerations tend to become less an end in themselves and more a necessary preliminary to setting up the equations for a calculation in the simplest and most expedient form. With regard to the interpretation of spectral intensity measurements and especially the polarization of absorption bands, pure symmetry considerations remain immensely useful as will be seen in Section 8.6.

One of the most commonly occurring of the lower symmetries in co-ordination compounds is D_{4h}. This is the point group of atoms surrounding and directly interacting with the metal atom in square planar complexes, of octahedral complexes which are distorted by elongation or compression along one of the fourfold axes and of *trans* disubstituted octahedral complexes such as *trans*-$[Co(NH_3)_4Cl_2]^+$. We shall discuss this one example to illustrate the general nature of the problems which arise when the symmetry is lower than cubic.

As shown in Table 8.3, the d orbitals form a basis for a representation of the group D_{4h} which contains the irreducible representations A_{1g}, B_{1g}, B_{2g}, and E_g. By referring to the character table for D_{4h} we can obtain the more specific information that the d orbitals correspond with these representations in the following way:

$$
\begin{aligned}
A_{1g}&: \quad d_{z^2} \\
B_{1g}&: \quad d_{x^2-y^2} \\
B_{2g}&: \quad d_{xy} \\
E_g&: \quad d_{xz}, d_{yz}
\end{aligned}
$$

Since there are four different symmetry species of orbitals we now require three parameters to specify the energy differences between them. The relative values of these parameters must be known in order to know the relative energies of these four types of orbital so that at least two *actual numbers*, ratios of two of the parameters to the third, perhaps, must be known before any sort of energy level diagram can be constructed. Where the deviation from perfect octahedral symmetry is small it can be assumed that the a_{1g} and b_{1g} levels arising from the splitting of the e_g levels in O_h will be separated by an energy which is comparable in magnitude to the separation of the b_{2g} and e_g levels arising from the t_{2g} levels in O_h, and that both of these energies will be small relative to the energy difference, Δ_0, initially existing between the e_g and t_{2g} levels in the octahedral environment. But still, there remains the question of the relative energies of a_{1g} versus b_{1g} and of b_{2g} versus e_g.

Relation of Energy Level Diagrams to Spectral and Magnetic Properties of Complexes

Among the most important uses of energy level diagrams of the sort we have been discussing are in the interpretation of spectral and magnetic properties of complexes and other compounds of the transition elements. For detailed discussion of these applications the reader is referred to

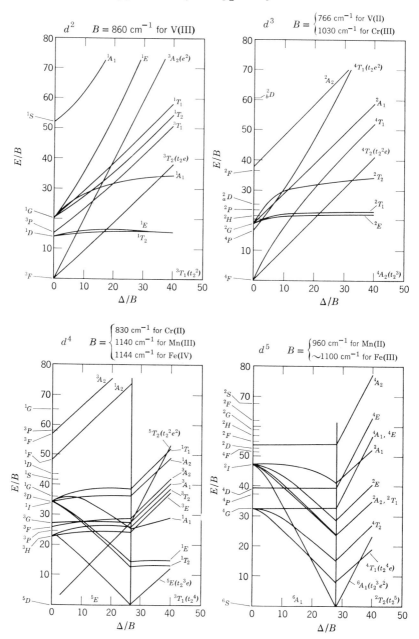

Figure 8.5 Energy level diagrams, after Tanabe and Sugano, *J. Phys. Soc. Japan*, **9**, 753 (1954), for the d^2–d^8 configurations, in octahedral symmetry.

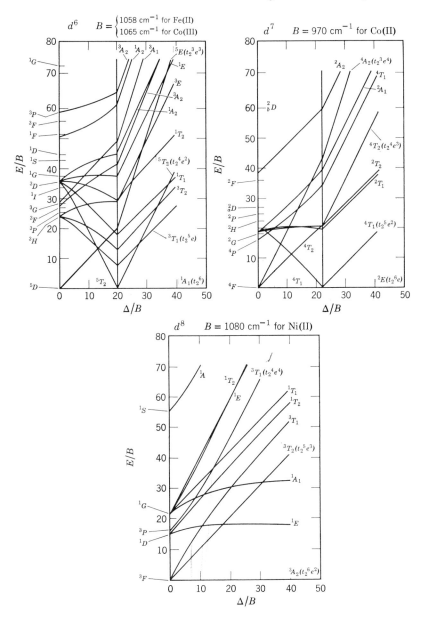

Figure 8.5   (*Continued.*)

several books dealing more broadly with ligand field theory,* but it is appropriate to give here a summary account of them.

The visible and near ultraviolet spectra of transition metal ions in chemical environments are due to transitions from their ground states to the various excited states as these are shown on the energy level diagrams in Figure 8.5. As will be discussed more fully in Section 8.6, these transitions are nominally forbidden by selection rules in first approximation but appear weakly because of breakdown of these selection rules in higher approximations. Transitions to excited states with the same spin multiplicity as the ground state are some 10^2 times stronger than those to states differing in spin quantum number, as might be expected. Thus the spin forbidden transitions cause absorption bands which are nearly always too weak to be observed in ordinary measurements.

By inspection of the energy level diagrams it is possible to see directly what sort of a spectrum the ion should have in the given environment. For example, it can be seen from Figure 8.3 that a d^2 ion in an octahedral complex, say $[V(H_2O)_6]^{3+}$, should have three spin-allowed transitions, from the $^3T_1$ ground state to the upper states $^3T_2$, $^3T_1$, and $^3A_2$. Experimentally, two absorption bands have been found at $\sim$17,000 cm^{-1} and $\sim$24,000 cm^{-1} and these may be assigned to the $^3T_1 \rightarrow {}^3T_2$ and $^3T_1 \rightarrow {}^3T_1$ transitions if Δ_0 is taken as $\sim$21,500 cm^{-1}. The $^3T_1 \rightarrow {}^3A_2$ transition would be expected to be at still higher energy at this value of Δ_0 and has not been definitely observed. As another example, let us consider the d^7 ion Co(II) in a tetrahedral environment, for example, in $[CoCl_4]^{2-}$. The energy level diagram is the same as that for a d^3 ion in an octahedral complex, and from Figure 8.5 we observe that three spin-allowed bands are to be expected. Again only two have been observed at $\sim$5500 cm^{-1} and $\sim$14,700 cm^{-1}. From the energy level diagram it follows that these must be assigned as the $^4A_2 \rightarrow {}^4T_1(F)$ and $^4A_2 \rightarrow {}^4T_1(P)$ transitions and it would then be predicted that the $^4A_2 \rightarrow {}^4T_2$ transition should lie in the range 3000–3500 cm^{-1}. In a few other tetrahedral complexes such a transition has been observed but is extremely weak. The reason for the weakness is discussed in Section 8.6. It is to be noted that Δ_t here is only 3000–3500 cm^{-1} as compared to the value of $\sim$21,500 cm^{-1} for $[V(H_2O)_6]^{3+}$ found earlier. This great difference is due to the combination of two effects. One is that for a particular metal ion and ligands, Δ_0, for the octahedral complex MX_6, is about twice as

* J. S. Griffith, *The Theory of Transition Metal Ions*, Cambridge University Press, 1961. C. J. Ballhausen, *Introduction to Ligand Field Theory*, McGraw-Hill, New York, 1962. L. E. Orgel, *Transition Metal Chemistry*, Methuen and Co., Ltd., London, 1960. F. A. Cotton and G. Wilkinson, *Advanced Inorganic Chemistry, A Comprehensive Course*, Interscience Publishers, a division of John Wiley and Sons, New York, 1962.

great as Δ_t, in the tetrahedral complex MX_4. Second, for octahedral complexes, an increase of one unit in the oxidation number of the metal causes Δ_0 to rise by a factor of 2–3.

Insofar as magnetic properties are concerned the energy level diagrams provide a ready explanation of the way in which the symmetry and strength of interaction of the environment determine the spin multiplicities of the metal ions in their compounds. Basically, two different situations arise. In one of these, exemplified by the octahedral d^1, d^2, d^3, d^8, and d^9 cases, the ground state is one derived from the lowest term of the free ion for all values of the parameter Δ_0, however large. Hence the number of unpaired electrons must be the same as that in the free ion, however strongly the ion may interact with its environment. In the other cases, namely d^4, d^5, d^6, and d^7, the ground state is derived from the lowest free-ion term only out to a certain critical value of Δ_0 beyond which a state of lower spin multiplicity originating in a higher free-ion term drops below it and hence becomes the ground state. For these systems therefore we can predict that for complexes and other compounds in which the perturbing effect of the environment as measured by Δ_0 is weak, there will be the maximum number of unpaired electrons, whereas for compounds in which the perturbing effect of the environment is very strong, greater than the critical value of Δ_0, there will be fewer (two or four fewer) unpaired electrons. Predictions of this sort have been found to be in remarkable accord with experimental observations. Similar predictions could be made for the various d^n systems in tetrahedral environments but are of little practical value since in real tetrahedral systems the value of Δ_t never seems to exceed the critical value, and hence all tetrahedral complexes known have the highest possible spin multiplicity.

There is also another way of deducing whether a given d^n ion in an octahedral environment will have only one possible spin multiplicity or several, and what these multiplicities will be, which is so simple that it can be used without reference to any published energy level diagrams and indeed even without use of pencil and paper. We consider the set of one-electron d orbitals split as shown in Figure 8.2 into the lower-lying t_{2g} subset and the upper-lying e_g subset. When an electron is to be placed in this set of d orbitals, two energy terms must be considered. If the electron enters the t_{2g} subset it will be more stable by an amount Δ_0 than if it enters the e_g subset. However, if in order to enter the t_{2g} subset it will have to enter an orbital which is already occupied by one electron, there will be a repulsive energy, usually called a pairing energy, P. If this pairing energy is greater than Δ_0 the electron will go into an e_g orbital despite the fact that this costs an energy Δ_0. Thus the critical value of

Δ_0 can be equated (approximately) to the pairing energy P. The latter can be estimated from spectroscopic data on the free ion.

With these considerations in mind we can make the following statements about the d electron distributions for the various d^n configurations in octahedral environments. For the d^1, d^2, and d^3 cases the electrons can enter the t_{2g} orbitals without any need of double occupancy of any orbital. Hence these ions will have one, two, and three unpaired electrons respectively, regardless of the magnitude of Δ_0. For the d^8 and d^9 ions all possible configurations require double occupancy of three and four orbitals respectively, and the lowest-energy configurations will always be those, $t_{2g}^6 e_g^2$ and $t_{2g}^6 e_g^3$, with the t_{2g} orbitals fully occupied regardless of the magnitude of Δ_0. Thus the ground states of d^1, d^2, d^3, d^8, and d^9 ions in octahedral environments must have the maximum number of unpaired electrons irrespective of the magnitude of Δ_0. For d^4, d^5, d^6, and d^7 ions, however, the electron distributions will depend on the magnitude of Δ_0 compared to P as indicated in the following table. The numbers in parentheses give the numbers of unpaired electrons.

CONFIGURATION	$\Delta_0 < P$	$\Delta_0 > P$
d^4	$t_{2g}^3 e_g$ (4)	t_{2g}^4 (2)
d^5	$t_{2g}^3 e_g^2$ (5)	t_{2g}^5 (1)
d^6	$t_{2g}^4 e_g^2$ (4)	t_{2g}^6 (0)
d^7	$t_{2g}^5 e_g^2$ (3)	$t_{2g}^6 e_g$ (1)

It will be seen that all these results are in accord with the conclusions which can be drawn from the energy level diagrams of Figure 8.5.

8.5   Estimation of Orbital Energies

The numerical evaluation of the energies of orbitals and states is fundamentally a matter of making quantum mechanical computations. As indicated in Chapter 1, quantum mechanics per se is not the subject of this book and indeed we have tried in general to avoid any detailed treatment of methods for solving the wave equation, emphasis being placed on the properties which the wave functions must have purely for reasons of symmetry and irrespective of their explicit analytical form. However, this discussion of the symmetry aspects of ligand field theory would be artificial and unsatisfying without some brief outline of the various models which may be used to make computations and also to visualize the nature of the interaction between the metal ion and its chemical environment.

Our discussion here of computational procedures will be very superficial and aimed at bringing out the physical features of the models; the reader is referred to several other books * for a full treatment of this subject and references to the original literature. Likewise, for further discussion of the interpretation of the chemical behavior of transition metal compounds in terms of ligand field theory, he is referred to two recent books.†

As noted in Section 8.1, there are three closely related theories of the electronic structures of transition metal complexes, all making quite explicit use of the symmetry properties of the problem but using different physical models of the interaction of the ion with its surroundings as a basis for computations. These three theories are the crystal field, ligand field, and molecular orbital theories. There is also the valence bond theory which makes less explicit use of symmetry but is nevertheless in accord with the essential symmetry requirements of the problem. We shall now briefly outline the physical model and the essentials of such computational procedures as exist in each one of these theories.

The Crystal Field Theory

This model of a complex or of a crystalline salt of a metal ion in a compound such as a halide or oxide is of an electrostatic, point charge, or point dipole type. The ligands or neighbors of the metal ion are treated as structureless, orbital-less point charges which set up an electrostatic field. The effect of this field on electrons in the d orbitals of the metal ion is then investigated.

Group theory alone has shown us that a single d electron in an ion which is at the center of an octahedron may be in either of two states. In one of these it will have either of two wave functions or one which is a linear combination of both, which, together, provide a basis for the E_g representation of the group O_h. In the other state it may have one of three wave functions or some linear combination of these, this set of three being such as to provide a basis for the T_{2g} representation of the

* J. S. Griffith, *The Theory of Transition Metal Ions*, Cambridge University Press, 1961. C. J. Ballhausen, *Introduction to Ligand Field Theory*, McGraw-Hill, New York, 1962.
† L. E. Orgel, *Transition Metal Chemistry*, Methuen and Co., Ltd., London, 1960. F. A. Cotton and G. Wilkinson, *Advanced Inorganic Chemistry, A Comprehensive Course*, Interscience Publishers, a division of John Wiley and Sons, New York, 1962.

group O_h. If we refer to the character table for the group O_h we note that the wave functions $d_{x^2-y^2}$ and d_{z^2} form a basis for the E_g representation. Hence we may consider these to be the orbitals which may be occupied by an e_g electron. Similarly a t_{2g} electron may be assumed to occupy one of the orbitals d_{xy}, d_{yz}, d_{xz}, since these form a basis for the T_{2g} representation of the group. We shall now show how the energies of electrons in these orbitals are estimated according to the electrostatic model of the crystal field theory.

We assume that each of the six ligands is either an anion such as O^{2-}, F^-, Cl^- ..., or a dipolar molecule such as $N^{\delta-}H_3^{\delta+}$, $O^{\delta-}H_2^{\delta+}$ ..., having its negative end close to the cation. In either case we may then look upon the environment of the cation as being that shown in Figure 8.6 in relation to a specific set of Cartesian axes. Before considering how, on the basis of such an electrostatic model, the actual magnitude of the energy difference between the e_g and t_{2g} states of the d electron might be computed, let us first consider the simpler, qualitative question of which state, e_g or t_{2g}, is the more stable.

Group theory tells us that both e_g orbitals have the same energy and that all three t_{2g} orbitals have the same energy. Hence we need only compare either of the e_g orbitals with any one of the t_{2g} orbitals to obtain the answer. Let us choose the $d_{x^2-y^2}$ and d_{xy} orbitals for our comparison. The shapes of these orbitals are indicated in Figure 8.7 by drawings in-

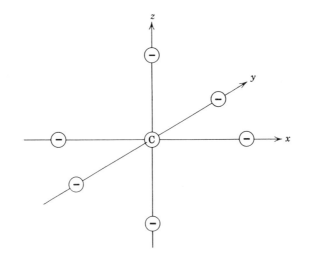

Figure 8.6   The electrostatic environment of a cation, C, surrounded by an octahedral array of anions or dipoles.

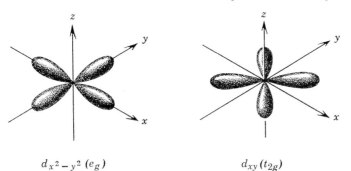

$d_{x^2-y^2}$ (e_g) d_{xy} (t_{2g})

Figure 8.7 Sketches showing the $d_{x^2-y^2}$ and d_{xy} orbitals, representative of the e_g and t_{2g} orbitals respectively, in relation to the coordinate axes.

tended to show surfaces enclosing a major fraction, say 90 per cent, of the electron density. Since the electron has a negative charge and the ligands are either negative or appear so to the electron, it is apparent that because of electrostatic repulsive forces the electron is more stable in the d_{xy} orbital than in the $d_{x^2-y^2}$ orbital. The interaction of the electronic charge with the charges of the ligands lying along the z axis will be the same in either case, but it is evident that the electronic charge is much more concentrated in the region of the other negative ligands in the $d_{x^2-y^2}$ orbital than it is in the d_{xy} orbital. Thus we know, qualitatively, that, insofar as the electrostatic model is a faithful representation of the true situation, the e_g orbitals are of higher energy than the t_{2g} orbitals.

It is easy to see the correctness of the group theoretical result that the d_{xy}, d_{xz}, and d_{yz} orbitals must all have the same energy. Each of these is identical in form to the other two, differing only in the plane in which its maxima lie. It is certainly not so obvious, merely on inspection, that the $d_{x^2-y^2}$ and d_{z^2} orbitals have the same energy. However, it is easy to grasp this equivalence using the following line of reasoning. We know from wave mechanics that there can be only five linearly independent solutions to the wave equation with the same value of the quantum number n (≥ 3) and with $l = 2$. However, we may write an infinite number of solutions initially and select any five linearly independent combinations we desire (see page 78). Accordingly, let us consider the following *six* functions for the angular parts of nd orbitals:

$$\psi_1' \approx xy \qquad \psi_4' \approx x^2 - y^2$$
$$\psi_2' \approx yz \qquad \psi_5' \approx z^2 - y^2$$
$$\psi_3' \approx xz \qquad \psi_6' \approx z^2 - x^2$$

Of these six the following set of five are usually selected:

$$\psi_1 = \psi_1' \approx xy$$

$$\psi_2 = \psi_2' \approx yz$$

$$\psi_3 = \psi_3' \approx xz$$

$$\psi_4 = \psi_4' \approx x^2 - y^2$$

$$\psi_5 = \frac{1}{\sqrt{2}}(\psi_5' + \psi_6') \approx 2z^2 - x^2 - y^2 \approx z^2$$

Thus we see that the d_{z^2} orbital can be regarded as a normalized linear combination of $d_{z^2-y^2}$ and $d_{z^2-x^2}$ orbitals. Now the $d_{x^2-y^2}$, $d_{z^2-y^2}$, and $d_{z^2-x^2}$ orbitals are obviously all of identical energy in an octahedral field, and, as shown on page 78, any linear combination of two degenerate wave functions has the same energy as each of its constituents. Thus we can see by geometrical reasoning that the d_{z^2} and $d_{x^2-y^2}$ orbitals are degenerate in an octahedral field, despite the fact that they may not clearly appear to be equivalent.

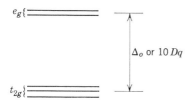

Figure 8.8 Splitting of d orbitals in an octahedral crystal field.

We may, on the basis of the foregoing argument, draw the simple energy level diagram, Figure 8.8, showing the relative energies of the e_g and t_{2g} orbitals. We know that the e_g levels are of higher energy than the t_{2g} levels, and we have denoted the magnitude of this difference by Δ_0 or $10Dq$, which are the symbols commonly used in the literature.

We may now consider whether it is possible to calculate the value of Δ_0 using an electrostatic model. To do so we consider anion ligands as point charges and dipolar ligands as point dipoles. For the latter we should also have to estimate the effective value of the dipole moment which would be equal to the permanent moment plus that induced by the positive charge of the metal ion. Finally, we should require knowledge of the metal-ligand distance and a proper radial wave function for the d electron. It would then be possible to perform a calculation of the e_g-t_{2g} separation. Such calculations have been carried out in a number of cases. For dipolar ligands, it is necessary to assume very unrealistic values for the effective dipole moments in order to get correct values of Δ_0. For ionic ligands the model gives results which are of the right order of magnitude but not much better than that. However, it is now generally recognized that this purely electrostatic model is too simple to be taken literally since, in all cases, the value of Δ_0 is determined by interactions other than purely electrostatic ones. Thus Δ_0 is best regarded as a phenomenological parameter to be determined from experiment rather than as one to be calculated from first principles using the crystal field model.

There is one further aspect of the splitting of the one-electron d orbitals in an octahedral field which must be noted. Suppose we consider the following *Gedanken* experiment. We surround an atom or ion by a concentric spherical shell of uniformly distributed negative charge, the total charge being $6q$ units. A set of ten d electrons in this ion will now have an energy E_S which is higher, due to repulsive forces between the electrons and the outer shell of negative charge, than its energy, E^0, in the free ion. However, since the charge distribution is spherical, the d electrons all have the same energy. Now suppose the total charge on this spherical shell is redistributed, but moving only on the surface of the sphere, so as to place six point charges, each q units in magnitude, at the six apices of an octahedron. This redistribution cannot change the energy of the d^{10} configuration as a whole, and yet we know that now six electrons are in t_{2g} orbitals and four are in e_g orbitals and that these orbitals differ in energy by Δ_0. These relationships are depicted in Figure 8.9. In order for the total energy of the d^{10} configuration to be the

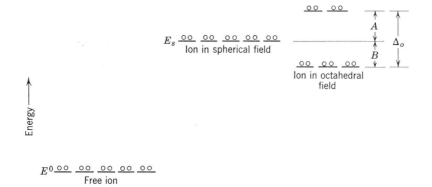

Figure 8.9 An energy diagram showing how the energies of the electrons in a d^{10} configuration are affected by spherical and octahedral electrostatic fields.

same in the octahedral field as it is in the spherical field, the following equations must hold:

$$6(E_S - B) + 4(E_S + A) = 10E_S$$

$$A + B = \Delta_0$$

Solving:

$$3B = 2A$$

Hence

$$A = \tfrac{3}{5}\Delta_0$$

$$B = \tfrac{2}{5}\Delta_0$$

It should be noted that the splitting, Δ_0, is generally of the order of one to three electron volts whereas the elevation of the set of d levels as a whole is of the order of twenty to forty electron volts. Thus it should always be borne in mind that the crystal and ligand field theories focus attention on only one relatively small aspect of the overall energy of formation of a complex.

For a d electron in the electrostatic field of four anions or dipoles arranged tetrahedrally around it, the splitting pattern can be derived by an analogous line of reasoning. Group theory tells us that the fivefold degenerate state of the d electron in the free ion is split into two states, one twofold degenerate, E, and one threefold degenerate, T_2. Reference to the character table for the T_d group shows that the former state will be one of the two orbitals d_{z^2} or $d_{x^2-y^2}$ or a linear combination thereof, and that the T_2 state will be one of the orbitals d_{xy}, d_{xz}, or d_{yz}, or some linear combination of these.

In order to find out the relative energies of the e and t_2 orbitals, let us place our tetrahedral complex in a set of coordinate axes as shown in Figure 8.10. Again we can make a comparison between either of the e orbitals and any one of the t_2 orbitals, and perhaps the best selection in order to visualize the relative electrostatic energies is again the pair d_{xy} and $d_{x^2-y^2}$. The difference in this case is much less striking than in the octahedral case, but it can be seen that qualitatively an electron in the d_{xy} orbital will have a higher potential energy than one in the $d_{x^2-y^2}$ orbital. If we call the energy separation between the e and t_2 orbitals Δ_t, then by an argument exactly analogous to the one used in the octahedral case we can show that the energies of the t_2 and e orbitals relative to their energies in a spherical shell of the same total charge will be as shown earlier in Figure 8.2.

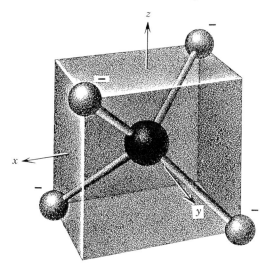

Figure 8.10 The electrostatic environment of a cation surrounded by a tetrahedral array of anions or dipoles.

The Ligand Field Theory

This is a modification of the crystal field theory in which we drop the assumption that the partially filled electron shell is one consisting of pure d orbitals. Instead it is admitted that there is overlap between the d orbitals of the metal and the orbitals of the ligand atoms.

There are various lines of evidence indicating that even in those complexes in which the binding might be expected to be most ionic, for example, in hexafluoro complexes such as CoF_6^{3-}, aquo ions such as $[Fe(H_2O)_6]^{2+}$, and so on, overlap of metal and ligand orbitals occurs to a small but significant extent. Thus there is direct evidence from ESR and NMR studies that spin density of the "d" electrons has a finite value at nuclei in the ligand molecules, and that in fact actual delocalization of the electron into ligand orbitals occurs. Numerical estimates from these data of the time spent by a "d" electron in ligand atom orbitals in species such as MnF_6^{4-} (in MnF_2) and $IrCl_6^{2-}$ are about 2–5 per cent per ligand atom. From this it can be concluded that the "d" orbitals have only about 80 ± 10 per cent d character and 10–30 per cent ligand orbital character. In reasonable accord with these observations is the fact that in complexes the interelectronic repulsion energies, which are responsible for the energy differences between the different terms of a d^n configuration, are only about 70 per cent of their magnitudes in the free ions.

There are two practical consequences of this recognition of overlap between metal and ligand orbitals. One is that we abandon all hope of making a priori calculations of orbital splittings by a pure point-charge electrostatic model using pure d wave functions. The general electrostatic expressions for the "d" orbital energies remain valid in their general form, but the crystal field parameters, effective charge or dipole of the ligands, metal-ligand distance, and the radial part of the d orbital wave functions, now lose their literal physical significance and must be considered as fictitious adjustable parameters.

Second, in constructing the energy level diagrams for d^n configurations, we must leave the separations between the various free-ion terms as functions of *adjustable* interelectronic repulsion parameters, rather than simply setting them down at the free-ion values. Practical energy level diagrams such as those in Figure 8.5 are interpreted using free-ion term separations equal to about 75 per cent of the separations spectroscopically observed for the free gaseous ions.

The Molecular Orbital Theory

The molecular orbital treatment of transition metal complexes uses the following strategy to obtain LCAO expressions for molecular orbitals. The valence shell orbitals of the ligands are used as a basis for a representation of the point group of the molecule, and this representation is decomposed into its component irreducible representations. The ligand orbitals are then combined into linear combinations belonging to these irreducible representations, and the interactions between ligand and metal orbitals of the same symmetry are computed. The energies obtained are then used to make linear combinations of the metal and ligand orbitals which are the true MO's of the complex.

Needless to say the calculation of the energies is the crucial and also the most difficult part of the process. Truly rigorous calculations have seldom been attempted. As in the few calculations for metal sandwich molecules, where the strategy is essentially the same, the energy calculations are approximations based on assumed proportionality between energy integrals and overlap integrals.*

We shall illustrate the MO treatment here by considering only the σ bonding in an octahedral complex. For a complex such as $[Co(NH_3)_6]^{3+}$ in which the ligand atoms have no available π orbitals, this treatment will be substantially complete in itself. For others such as, for example,

---

* For an instructive example see C. J. Ballhausen and H. B. Gray, *Inorg. Chem.*, **1**, 111 (1962).

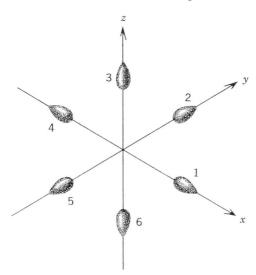

Figure 8.11 A set of six ligand σ orbitals in an octahedral complex and a numbering system for them.

$[\mathrm{Fe(CN)_6}]^{3-}$, in which the π orbitals of the ligands undoubtedly play an important role in the bonding, it would be necessary to supplement it by a similar treatment of the π bonding.

Figure 8.11 shows the set of ligand σ orbitals which we shall consider and a numbering system for them. Using these six orbitals as a basis for a representation of the group O_h, we obtain the following results:

O_h	E	$8C_3$	$6C_2$	$6C_4$	$3C_2(= C_4{}^2)$	i	$6S_4$	$8S_6$	$3\sigma_h$	$6\sigma_d$
Γ_σ	6	0	0	2	2	0	0	0	4	2

$$\Gamma_\sigma = A_{1g} + E_g + T_{1u}$$

We must now construct LCAO expressions for combinations of these six σ orbitals such that they belong to the irreducible representations listed. For A_{1g} this is extremely easy. Since all of the σ orbitals are permuted with one another by the symmetry operations, an LCAO having A_{1g} symmetry must contain each one with the same coefficient so that none of these permutations can change the LCAO into anything but itself. Hence the normalized expression must be:

$$\psi_{A_{1g}} = \frac{1}{\sqrt{6}} (\sigma_1 + \sigma_2 + \sigma_3 + \sigma_4 + \sigma_5 + \sigma_6)$$

The easiest, but not entirely general, way to obtain the LCAO expressions for the degenerate orbitals is to note that the metal $d_{x^2-y^2}$ and d_{z^2} orbitals belong to the E_g representation and that the metal p orbitals belong to the T_{1u} representation. Thus the desired LCAO's of ligand σ orbitals may be obtained by taking combinations which match in the magnitudes and signs of their coefficients the amplitudes and signs of the lobes of these atomic orbitals of the metal atom. Referring to Table 6.1, we can readily write the following normalized LCAO expressions:

$$\psi_{E_g}a = \frac{1}{\sqrt{12}}(2\sigma_3 + 2\sigma_6 - \sigma_1 - \sigma_2 - \sigma_4 - \sigma_5)$$

$$\psi_{E_,}b = \tfrac{1}{2}(\sigma_1 + \sigma_4 - \sigma_2 - \sigma_5)$$

$$\psi_{T_{1u}}a = \frac{1}{\sqrt{2}}(\sigma_1 - \sigma_{\cdot})$$

$$\psi_{T_{1u}}b = \frac{1}{\sqrt{2}}(\sigma_2 - \sigma_5)$$

$$\psi_{T_{1u}}c = \frac{1}{\sqrt{2}}(\sigma_3 - \sigma_6)$$

Now for the metal atom, inspection of the O_h character table shows that the valence shell orbitals belong to the irreducible representations in the following way:

$$(d_{x^2-y^2}, d_{z^2}): \quad E_g$$
$$(d_{xy}, d_{yz}, d_{zx}): \quad T_{2g}$$
$$s: \quad A_{1g}$$
$$(p_x, p_y, p_z): \quad T_{1u}$$

We therefore see that six MO's for σ bonding will arise by interaction of metal orbitals with ligand σ LCAO's of the types A_{1g}, E_g, and T_{1u}, while the metal T_{2g} orbitals will not participate in the MO's for σ bonding and are thus nonbonding in this sense.

We have now arrived at the point of calculating the interaction energies, that is, evaluating integrals of the type

$$\int \phi_i \mathfrak{K} \psi_i \, d\tau$$

where ϕ_i represents one of the metal atom orbitals of the ith representation and ψ_i represents the corresponding LCAO made up of ligand σ orbitals. Such calculations have not been made and to proceed further we can only rely on very rough estimates of the relative magnitudes of such interaction energies. From the approximate separations of the orbitals of the metal ion (known experimentally) and from the difference in the ionization potentials of metal atom or ion and ligands, together with rough estimates of the interaction energies, an energy level diagram such as that shown in Figure 8.12 can be constructed. It should be emphasized that this diagram is only schematic in the sense that the various energy differences are only indicated to what are probably the correct *relative* orders of magnitude, and even to this extent may be somewhat inaccurate. For example, the t_{1u} orbitals might be a little below rather than a little above the a_{1g} orbital.

The features of this diagram most worthy of emphasis are the following. We note that as a result of the bonding there has arisen, near the center of the diagram, a set of t_{2g} orbitals and a set of $e_g{}^*$ orbitals at somewhat higher energy, an arrangement quite analogous to that obtained in the crystal field theory. The t_{2g} orbitals are in this case pure metal d

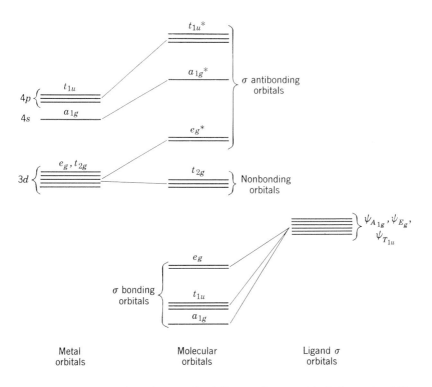

Figure 8.12   A schematic MO energy level diagram for an octahedral complex, ML_6, in which the ligands have no significant π interaction with the metal.

orbitals while the $e_g{}^*$ orbitals are MO's, containing contributions from both ligand σ orbitals and metal de_g orbitals. Since, however, the energy of the $e_g{}^*$ MO's is much closer to the energy of the de_g orbitals than to the energy of the ligand σ orbitals, the de_g orbitals make much the larger contribution to the $e_g{}^*$ MO's. Thus, in summary, the MO treatment indicates that there will arise from the interaction of the metal d orbitals with the octahedral environment two sets of MO's, an $e_g{}^*$ set and a t_{2g} set, with the former of higher energy and consisting mostly or perhaps almost entirely of metal de_g and dt_{2g} orbitals. Clearly this is the same qualitative result as that given by ligand field theory.

The molecular orbital theory is more complete and more flexible than the ligand field theory, however, in that it can take into account any degree of mixing of the metal and ligand orbitals and it also considers the behavior of orbitals other than those derived from the metal d orbitals. When the ligands contain π orbitals the interaction of these with the metal dt_{2g} orbitals may be included in the treatment. The result of such an interaction will be to produce a set of t_{2g} MO's in the same energy range as the dt_{2g} orbitals, of either higher or lower energy depending on the nature of the π interaction. Thus the MO theory provides a good conceptual picture of how the arrangement of energy levels in the complex is determined by the chemical bonding, a picture which is in general less artificial than that given by the ligand field and especially the crystal field theories. Its disadvantage relative to these simpler theories is that it does not provide a practical method for obtaining numerical values of the energies.

The Valence Bond Theory

In this approach to the bonding of a metal to neighboring ions or ligands the symmetry plays an important role because it is necessary to construct hybrid orbitals on the metal atom or ion in the directions which will give the best overlap with the filled σ orbitals of the ligands. We have already seen in Chapter 6 how to work out the required combinations of the atomic orbitals of the metal. For the octahedral case it will be recalled that the required orbitals had to be those belonging to the A_{1g}, E_g, and T_{1u} representations of the group O_h, and that for an atom having only s, p, and d orbitals in its valence shell, the only possible combination is $sp_xp_yp_zd_{z^2}d_{x^2-y^2}$. In the valence bond approach we envision the overlap of these properly oriented σ hybrid orbitals with the filled σ orbitals of the ligands to form electron pair bonds between the metal and each ligand atom.

A little reflection will show that this procedure is very similar to a part of the procedure used to construct the MO energy level diagram for an octahedral complex. Exactly the same set of metal orbitals is used in both cases, and the set of six localized σ bonds envisioned in the valence bond treatment corresponds directly with the six σ bonding molecular orbitals in Figure 8.12. To this extent the VB and MO treatments are really only two ways of formulating the same physical situation, and both take rigorous account of the inherent symmetry of the problem.

However, the obvious difference between the two theories is that while the VB treatment, having provided a description of the six electron pairs responsible for the σ bonding, goes no further, the MO treatment also gives an account of the other orbitals present. This failure of the valence bond theory, except in much more elaborate and unwieldy form, to provide information about orbitals other than the bonding orbitals (especially its complete omission of the antibonding orbitals) of course places severe limitations on its flexibility and its applicability. These limitations show up chiefly in the following three respects.

1. Since the simple VB approach does not even consider the existence of unfilled antibonding orbitals, it cannot explain the absorption spectra of complexes nor does it even imply that such spectra should exist.

2. Since it does not lead to explicit expressions for the composition of the orbitals housing the bonding electrons, it does not directly provide a basis for quantitative treatment (either numerical evaluation or mere relative estimation) of bond energies and stabilities of the complexes.

3. The VB treatment does provide a means of relating the number of unpaired electrons to the symmetry of the complex but one which is subject to limitations and uncertainties in several cases. Since it does not recognize the existence of the antibonding orbitals, when two of the d orbitals are used in forming the σ bonds it is as though they simply vanished without a trace and the d electrons of the metal must occupy the remaining three d orbitals as best they can. Of course, when there are only one, two, or three d electrons, we obtain the same results as are given by the crystal field, ligand field, and molecular orbital theories, namely, that these electrons will remain entirely unpaired regardless of how strong the σ bonding may be. For the other cases, however, the VB treatment runs into difficulties from which it may only be salvaged by the introduction of alarmingly *ad hoc* hypotheses as to the ionic or covalent character of the bonds and the use of orbitals beyond the valence shell of the metal.

To illustrate, let us consider the situation with octahedrally coordinated Co(III). In $[CoF_6]^{3-}$ there are four unpaired electrons, while in $[Co(NH_3)_6]^{3+}$ there are no unpaired electrons. As we have seen, in the ligand field and molecular orbital theories these facts are readily explained as the result of Δ being in the former case less than the spin-pairing energy and in the latter case greater than the spin-pairing energy. Nothing need be said specifically about the degree of covalent character of the metal ligand bonds (although the MO method provides a basis for setting about such a calculation), and there is no need to make any arbitrary assumption that $4d$ orbitals (so-called "outer orbitals") assume a predominant role in the bonding in either complex.

The VB treatment, however, assumes that two d orbitals are entirely occupied by σ bonding electrons leaving the six d electrons no choice but to pair up in the remaining three d orbitals. It thus accounts for the diamagnetism of $[Co(NH_3)_6]^{3+}$ very well but runs into difficulty explaining the presence of four unpaired electrons in $[CoF_6]^{3-}$. Two ways of meeting this difficulty have been suggested. One is to assume that in $[CoF_6]^{3-}$ there is no covalent bonding—or at least none involving the d orbitals (incomplete hybridization)—so that these orbitals remain available to the six d electrons. While it is not particularly unreasonable to propose this, it does have a distinctly "after-thoughtish" or *ad hoc* character, and has been rendered even less appealing than necessary through having been stated often in rather bizarre ways. The commonest description of this situation in the VB literature has been to characterize the bonding in a compound such as $[CoF_6]^{3-}$ as, simply and without further qualification, "ionic." It seems to be implied in this description that the force of attraction can be purely electrostatic in $[CoF_6]^{3-}$ while it is covalent in $[Co(NH_3)_6]^{3+}$. Such a striking qualitative difference in CoF and CoN bonds cannot be considered real. Alternatively, the use of only the s and p orbitals in the σ bonding has been described as four tetrahedral bonds resonating among six positions, which seems to be an undesirably devious way of describing the situation, one which can hardly be recommended as a conceptually simple picture.

The other way of modifying the VB treatment to account for the existence of four unpaired electrons in $[CoF_6]^{3-}$ (and of four in certain octahedral Mn(III) complexes, five in some Mn(II) and Fe(III) complexes, four in various Fe(II) complexes, and so on) is to postulate that the d orbitals used in the hybrid orbitals come from the $4d$ shell. This is the concept of "outer orbital hybridization." But this idea also is highly *ad hoc;* it is difficult to believe that with some ligands only the $3d$ orbitals are necessary while with others the metal atom finds it better to use only $4d$ orbitals.

A particularly significant example of the incorrect descriptions of electronic structures that can be obtained because the VB theory ignores the presence of antibonding orbitals occurs with planar Cu(II) complexes. In order to form the four σ bonds, we have seen (page 98) that the $d_{x^2-y^2}$ orbital, the p_x and p_y orbitals, and an s orbital must be used. For Cu(II), d^9, this leaves one electron which cannot be accommodated in the four unused d orbitals; the lowest unoccupied metal orbital is the $4p_z$ orbital, and according to the VB treatment this is where the ninth electron should be. However, electron spin resonance data on several square complexes show that the unpaired electron in these compounds is in an orbital with $x^2 - y^2$ symmetry and not in one of z symmetry. This, of course, is exactly what would be predicted by the crystal field, ligand field, or molecular orbital theories. In crystal field and ligand field theory we would expect the $d_{x^2-y^2}$ orbital to be the highest energy d orbital, since it has its lobes uniquely concentrated in the direction of the ligands; thus the electrons would occupy the other more stable d orbitals in pairs with only one electron in the least stable orbital. In the MO approach the $d_{x^2-y^2}$ orbital is the only one which can participate in the σ bonding, and hence there will arise an antibonding orbital of $x^2 - y^2$ symmetry lying well above the other d orbitals. So long as it also lies below the other σ antibonding orbitals and the p_z orbital, it will be occupied by the unpaired electron while the other eight electrons will fill the four d orbitals not involved in the σ bonding.

Thus, in summary, the VB treatment is quite correct in relation to symmetry requirements but is seriously inadequate as a bonding model due to its incomplete coverage of all the important orbitals. For a great many problems involving nontransition elements it is extremely valuable, and for certain transition metal compounds, such as metal carbonyls, it provides a satisfactory picture of the principal features of the bonding. However, for most of the transition metal complexes, it is unwieldy, inadequate, and sometimes misleading, and the other models are greatly to be preferred.

8.6 Symmetry Considerations Regarding Selection Rules and Spectral Intensities *

With probably only a very few exceptions, the process by which electromagnetic radiation is absorbed by an atom or molecule so as to excite it from a state with the wave function Ψ to a state of higher energy with the wave function Ψ' involves the interaction of the oscillating electric

---

* While we shall discuss here only applications to metal complexes it should be noted that the methods are quite general and are applicable to other molecular systems such as aromatic hydrocarbons.

vector of the radiation with what is classically considered as an oscillating dipole in the atom or molecule. The critical requirements for this *electric dipole* process to occur are represented in quantum mechanics by two equations. One is

$$E' - E = h\nu \tag{8.6-1}$$

in which $E' - E$ is the difference in the energies of the states represented by Ψ' and Ψ, and $h\nu$ is Planck's constant times the frequency of the radiation. The second equation is

$$I \propto \int \Psi' \mu \Psi \, d\tau \tag{8.6-2}$$

in which I is the intensity of the absorption band and μ is an operator corresponding to the vector sum of the three classical components of an electric dipole, viz.,

$$\mu = \sum_i e_i x_i + \sum_i e_i y_i + \sum_i e_i z_i \tag{8.6-3}$$

where e_i represents the charge of the ith particle and x_i, y_i, z_i represent its coordinates. On inserting 8.6-3 into 8.6-2 we obtain three equations. Further, since the e_i are scalars they may be absorbed into the proportionality constants and we obtain

$$I_x \propto \int \Psi' x \Psi \, d\tau$$

$$I_y \propto \int \Psi' y \Psi \, d\tau \tag{8.6-4}$$

$$I_z \propto \int \Psi' z \Psi \, d\tau$$

The physical meaning of these equations is that the intensity of absorption of light with its electric vector oscillating along the x axis, I_x, will be proportional to the magnitude of $\int \Psi' x \Psi \, d\tau$, with parallel statements regarding I_y and I_z.

Now, if one of these integrals has a finite magnitude we can only determine its numerical value by inserting explicit expressions for Ψ' and Ψ into the integrals and evaluating them. However, in all cases we can first of all find out by pure symmetry arguments whether the integral is capable of having any finite magnitude or whether it must be identically zero. It is to the solution of this problem under various circumstances that we now turn. In order to do this we will use the results of Section 5.2 concerning the representations of direct products.

Centrosymmetric Complexes; Vibronic Coupling

In a complex which possesses a center of symmetry, all states arising from a d^n configuration have the g character inherent in the d orbitals. Since the dipole moment vectors belong to odd representations all of the integrals such as $\int \psi'_g x \psi_g \, d\tau$ are identically zero because the direct product of two g functions can never span any u representations. On this basis alone, we would predict that transitions between the various states arising from d^n configurations in octahedral environments would have zero absorption intensity. In fact, these transitions do take place but the absorption bands are only $\sim 10^{-3}$ times the intensity expected for symmetry-allowed electronic transitions. Thus the prediction we have made is substantially correct but at the same time there is obviously some intensity-giving mechanism which has been overlooked.

It is generally accepted, following Van Vleck, that this mechanism is that called vibronic coupling—that is, a coupling of *vibrational* and *electronic* wave functions. In a qualitative sense we may say that some of the vibrations of the complex distort the octahedron in such a way that the center of symmetry is destroyed as the vibration takes place. The states of the d^n configuration then no longer retain rigorously their g character and the transitions become "slightly allowed." Figure 8.13 shows the approximate nature of several of the modes of vibration of an octahedron which do destroy the symmetry center.

This phenomenon of vibronic coupling can be treated very effectively using group theoretical methods. As will be shown in Chapter 9, the vibrational wave function of a molecule can be written as the product of

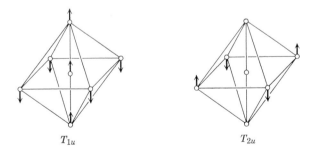

T_{1u} T_{2u}

Figure 8.13   Two of the normal vibrations of an octahedral AB_6 molecule in which the displacements of the atoms destroy the center of symmetry. There is also another type of T_{1u} vibration not shown here which has the same property.

wave functions for individual modes of vibration called *normal modes*, of which there will be $3n - 6$ for a nonlinear, n-atomic molecule. That is, we can express the complete vibrational wave function, ψ_v, as a product of $3n - 6$ functions each pertaining to one of the normal modes, viz.,

$$\psi_v = \prod_{i=1}^{3n-6} \psi_i$$

It is further shown in Chapter 9 that when each of the normal modes is in its ground state each of the ψ_i is totally symmetric and hence ψ_v is totally symmetric. If one of the normal modes is excited by one quantum number, the corresponding ψ_i may then belong to one of the irreducible representations other than the totally symmetric one, say Γ_i, and thus the entire vibrational wave function ψ_v will belong to the representation Γ_i. Simple methods for finding the representations to which the first excited states of the normal modes belong are explained in Chapter 9. In this section we will quote without proof results obtained by those methods.

To a first approximation, and usually a rather good one, the complete wave function, Ψ, for a molecule can be written as a product of an electronic wave function, ψ_e, a vibrational wave function, ψ_v, and a rotational wave function, ψ_r, viz.,

$$\Psi = \psi_e \psi_v \psi_r$$

It is then assumed that none of these factors of the complete wave function are interdependent so that instead of having to solve one large wave equation

$$\mathcal{H}\Psi = E\Psi$$

it is possible to solve three simpler ones

$$\mathcal{H}\psi_e = E_e\psi_e$$

$$\mathcal{H}\psi_v = E_v\psi_v$$

$$\mathcal{H}\psi_r = E_r\psi_r$$

and write the total energy as a simple sum of the electronic, vibrational, and rotational energies, namely,

$$E = E_e + E_v + E_r$$

This is, of course, only an approximation and though it works well for many purposes, one of its limitations is that it cannot explain the low but finite intensity of the transitions between states of d^n configurations in centrosymmetric environments as we have shown above.

The way out of the difficulty is to drop the assumption that ψ_e and ψ_v are entirely independent, though retaining the approximation that ψ_r can be treated as independent of these other two. Thus it is not the values of integrals like

$$\int \psi_e' x \psi_e \, d\tau$$

which we must consider but rather it is the values of the integrals

$$\int (\psi_e' \psi_v') x (\psi_e \psi_v) \, d\tau$$

It is easy to show by symmetry arguments that the latter do not in general vanish. First, we note that if we assume that in the lower state, $\psi_e \psi_v$, the molecule is in its vibrational ground state, then ψ_v is totally symmetric and we can ignore it. Our problem then is to decide whether there are any vibrational wave functions belonging to representations such that although the direct product representation of $\psi_e' x \psi_e$ does not contain the totally symmetric representation, the direct product representation of $\psi_e' \psi_v' x \psi_e$ does. Whenever this is so the transition will be vibronically allowed. According to the results of Section 5.2 the integral will be nonzero if there is any normal mode of vibration whose first excited state, ψ_v' belongs to one of the representations spanned by $\psi_e' x \psi_e$.

In order to show how this is done let us take a simple example. For the ion $[Co(NH_3)_6]^{3+}$, the ground state, ψ_e, transforms as $^1A_{1g}$. There are two excited states with the same spin ($S = 0$) which belong to the representations T_{1g} and T_{2g}. In the group O_h the coordinates x, y, z jointly form a basis for the T_{1u} representation. Thus, for the $^1A_{1g} \rightarrow {}^1T_{1g}$ transition the direct product representation of $\psi_e'(x, y, z)\psi_e$ is given by

$$\Gamma[\psi_e'(x, y, z)\psi_e] = T_{1g} \times T_{1u} \times A_{1g}$$

$$= T_{1g} \times T_{1u}$$

This can be reduced to

$$A_{1u} + E_u + T_{1u} + T_{2u}$$

Thus, if there are any normal vibrations whose first excited states belong to any of these representations, there will be nonvanishing intensity integrals. By the methods of Chapter 9 it is easily found that the symmetries of the normal modes of an octahedral AB_6 molecule are

$$A_{1g}, \ E_g, \ 2T_{1u}, \ T_{2g}, \ T_{2u}$$

Thus, while the pure electronic transition $^1A_{1g} \rightarrow {}^1T_{1g}$ is not allowed, all those transitions in which there is simultaneous excitation of a vibration of T_{1u} or T_{2u} symmetry are allowed.

Similarly, for an $^1A_{1g} \rightarrow {}^1T_{2g}$ transition, we find

$$\Gamma[\psi_e'(x, y, z)\psi_e] = T_{2g} \times T_{1u} \times A_{1g}$$
$$= T_{2g} \times T_{1u}$$
$$= A_{2u} + E_u + T_{1u} + T_{2u}$$

Thus the $^1A_{1g} \rightarrow {}^1T_{2g}$ transition can also occur so long as there is simultaneous excitation of a T_{1u} or T_{2u} vibration.

Vibronic Polarization

For an octahedral complex we see that the direction of vibration of the electric vector of the light makes no difference, for the directions x, y, and z are equivalent in the sense that they are interchangeable by the symmetry operations of the molecule. However, in less symmetrical complexes in which x, y, and z do not all belong to the same representation, we encounter the phenomenon of *polarization*.

Let us suppose that we place a polarizing prism between the light source and the sample. If the sample is a single crystal in which the molecules all have the same orientation relative to the crystallographic axes, we can so orient the crystal that the direction of the electric vector of the light will correspond to the x, y, or z direction in a coordinate system for the molecule. It is then possible that some transition may occur only for one or two of these orientations but not for all three.

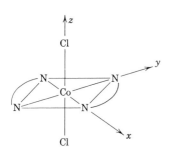

Figure 8.14   A sketch of the *trans*-dichlorobisethylenediaminecobalt-(III) ion showing a set of reference axes.

As an example, let us consider a *trans*-substituted octahedral complex such as *trans*-dichlorobisethylenediaminecobalt(III) which is pictured in Figure 8.14 with a set of coordinate axes. Although the symmetry is no longer cubic, there is still a center of inversion so that *d-d* transitions can only have finite intensity if there is vibronic coupling. Since it is only vibrations in the part of the molecule including and immediately surrounding the cobalt ion which would be expected to have any appreciable interaction with the electronic wave functions of the metal ion, we shall restrict attention to the normal vibrations of a *trans*-[CoCl$_2$N$_4$] group, which has local symmetry D_{4h}. The methods of Chapter 9 will tell us that for such a group the first excited states of the normal modes have the following symmetries:

$$2A_{1g},\ B_{1g},\ B_{2g},\ E_g,\ 2A_{2u},\ B_{1u},\ 3E_u$$

For the *trans*-dichloro complex the ground state will be a $^1A_{1g}$ state, as in a strictly octahedral complex, but the excited singlet states $^1T_{1g}$ and $^1T_{2g}$ will be split as follows (cf. the correlation table, Appendix IIB):

$$T_{1g}:\ A_{2g} + E_g$$
$$T_{2g}:\ B_{2g} + E_g$$

Thus the possible transitions from the ground state to excited states will be of the following types so far as symmetry of the electronic states is concerned:

$$(1)\ A_{1g} \rightarrow A_{2g}$$
$$(2)\ A_{1g} \rightarrow B_{2g}$$
$$(3)\ A_{1g} \rightarrow E_g$$

For these transitions we obtain the following results for the representations of the purely electronic dipole integrals:

	$A_{1g} \rightarrow A_{2g}$	$A_{1g} \rightarrow B_{2g}$	$A_{1g} \rightarrow E_g$
$\int \psi_e' z \psi_e\, d\tau$	A_{1u}	B_{1u}	E_u
$\int \psi_e'(x, y)\psi_e\, d\tau$	E_u	E_u	$A_{1u} + A_{2u} + B_{1u} + B_{2u}$

Comparing these results with the list of the symmetries of the first excited states of the normal vibrations, we can immediately write down the following predictions for the polarizations of the transitions:

	POLARIZATION WITH VIBRONIC COUPLING	
TRANSITION	z	(x, y)
$A_{1g} \rightarrow A_{2g}$	Forbidden	Allowed
$A_{1g} \rightarrow B_{2g}$	Allowed	Allowed
$A_{1g} \rightarrow E_g$	Allowed	Allowed

These results have actually been used to analyze experimental data. Figure 8.15 shows the experimental observations of Yamada et al.* on

---

* S. Yamada et al., *Bull. Chem. Soc. Japan*, **25**, 127 (1952); **28**, 222 (1955).

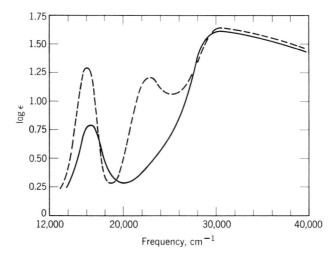

Figure 8.15 Dichroism of *trans*-[Co(en)₂Cl₂] after the results of Yamada et al. (*loc. cit.*) on *trans*-[Co(en)₂Cl₂]Cl·HCl·2H₂O. The full line shows the spectrum with light polarized parallel (or nearly parallel) to the Cl—Co—Cl axis and the dashed line shows the spectrum with light polarized perpendicular to the Cl—Co—Cl axis.

trans-[Co(en)₂Cl₂]Cl·HCl·2H₂O. It can be seen that there are three regions of absorption. From about 27,000 to about 40,000 cm⁻¹ the absorption exhibits no significant polarization. At ∼22,000 cm⁻¹ there is a strongly polarized band which is absent for light parallel to z but present for light perpendicular to z, while at ∼16,000 cm⁻¹ there is a band which shows some difference in intensity for the two directions but is clearly present in both directions of polarization. The results of the above analysis permit a simple interpretation of these observations. The bands at ∼16,000 and ∼22,000 cm⁻¹ are assigned respectively to transitions to the E_g and A_{2g} components of the T_{1g} state existing in O_h symmetry since an $A_{1g} \rightarrow E_g$ transition is vibronically allowed for both directions, but an $A_{1g} \rightarrow A_{2g}$ transition is vibronically forbidden for z polarization. The broad absorption above ∼27,000 cm⁻¹ may be assigned to the unresolved transitions from the A_{1g} ground state to the E_g and B_{2g} states coming from the T_{2g} state for O_h symmetry. An interpretation along these lines was first given by Ballhausen and Moffitt * who also showed that independent calculations and experimental evidence would lead to the expectation that the order of the excited levels should be as postulated in order to explain the polarization data.

* C. J. Ballhausen and W. Moffitt, *J. Inorg. Nucl. Chem.*, **3**, 178 (1956).

Noncentrosymmetric Complexes

When the complex lacks a center of symmetry even in its equilibrium configuration, the "d-d" transitions become allowed as simple changes in the electronic wave functions. The breadth of the absorption bands shows that the electronic transitions are still accompanied by vibrational changes but these vibrational changes are not in themselves essential to the occurrence of the transition. The way in which the noncentrosymmetric ligand field alters the d wave function so that the states of the "d^n" configuration no longer have rigorous g character is believed to be by making possible the mixing of d and p orbitals. We have already shown on page 95 that in a tetrahedral field the p orbitals and the d_{xy}, d_{xz}, and d_{yz} orbitals belong to the same (T_2) representation, and that to some finite degree the two sets of T_2 orbitals which will be found among the orbitals arising from the valence shell atomic orbitals of a transition metal atom must each have both p and d character. Then if two different electronic states of the "d^n" configuration of a metal ion contain different amounts of p character, a transition from one to the other will be to a certain extent a $d \rightarrow p$ or $p \rightarrow d$ transition, which are highly allowed even in the free atom since the d orbitals are even to inversion and the p orbitals odd. The exact extent to which this mixing occurs and the resulting intensity of the transition must, of course, be computed using explicit wave functions, but symmetry considerations alone can tell us whether it is possible for a particular transition to acquire any intensity at all in this way.

As a first illustration let us consider the optical transitions in a tetrahedral complex of Co(II). The ground state belongs to the A_2 representation of the tetrahedral point group T_d, and there are two excited states of T_1 symmetry and one of T_2 symmetry. The character table for T_d tells us that the coordinates x, y, and z form a basis for the T_2 representation. For the $A_2 \rightarrow T_1$ transitions we then see that the intensity integral will span the representations in the direct product of $A_2 \times T_1 \times T_2$ and this reduces as follows

$$A_2 \times T_1 \times T_2 = A_1 + E + T_1 + T_2$$

Since the A_1 representation is present it follows that these transitions are allowed by the symmetry of the purely electronic wave functions. For the $A_2 \rightarrow T_2$ transition we must consider the direct product $A_2 \times T_2 \times$

T_2 which reduces as follows:

$$A_2 \times T_2 \times T_2 = A_2 + E + T_1 + T_2$$

We see that the $A_2 \rightarrow T_2$ transition is not allowed by the symmetry of the pure electronic wave functions and whatever intensity it may have must be attributed to vibronic interaction. In agreement with this prediction, it has been found that the $A_2 \rightarrow T_2$ transition is observed but with an intensity 10 to 100 times smaller than those of the $A_2 \rightarrow T_1$ transitions in the systems (for example, Co(II) in ZnO) which have been studied.

Polarization of Electronically Allowed Transitions

Just as with vibronically allowed transitions, in symmetry groups in which all Cartesian axes are not equivalent (noncubic groups), it is found that, in general, transitions will be allowed only for certain orientations of the electric vector of the incident light. One class of compounds in which this phenomenon has been studied both theoretically and experimentally are *tris* chelate compounds such as *tris*-(acetylacetonato)-M(III) and *tris*-(oxalato)M(III) complexes. In these complexes the six ligand atoms form an approximately octahedral array but the true molecular symmetry is only D_3. There is no center of symmetry in these molecules so that the pure electronic selection rules might be expected to be dominant.

For the *tris*-(oxalato)Cr(III) ion, $[Cr(C_2O_4)_3]^{3-}$, the electronic states are those into which the states of a complex of O_h symmetry are reduced when the symmetry is reduced to D_3. From the correlation table (Appendix IIB) we see that the correlation of the O_h and D_3 states is as follows:

O_h	D_3	
A_{2g}	A_2	(Ground state)
T_{1g}	$A_2 + E$	
T_{2g}	$A_1 + E$	

Thus in D_3 symmetry we want to know the polarizations of the following types of transitions: $A_2 \rightarrow A_1$, $A_2 \rightarrow A_2$, and $A_2 \rightarrow E$. Noting in the character table for D_3 that z belongs to the A_2 representation and (x, y) to the E representation, we obtain the following results for the irreducible representations spanned by the dipole integrals for each of these transitions:

	$A_2 \rightarrow A_1$	$A_2 \rightarrow A_2$	$A_2 \rightarrow E$
$\int \psi'_e z \psi_e \, d\tau$	A_1	A_2	E
$\int \psi'_e (x, y) \psi_e \, d\tau$	E	E	$A_1 + A_2 + E$

Thus the selection rules are:

TRANSITION	POLARIZATION OF INCIDENT RADIATION	
	z	(x, y)
$A_2 \rightarrow A_1$	Allowed	Forbidden
$A_2 \rightarrow A_2$	Forbidden	Forbidden
$A_2 \rightarrow E$	Forbidden	Allowed

It can be seen that these are very powerful selection rules indeed. On the other hand, we might have assumed that the symmetry of the environment of the metal ion could have been adequately approximated by considering only the six coordinated oxygen atoms. In this case, the symmetry would be D_{3d} in which there is a center of inversion and the transitions would be governed by vibronic selection rules. When these are worked out it is found that all of the transitions are vibronically permitted. Thus, experimental study of the polarizations should provide clear-cut evidence as to the correct effective symmetry and selection rules. Such a study has been reported * and shows conclusively that the selection rules followed are those given above for pure electronic transitions in D_3 symmetry.

8.7   Double Groups and Their Uses

In Section 8.3 we showed that for an orbital or state wave function having angular momentum quantum number l (or L) the character of the representation for which this forms a basis, under a symmetry operation which consists in rotation by an angle α, is given by

$$\chi(\alpha) = \frac{\sin (l + \frac{1}{2})\alpha}{\sin (\alpha/2)} \qquad (8.3\text{-}2)$$

* T. S. Piper and R. L. Carlin, *J. Chem. Phys.*, **35**, 1809 (1961). These authors also give selection rules and experimental data for the oxalato complexes of the trivalent ions of Ti, V, Mn, Fe, and Co.

We then applied this formula to various types of single electron wave functions, for example, s, p, d, f, g, and to wave functions for various Russell-Saunders terms characterized by integral values of the quantum number L.

There are, however, many cases of interest in which we may want to determine the splitting of a state which is well characterized by its total angular momentum, J. This will in fact be the only thing of importance in the very heavy elements, for example, the rare-earth ions, where states of particular L cannot be used since the various free-ion states of different J are already separated by much greater energies than the crystal field splitting energies.

Now $J = L + S$, and for ions with an odd number of electrons S and hence J must be half integral numbers. For states in which J is an integer, the characters can be obtained using the above formula by simply replacing l by J. However, when J is half integral a difficulty arises. We know that a rotation by 2π is an identity operation and therefore it should be true that

$$\chi(\alpha) = \chi(\alpha + 2\pi)$$

It can easily be seen that this is true when L or J is an integer. However, when J is half integral we have

$$\chi(\alpha + 2\pi) = \frac{\sin (J + \tfrac{1}{2})(\alpha + 2\pi)}{\sin (\alpha + 2\pi)/2} = \frac{\sin [(J + \tfrac{1}{2})\alpha + 2\pi]}{\sin [\alpha/2 + \pi]}$$

$$= \frac{\sin (J + \tfrac{1}{2})\alpha}{- \sin (\alpha/2)}$$

$$= -\chi(\alpha)$$

Since the characters of a representation must be uniquely defined we see that those we would obtain by the above procedure when J is half integral cannot belong to true representations.

A simple device for avoiding this difficulty was proposed by Bethe. We introduce the fiction (mathematically possible but not physically significant) that rotation by 2π be treated as a symmetry operation but not as an identity operation. We must then expand any ordinary rotation group by taking the product of this new operation, which we shall call R, with all of the existing rotations. The new group will therefore contain twice as many operations and more classes and representations (though not twice as many) than the simple rotation group with which we start. This new group is called a *double group*.

In working out the various products $C_n{}^m R$ and $RC_n{}^m$ we first note that two rotations about the same axis commute so that $C_n{}^m R = RC_n{}^m$. If

$n = 2$ we have RC_2 which is a special case since

$$\chi(\pi) = \chi(3\pi) = 0$$

For rotation by any other angle, viz., $m2\pi/n$, it is not difficult to show that the following equality holds generally:

$$\chi[m2\pi/n + 2\pi] = \chi[(n - m)2\pi/n]$$

In order to evaluate the characters of E and R, that is $\chi(0)$ and $\chi(2\pi)$ we must evaluate the limit of an indeterminate form, for as $\alpha \to 0$ or $\alpha \to 2\pi$

$$\frac{\sin (J + \frac{1}{2})\alpha}{\sin (\alpha/2)} \to \frac{0}{0}$$

This may easily be done using l'Hospital's rule and the results are

$$\chi(0) = 2J + 1$$

$$\chi(2\pi) = \begin{cases} 2J + 1 & \text{when } J \text{ is an integer} \\ -(2J + 1) & \text{when } J \text{ is a half integer} \end{cases}$$

After we have worked out the characters for all of the new operations, $C_n{}^m R$, of the double group, we will then collect them together into classes using the same rule as for simple groups that all operations having the same characters are in the same class. Thus in general we shall find the following classes in double rotation groups:

(1) E
(2) R
(3) C_2 and $C_2 R$
(4) C_n and $C_n^{n-1} R$
(5) $C_n{}^m$ and $C_n^{n-m} R$

We can then determine the number and dimensions of the irreducible representations using the familiar rules that there are as many irreducible representations as there are classes and that the sum of the squares of the dimensions of the irreducible representations must equal the group order.

In order to illustrate this procedure let us consider the group D_4 and the corresponding double group D_4'. The eight operations of D_4 are E, C_4, $C_4{}^3$, C_2, $2C_2'$, $2C_2''$. According to the general results given above, the sixteen operations of D_4' may be arranged into the following classes:

$$E \quad R \quad C_4 \quad C_4{}^3 \quad C_2 \quad 2C_2' \quad 2C_2''$$
$$C_4{}^3 R \quad C_4 R \quad C_2 R \quad 2C_2' R \quad 2C_2'' R$$

There are seven classes so there must be seven irreducible representations, and their orders, l_i, must satisfy the equation

$$l_1{}^2 + l_2{}^2 + l_3{}^2 + l_4{}^2 + l_5{}^2 + l_6{}^2 + l_7{}^2 = 16$$

It is easy to convince oneself that the only combination of positive integers satisfying this equation is 1, 1, 1, 1, 2, 2, 2. Thus there are four one-dimensional and three two-dimensional irreducible representations of the double group D_4'.

Double groups are of greatest importance for transition metal complexes. In Appendix III we give the character tables for the double groups D_4' and O' corresponding to the simple rotation groups D_4 and O. Several features of these tables should be noted. First, there are two systems for labeling the representations. One is an adaptation of the Mulliken system for simple groups in which we use paired Mulliken symbols. The other is Bethe's original system in which we use a serially indexed set of Γ_i's. Second, it will be noted that among the representations of the double groups are all the representations of the simple group. Whenever we form a representation using a wave function having an integral value of angular momentum, l, L, S, or J, it will either be one of these representations or it will be reducible to a sum of only these representations. In other words, when the angular momentum quantum number used is integral we have no need of the double group. However, when the angular momentum quantum number, s, S, or J, is half integral we will obtain one of the new representations not occurring in the simple group, or a representation which can be reduced to a sum containing only these new irreducible representations. It will be noted that these new representations all have an even order, 2, 4, and so on. Thus all wave functions of a system must be at least twofold degenerate. This is a manifestation of Kramer's theorem that in the absence of an external magnetic field, the spin degeneracy of a system having an odd number of electrons must always persist even when the low symmetry of the environment lifts all other degeneracies.

The direct products of representations of double groups can be taken in the usual way and reduced to sums of irreducible representations.

In order to illustrate the utility of double groups let us consider several examples. Suppose we have an ion with one d electron in a planar complex. Real examples of this case are represented by complexes of Cu(II) and Ag(II) (where we virtually have one positron, but this behaves as one electron except in the signs of the energies). In each case there will be two states with J values of $l \pm \frac{1}{2} = 2 \pm \frac{1}{2}$, namely $J = \frac{3}{2}$ and $J = \frac{5}{2}$. Using Equation 8.3-2, we find that these form bases for the following representations:

D_4'	E	R	$2C_4$	$2C_4R$	$2C_2$	$4C_2'$	$4C_2''$
$\Gamma_{3/2}$	4	-4	0	0	0	0	0
$\Gamma_{5/2}$	6	-6	$-\sqrt{2}$	$\sqrt{2}$	0	0	0

These can be reduced in the standard way giving

$$\Gamma_{3/2} = \Gamma_6 + \Gamma_7$$

$$\Gamma_{5/2} = \Gamma_6 + 2\Gamma_7$$

The procedure we have used would be particularly appropriate in the case of Ag(II) where the two J states are already well separated in the free ion because of a very large spin-orbit coupling. An energy level diagram of the following sort could then be drawn:

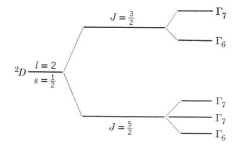

This illustrates how the two J states would be further split up by an environment of D_{4h} symmetry.

If the spin-orbit coupling is relatively small we might wish to consider first the splitting of the ^2D state by the environment, and then consider the further splitting of the resulting states by spin-orbit coupling. To do this we first use the D_{4h} character table to find that the ^2D state splits into A_{1g}, B_{1g}, B_{2g}, and E_g. These representations in D_{4h} can easily be seen to correspond, respectively, to A_1, B_1, B_2, and E in D_4, and to Γ_1, Γ_3, Γ_4, and Γ_5 in D_4'. This analysis has dealt with the orbital part of the wave function (see Section 8.2, especially Equation 8.2-1). For the spin part, ψ_s in Equation 8.2-1, we find the representation for which the spin angular momentum, $s = \frac{1}{2}$, forms a basis in the double group D_4'. Using the formulae given above we easily obtain

D_4'	E	R	$2C_4$	$2C_4R$	$2C_2$	$4C_2'$	$4C_2''$
$\Gamma_{1/2}$	2	-2	$\sqrt{2}$	$-\sqrt{2}$	0	0	0

Thus

$$\Gamma_{1/2} = \Gamma_6$$

Now, to find the representation of a wave function which is a product of two other functions we must obtain the representation of the direct product of the two functions. The characters of this representation are the products of the characters of the representations of the two functions. Thus, using the character table for D_4' we obtain the results

$$\Gamma_1 \times \Gamma_6 = \Gamma_6$$

$$\Gamma_3 \times \Gamma_6 = \Gamma_7$$

$$\Gamma_4 \times \Gamma_6 = \Gamma_7$$

$$\Gamma_5 \times \Gamma_6 = \Gamma_6 + \Gamma_7$$

Of course the final results are the same as those previously obtained. The manner in which we obtain them is unimportant so far as pure symmetry considerations are concerned, but we would normally choose the first method in a case where we would expect the splitting between the free-ion states with $J = \frac{3}{2}$ and $J = \frac{5}{2}$ to be greater than the further splittings caused by the environment and the second method when we expected the splitting of the Russell-Saunders term, ^2D, by the environment to be much larger than the splittings due to spin-orbit coupling. In the latter case our energy level diagram for one electron might look somewhat as follows:

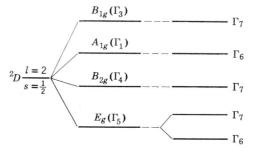

In this example the relative order of the orbitals is somewhat arbitrary. Only by solving an appropriate wave equation could the actual order be determined in a particular case, but the results would have to correspond with this diagram in the types and number of each type of the wave functions obtained.

Molecular Vibrations

9.1 Introductory Remarks

A molecule possesses three types of internal energy. These are, in the usual decreasing order of their magnitudes, electronic, vibrational, and rotational energies. In preceding chapters we have dealt with the use of symmetry properties in understanding the electronic states of various kinds of molecules. The rotational energy states have no symmetry properties of importance in ordinary chemical processes and will not concern us directly in this book. That leaves then the subject of molecular vibrations, to which symmetry arguments may be very fruitfully applied.

All molecules, at all temperatures, including even the absolute zero, are continually executing vibrational motions, that is, motions in which the distances and internal angles of the molecule change periodically without producing any net translation of the center of mass of the molecule or imparting any net angular momentum (rotatory motion) to the molecule. Of course the molecule may, and if free certainly will, be traveling through space and rotating, but we may divorce our attention from these motions by supposing that we are seated at the center of gravity of the molecule and that we travel and rotate with it. Then it will not appear to us to be undergoing translation or rotation and our full attention may be focused on its internal or *genuine* vibrations.

While a cursory glance at a vibrating molecule might suggest that its vibratory motion is random, close inspection and proper analysis reveals a basic regularity and simplicity. It is the underlying basis for this simplicity which we shall formulate in this chapter. We shall also develop working methods by which all of the analysis of molecular motions which symmetry alone allows may be rapidly and reliably performed.

9.2   The Symmetry of Normal Vibrations

The complex, random, and seemingly aperiodic internal motions of a vibrating molecule are the result of the superposition of a number of relatively simple vibratory motions known as the *normal vibrations* or *normal modes of vibration* of the molecule. Each of these has its own fixed frequency. Naturally, then, when many of them are superposed, the resulting motion must also be periodic, but it may have a period so long as to be difficult to discern.

The first question to be considered regarding the normal modes is that of their number in any given molecule. This, fortunately, is a very easy one to answer, and doubtless many readers will know the answer already. An atom has three degrees of motional freedom. It may move from an initial position in the x direction independent of any displacement it may or may not undergo in the y and z direction, in the y direction independent of whether or not it moves in the x or z directions, and so on. In a molecule consisting of n atoms there will thus be $3n$ degrees of freedom. Let us now suppose that all n atoms simultaneously move by the same amount in the x direction. This will displace the center of mass of the entire molecule in the x direction without causing any alteration of the internal dimensions of the molecule. The same may of course be said of similar motions in the y and z directions. Thus, of the $3n$ degrees of freedom of the molecule, three are not genuine vibrations but only translations. Similarly, concerted motions of all atoms in circular paths about the x, y, and z axes do not constitute vibrations either, but instead, molecular rotations. Thus, of the $3n$ degrees of motional freedom, only $3n - 6$ remain to be combined into genuine vibratory motions.

We make note here of the special case of a linear molecule. In that case rotation of the molecule may occur about each of two axes perpendicular to the molecular axes, but "rotation" of nuclei about the molecular axis itself cannot occur since all nuclei lie on the axis. Thus an n-atomic linear molecule has $3n - 5$ normal modes.

Let us now look at the normal modes of vibration of a molecule which is as simple as possible and yet exemplifies all general features ordinarily encountered. The planar ion CO_3^{2-} will do for this purpose. As a nonlinear four-atomic species, it must have $3(4) - 6 = 6$ normal modes. In Figure 9.1 we have depicted these vibrations. In each drawing the length of an arrow relative to the length of another arrow in the same drawing shows how much the atom to which it is attached is displaced at any instant relative to the simultaneous displacement of the atom to which the other arrow is attached. The lengths of the arrows relative to interatomic distances in the drawings, however, are exaggerated.

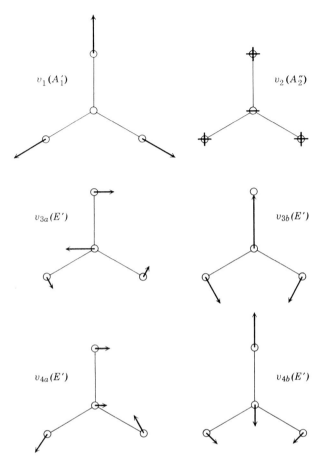

$v_1(A_1')$ $v_2(A_2'')$

$v_{3a}(E')$ $v_{3b}(E')$

$v_{4a}(E')$ $v_{4b}(E')$

Figure 9.1. The six normal modes of vibration of the carbonate ion.

As may be seen in the particular case of CO_3^{2-}, which is used for illustration, normal modes have two important properties:

(1) Each of the vectors representing an instantaneous atomic displacement may be regarded as the resultant of a set of three basis vectors.

(2) Each of the normal modes forms a basis for or "belongs to" an irreducible representation of the molecule.

Let us first consider the ways in which we might regard the displacement vectors in the normal modes as resultants of some set of basis vectors. There are many ways in which the set of basis vectors might be chosen, but only two are of interest. In the first, we attach a separate Cartesian coordinate system to each atom with the atom at the origin and all x axes, all y axes, and all z axes parallel and pointing in the same direction (cf. Figure 9.3). In each small coordinate system we place unit vectors along the x, y, and z axes. Now, the vector representing the displacement of a given atom, the ith atom, may be expressed as the vector sum of Cartesian displacement vectors of that atom, x_i, y_i, and z_i. We may call this process resolution of a general displacement into Cartesian displacements. It will be noted that the three translational motions and the three (or two) rotational motions may also be resolved into vector sums of Cartesian displacements. Thus all $3n$ degrees of motional freedom of the molecule may be represented by suitable combinations of the $3n$ Cartesian displacements.

The second important way of resolving the displacement vectors of the normal modes is to use basis vectors related to the internal coordinates of the molecule, that is, the interatomic distances and bond angles. There is no unique way of doing this. Normally, however, we choose first the changes in interatomic distances between bonded atoms and then as many changes in bond angle (taking care that those chosen are all independent) as are necessary to provide a set of $3n - 6$ internal displacement vectors. For example, in the carbonate ion we require six internal displacement vectors to represent the six normal modes. We choose first changes in the three C—O distances. Next we may choose changes in two of the three OCO angles. Our sixth choice might be a change in the remaining OCO angle or a change in the angle between a C—O bond axis and the molecular plane.

Let us consider now the second important property of the normal modes, namely, their symmetry. It is easy to see by comparison of the diagrams in Figure 9.1 and the character table for the group D_{3h}, to which the carbonate ion belongs, that each normal mode (or pair of normal modes) transforms exactly as required by the characters of the representation to which it belongs. These representations are noted in parentheses on Figure 9.1. Clearly the set of vectors representing ν_1 is carried into itself by all operations; hence it belongs to the A_1' representation. It is equally obvious that the set of vectors representing ν_2 is carried into itself by the operations E, C_3, and σ_v, but into the negative of itself by C_2, S_3, and σ_h. Thus this mode belongs to the A_2'' representation as stated in Figure 9.1.

The ν_{3a} and ν_{3b} together form the basis for the E' representation of the group D_{3h}. Clearly the identity operation takes each component into itself, as required by the character of 2. We can express this symbolically as follows:

$$E(\nu_{3a}) = \nu_{3a} + 0\nu_{3b}$$
$$E(\nu_{3b}) = 0\nu_{3a} + \nu_{3b}$$

The matrix of the coefficients on the right side of the above set of equations is

$$\begin{bmatrix} 1 & 0 \\ 0 & 1 \end{bmatrix}$$

It is, of course, a two-dimensional unit matrix with the character 2. The effect of a threefold rotation on either ν_{3a} or ν_{3b} is to take it into a linear combination of both ν_{3a} and ν_{3b}. Figure 9.2 illustrates this for the case of a clockwise rotation of ν_{3a} by $2\pi/3$, to give a mode which we have labeled

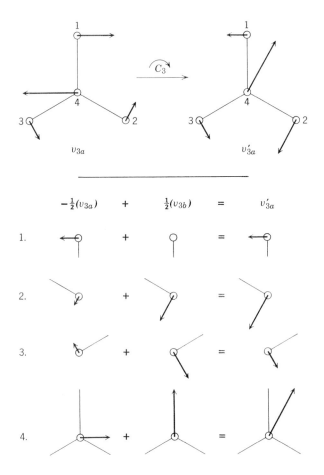

Figure 9.2 Vector diagrams showing how a threefold rotation transforms ν_{3a} into ν'_{3a} and how the latter is a linear combination of ν_{3a} and ν_{3b}; specifically, $\nu'_{3a} = -\frac{1}{2}\nu_{3a} + \frac{1}{2}\nu_{3b}$.

ν'_{3a}. In the lower part of Figure 9.2 it is shown in detail how each of the displacement vectors in ν'_{3a} is the vector sum of $-\frac{1}{2}\nu_{3a}$ and $\frac{1}{2}\nu_{3b}$. Thus we can write

$$C_3(\nu_{3a}) = -\tfrac{1}{2}\nu_{3a} + \tfrac{1}{2}\nu_{3b}$$

It can similarly be shown that application of a clockwise rotation by $2\pi/3$ to ν_{3b} would produce a mode which could be expressed as the following linear combination of ν_{3a} and ν_{3b}:

$$C_3(\nu_{3b}) = -\tfrac{3}{2}\nu_{3a} - \tfrac{1}{2}\nu_{3b}$$

Now the matrix of the coefficients of these two transformations is:

$$\begin{bmatrix} -\frac{1}{2} & \frac{1}{2} \\ -\frac{3}{2} & -\frac{1}{2} \end{bmatrix}$$

and its character is -1 as required by the character table.

It is easy to see that the operation C_2 transforms ν_{3a} into the negative of itself and ν_{3b} into itself. Thus a matrix is obtained which has only the diagonal elements -1 and 1 and the character 0 as required by the character table. It is equally easy to see that σ_h carries each component of ν_3 into itself so that the matrix of the transformation has only the diagonal elements 1 and 1 and hence a character of 2. We could carry out similar reasoning for the remaining operations applied to ν_{3a} and ν_{3b} and also with respect to the application of all of the operations in the group to ν_{4a} and ν_{4b}, and it would be found that they satisfy the requirements of the characters of the E' representation in every respect.

9.3 Determining the Symmetry Types of the Normal Modes

The two characteristic features of normal modes of vibration which have been stated and discussed above lead directly to a simple and straightforward method of determining how many of the normal modes of vibration of any molecule will belong to each of the irreducible representations of the point group of the molecule. This information may be obtained entirely from knowledge of the molecular symmetry and does not require any knowledge, or by itself provide any knowledge, of the frequencies or detailed forms of the normal modes.

We have illustrated in detail for the case of CO_3^{2-} how the normal modes of genuine vibration have symmetry corresponding to one or

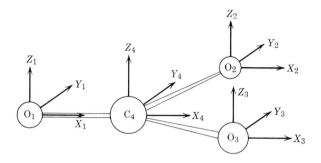

Figure 9.3 The set of $3n = 12$ Cartesian displacement vectors used in determining the reducible representation spanning the irreducible representations of the normal modes of CO_3^{-2}.

another of the irreducible representations of the molecule. This is true for every molecule, though we shall not offer the proof here.* It is also true that the nongenuine vibrations, the translational and rotational motions, transform according to irreducible representations of the molecular point group. Moreover the entire set of $3n$ normal modes may be expressed as functions of a set of $3n$ Cartesian displacements, as described in the preceding section. It is also evident that we may use the $3n$ Cartesian displacement vectors as the basis for a reducible representation of the molecular symmetry group. This representation will contain (or, as is sometimes said, span) the set of irreducible representations to which all of the normal modes, genuine and nongenuine, belong.

We shall now illustrate this using CO_3^{2-} as an example. A number of further examples will be found in Section 9.7. The first step must be to determine the symmetry group to which the molecule belongs, as described in Chapter 3, especially Section 3.10. CO_3^{2-} belongs to the D_{3h} group. Figure 9.3 shows the CO_3^{2-} ion with the sets of Cartesian displacement vectors attached to each atom. There are of course $3n = 12$ in all and the representation will therefore be of dimension 12. We turn now to the character table for the group D_{3h}. The first operation, naturally, is the identity operation. When this is applied to the set of vectors each remains in place, that is, remains identical with itself. We may express this as shown in Figure 9.4. We assume that the symmetry

---

* Rigorous proof, which involves more quantitative discussion of the mechanics of the normal vibrations and the use of explicit expressions for the kinetic and potential energies, may be found in more specialized texts, for example, in *Molecular Vibrations* by Wilson, Decius, and Cross.

	X_1	Y_1	Z_1	X_2	Y_2	Z_2	X_3	Y_3	Z_3	X_4	Y_4	Z_4
X_1'	1	0	0	0	0	0	0	0	0	0	0	0
Y_1'	0	1	0	0	0	0	0	0	0	0	0	0
Z_1'	0	0	1	0	0	0	0	0	0	0	0	0
X_2'	0	0	0	1	0	0	0	0	0	0	0	0
Y_2'	0	0	0	0	1	0	0	0	0	0	0	0
Z_2'	0	0	0	0	0	1	0	0	0	0	0	0
X_3'	0	0	0	0	0	0	1	0	0	0	0	0
Y_3'	0	0	0	0	0	0	0	1	0	0	0	0
Z_3'	0	0	0	0	0	0	0	0	1	0	0	0
X_4'	0	0	0	0	0	0	0	0	0	1	0	0
Y_4'	0	0	0	0	0	0	0	0	0	0	1	0
Z_4'	0	0	0	0	0	0	0	0	0	0	0	1

Figure 9.4   The matrix expressing the effect of the identity operation on the set of Cartesian displacement coordinates (Figure 9.3) for CO_3^{2-}.

operation is applied only to the set of vectors, moving them but leaving the nuclei themselves fixed. Thus we may specify or label each vector prior to the operation by stating its direction and the number of the atom to which it is attached, viz., X_1 or Z_4. For the same vector after the symmetry operation we use the same symbol primed, whether the vector has moved in any way or not. The left vertical column on Figure 9.4 lists the vectors after application of the symmetry operation and the top horizontal row lists the original set. The purpose of Figure 9.4 and a similar device for each symmetry operation is to express the composition of the primed vectors in terms of those in the original, unprimed set. In this case the results are trivial: each primed vector is identical with the corresponding unprimed vector. The square array of numbers so obtained is a matrix describing the effect of the symmetry operation upon the set of vectors, and its character is the character corresponding to the particular operation in the reducible representation we are seeking. Thus, for the identity operation, we have here a character of 12.

We now apply a threefold rotation to the set of Cartesian displacement vectors with the results pictured in Figure 9.5. Again we wish to construct the matrix expressing these results. This is a trifle tedious but requires no more than the simplest trigonometry. For example, as Figure 9.6 shows, X_1' can be expressed as $-1/2X_2 - (\sqrt{3}/2)Y_2$, and this result has been entered in the first row of the matrix, Figure 9.7. The reader should have no difficulty in verifying the other entries in Figure 9.7. The character of this matrix has the value zero.

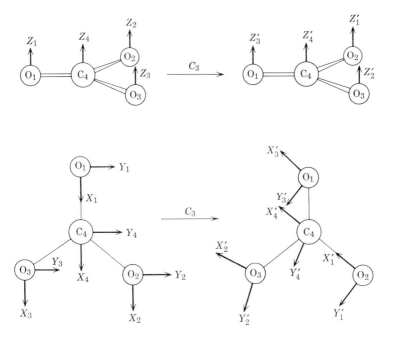

Figure 9.5   Diagrams showing the effect of a threefold rotation on the set of Cartesian displacement vectors.

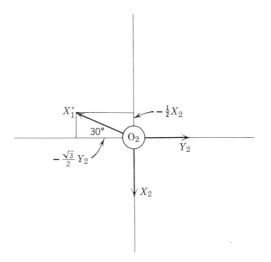

Figure 9.6   Diagrams showing the resolution of the displacement vector X_1' into its X_2 and Y_2 components.

	X_1	Y_1	Z_1	X_2	Y_2	Z_2	X_3	Y_3	Z_3	X_4	Y_4	Z_4
X_1'	0	0	0	$-1/2$	$-\sqrt{3}/2$	0	0	0	0	0	0	0
Y_1'	0	0	0	$\sqrt{3}/2$	$-1/2$	0	0	0	0	0	0	0
Z_1'	0	0	0	0	0	1	0	0	0	0	0	0
X_2'	0	0	0	0	0	0	$-1/2$	$-\sqrt{3}/2$	0	0	0	0
Y_2'	0	0	0	0	0	0	$\sqrt{3}/2$	$-1/2$	0	0	0	0
Z_2'	0	0	0	0	0	0	0	0	1	0	0	0
X_3'	$-1/2$	$-\sqrt{3}/2$	0	0	0	0	0	0	0	0	0	0
Y_3'	$\sqrt{3}/2$	$-1/2$	0	0	0	0	0	0	0	0	0	0
Z_3'	0	0	1	0	0	0	0	0	0	0	0	0
X_4'	0	0	0	0	0	0	0	0	0	$-1/2$	$-\sqrt{3}/2$	0
Y_4'	0	0	0	0	0	0	0	0	0	$\sqrt{3}/2$	$-1/2$	0
Z_4'	0	0	0	0	0	0	0	0	0	0	0	1

Figure 9.7   The matrix expressing the effect of the operation C_3 on the set of Cartesian displacement coordinates for CO_3^{2-}.

Before proceeding further, we take note of a labor-saving procedure. The operation C_3 shifts all of the vectors originally associated with atom 1 to atom 2. Thus when we write down the components of X_1', Y_1', and Z_1' we find that they come entirely from the set X_2, Y_2, Z_2. This being so, the diagonal elements in the first three rows are all zero. Since all of the vectors initially on atom 2 are rotated to atom 3 there are no nonzero diagonal elements in the next three rows. For the same reason, there are none in the next three rows either. It is only the vectors X_4, Y_4, and Z_4, which the operation C_3 merely shuffles among themselves but does not shift to a different atom, which contribute nonzero diagonal elements. Thus we could have determined the character of the C_3 matrix by ignoring all those vectors which are shifted from one atom to another when the molecule is rotated and taking account of only those which remain associated with the same atom. Henceforth we shall approach the task in this way.

When the molecule is subjected to a twofold rotation we see that vectors on two of the oxygen atoms, let us say numbers 2 and 3, are shifted. Thus we know that these vectors will contribute nothing to the character of the matrix. For each of the other two atoms, O_1 and C_4, however, the Z vectors are transformed into the negatives of themselves, two Y vectors go over into their own negatives, while the X vectors remain unchanged. These results are expressed in the abbreviated matrix of Figure 9.8, in which only the elements relating to the vectors on atoms 1 and 4 are given. The value of the character is seen to be -2.

The character of the matrix corresponding to the operation σ_h may be found without writing out any part of the complete matrix itself. We note that the operation σ_h does not shift any vectors from one atom to another. Hence no set of vectors may be summarily ignored. We note further that each set of vectors will be affected by σ_h in exactly the same way. Thus whatever contribution to the character is made by one of the four sets may simply be multiplied by four in order to get the total value of the character. In any one set, σ_h transforms the X and Y vectors into themselves and the Z vector into its own negative. Thus the submatrix for this set of vectors will be diagonal with the elements 1, 1, -1 and hence a character of 1. The character of the entire matrix corresponding to the operation σ_h is thus 4.

The operation S_3 shifts all the vectors on oxygen atoms so we know that these nine vectors can be ignored. The effect of S_3 on the vectors of the carbon atom can be found quickly by recalling the effect of C_3 on the same set, as shown in the lower right portion of Figure 9.7. S_3 is simply C_3 followed by σ_h so that its effect on X_4 and Y_4 is the same as that of C_3. However, whereas C_3 left Z_4 unaffected, S_3 transforms it into its negative. Thus S_3 acting on the displacement vectors of the carbon atom causes the following elements to appear along the diagonal of the matrix: $-\frac{1}{2}$, $-\frac{1}{2}$, -1. The character of the entire matrix is therefore -2.

Finally, we have to consider the operation σ_v. Let us choose the plane passing through O_1 and C_4. The vectors on atoms 2 and 3, which are shuffled by reflection through this plane, may be dismissed from consideration. It is obvious by inspection that X_1, Z_1, X_4, and Z_4 go into themselves while Y_1 and Y_4 go into the negative of themselves by reflection of these sets of vectors through the σ_v considered. Thus the diagonal elements generated are 1, 1, 1, 1, -1, and -1, and the character of the entire matrix corresponding to σ_v has the value 2.

	X_1	Y_1	Z_1	X_4	Y_4	Z_4
X_1'	1	0	0			
Y_1'	0	-1	0			
Z_1'	0	0	-1			
X_4'				1	0	0
Y_4'				0	-1	0
Z_4'				0	0	-1

Figure 9.8 Abbreviated matrix for the operation C_2 on the Cartesian displacement vectors of CO_3^{2-}.

D_{3h}	E	$2C_3$	$3C_2$	σ_h	$2S_3$	$3\sigma_v$		
A_1'	1	1	1	1	1	1		$x^2 + y^2, z^2$
A_2'	1	1	-1	1	1	-1	R_z	
E'	2	-1	0	2	-1	0	(x, y)	$(x^2 - y^2, xy)$
A_1''	1	1	1	-1	-1	-1		
A_2''	1	1	-1	-1	-1	1	z	
E''	2	-1	0	-2	1	0	(R_x, R_y)	(xz, yz)
Γ_t	12	0	-2	4	-2	2		

Figure 9.9   The character table for the group D_{3h} with the characters for the representation generated from the twelve Cartesian displacement coordinates appended.

In Figure 9.9 we reproduce the character table of the group D_{3h} and append to it the results just obtained for the characters of the operations in the reducible representation for which the twelve Cartesian displacement coordinates form a basis. This may be reduced by the methods of Section 4.3 with the following result:

$$\Gamma_t = A_1' + A_2' + 3E' + 2A_2'' + E''$$

We know that of the twelve normal modes of the molecule only six are genuine vibrations while three are translations and three are rotations. We can easily strike the nongenuine ones from the above list by reference to the information on the right side of the character table. The translatory motions must belong to the same representations as do the coordinates x, y, and z. Thus we delete from the above list one of the E' and one of the A_2'' species. We see that rotation about the z axis is a motion having A_2' symmetry and that rotations about the x and y axes are a degenerate pair having E'' symmetry. We therefore strike the A_2' and the E'' from our list. This then leaves the following list of the representations to which the six genuine normal modes of the molecule belong:

$$\Gamma_g = A_1' + 2E' + A_2''$$

These results are, of course, in agreement with the information given in Figure 9.1.

We conclude this section by summarizing the procedure developed and the meaning of the results that it provides. In order to find out how many genuine normal modes of vibration of a molecule there are belonging to each irreducible representation of the molecular symmetry group, we merely have to form the reducible representation which is generated on applying the operations of the group (actually just one operation from each class) to the set of Cartesian displacement vectors. This gives directly the symmetry types of both the genuine and the nongenuine modes from which list those of the translations and rotations may be removed immediately by use of information explicit in the character table. The process of finding the characters of the reducible representation is greatly simplified by recognizing that none of those vectors which are shifted to different atoms by a symmetry operation make any contribution to the value of the character of the matrix corresponding to that operation. The final result is a list of irreducible representations of the molecular symmetry group such that the sum of their dimensions equals the number of internal or genuine modes of vibration of the molecule. There is a genuine normal mode having symmetry corresponding to each of the irreducible representations in the list.

9.4 Contributions of Particular Internal Coordinates to Normal Modes

We noted in Section 9.3 that the normal modes could be expressed not only as functions, that is, vector sums, of a set of Cartesian displacement vectors but also as functions of a set of internal displacement vectors. We have seen how the former relationship is utilized in determining the total number of normal modes of each symmetry type. We use the second relationship mainly to gain information on how the stretching of bonds and bending of the bond angles contribute to the normal modes according to their symmetry types. For instance, inspection of Figure 9.1 reveals that the A_1' vibration is one involving purely the stretching of C—O bonds while the A_2'' vibration involves only bending or deformation of the molecule out of the equilibrium plane. The E' vibrations, however, are clearly not of this "purity"; both involve a mixture of C—O stretching and in-plane deformation of the OCO angles. We may ask: Could these facts have been deduced from symmetry considerations alone without knowledge of the actual forms of the normal modes? The answer to this question is in the affirmative and it is our purpose in this section to explain how such information is obtained.

Suppose we choose as a set of three internal displacement coordinates stretchings of the three C—O bonds, and use these as the basis for a three-dimensional representation of the symmetry group. The irreducible representations spanned by this representation will include only those to which belong normal modes involving C—O stretching. From

Figure 9.1, we anticipate that the answer will be $A_1' + E'$. Let us carry through the procedure outlined and see if we do obtain this answer. In so doing we will make use of the same shortcut developed above in handling Cartesian displacement vectors. Any vector which is shifted to a different position by a given symmetry operation will contribute nothing to the value of the character of the corresponding matrix.

The various symmetry operations will affect our set of C—O bond stretchings in the same way as they will affect the set of C—O bonds themselves. With this in mind we can determine the desired characters very quickly as follows. For the operation E the character equals 3 since each C—O bond is carried into itself. The same is true for the operation σ_h. For the operations C_3 and S_3 the characters are zero because all C—O bonds are shifted by these operations. The operations C_2 and σ_v have characters of 1 since each of these operations carries one C—O bond into itself but interchanges the other two. The set of characters, listed in the same order as are the symmetry operations at the top of the D_{3h} character table, are thus: 3 0 1 3 0 1. This representation reduces to $A_1' + E'$ as it should according to our previous discussion. Thus we have shown that normal modes of symmetry types A' and E' must involve some degree of C—O stretching. Since there is only one A_1' mode we can state further that this mode must involve entirely C—O stretching.

As a second set of internal displacement coordinates we may choose the increments or decrements to the three OCO angles. Before using this set to form a representation which will tell us the normal coordinates which involve in-plane OCO bends, we must be careful to note that all of the coordinates in the set are *not* independent. If all three of the angles were to increase by the same amount at the same time, the motion would have A_1' symmetry. However, it is obviously impossible for all three angles simultaneously to expand within the plane. Thus the A_1' representation which we shall find when we have reduced the representation is to be discarded as spurious. A set of three increases in the three OCO angles will be affected by the symmetry operations in the same way as the three angles themselves, so we may make use of the angles in determining the characters. The operation E transforms each angle into itself, giving a character of 3 for this operation. So also does the operation σ_h. The operations C_3 and S_3 shift all of the angles so these operations have characters of zero. The operations C_2 and σ_v each leave one angle unshifted but interchange the other two, thus having characters of 1. The complete set of characters, again in the order in which the symmetry operations are listed is: 3 0 1 3 0 1. This representation reduces to $A_1' + E'$. Disregarding the A_1' for the reason explained above, we have the result that in-plane bending of the OCO angles contributes to vibrations of E' symmetry. This result is seen to be in agreement with the actual nature of the normal modes as shown in Figure 9.1.

Since there remains only one other kind of internal coordinate, namely changes in the angles between the C—O bonds and the plane of the ion, and only one normal mode unaccounted for, we may naturally conclude that this remaining mode, of A_2'' symmetry, must consist entirely of out-of-plane bending of the ion, which is, of course, correct. However, we may bring more positive reasoning than this to bear on the problem. It is evident that normal modes involving C—O stretching, OCO in-plane angle bending, or both must by nature be symmetric with respect to reflection through the plane of the molecule. All vectors used to indicate the displacements in such vibrations will lie in the plane and cannot be affected by reflection through the plane in which they lie. Since a mode of A_2'' symmetry must be antisymmetric to σ_h, according to the character table, we might have seen that the A_2'' mode would not involve C—O stretching or in-plane OCO bending without any knowledge as to which vibrations did involve such internal displacements. Moreover, it is obvious that only a vibration in which all displacements are perpendicular to the molecular plane can belong to the A_2'' representation.

Further illustrations of this procedure will be found in Section 9.7.

9.5   Selection Rules for Fundamental Vibrational Transitions

Normal Coordinates

In Sections 9.2 and 9.3 we discussed in a pictorial way the idea of normal modes of vibration. It was stated that they may be visualized as combinations of displacements of all the atoms such that as the molecule executes the normal vibration the relative magnitudes and directions of these displacements remain fixed but their absolute magnitudes vary periodically according to the frequency of the mode. Corresponding to the ith normal mode we may write a *normal coordinate*, ξ_i, as a linear combination of the displacement coordinates of all atoms in the molecule. Each displacement coordinate is given a coefficient to correspond to the correct relation between the magnitudes and directions of the atomic displacements at any arbitrary time in the course of the vibration. The displacement coordinates used to write the normal coordinate may be either internal coordinates or Cartesian coordinates.

To illustrate, let us consider ν_1 of the carbonate ion, Figure 9.1. In internal coordinates the normal coordinate can be written down at once;

numbering the CO bonds from 1 to 3 and using Δ_i to represent an extension of the ith bond, we have

$$\xi_1 = \Delta_1 + \Delta_2 + \Delta_3 \qquad (9.5\text{-}1)$$

To write ξ_1 in terms of Cartesian displacement coordinates we have only to resolve each of the displacement vectors, Δ_i, into Cartesian displacement vectors. Assuming the molecule to lie in the xy plane and taking the length of a unit Cartesian displacement vector, x_i or y_i, to be equal to the length of Δ_1, we obtain:

$$\Delta_1 = y_1$$
$$\Delta_2 = (\sqrt{3}/2)x_2 - (1/2)y_2$$
$$\Delta_3 = -(\sqrt{3}/2)x_3 - (1/2)y_3$$

We have used the sines and cosines of 30° and 60° to obtain the coefficients. Hence, in terms of Cartesian displacement vectors, we have

$$\xi_1 = (\sqrt{3}/2)(x_2 - x_3) + (1/2)(2y_1 - y_2 - y_3) \qquad (9.5\text{-}2)$$

An important property of the expressions for the normal coordinates is that each one is a function which forms a basis for the representation of the molecular point group to which the normal mode belongs. Indeed we construct the normal coordinates, either implicitly as above or explicitly, so that they have this property. It is easy to see, for example, that ξ_1, e.g. 9.5-1, is totally symmetric. Similarly, for ν_2 we can write, in Cartesian displacements, the normal coordinate ξ_2 as

$$\xi_2 = 12(z_1 + z_2 + z_3) - (3 \times 16)z_4 \qquad (9.5\text{-}3)$$

in which we number the oxygen atoms 1–3 and the carbon atom 4 and the weighting factors are obtained from the atomic masses and adjusted so that there is no net translation of the center of gravity of the molecule. It can readily be seen that ξ_2 obeys all the symmetry requirements of a function which generates the A_2'' representation of the group D_{3h}.

In conclusion, it should be noted that to be fully correct for mathematical purposes, the expressions for the normal coordinates should be normalized. Normalization is carried out by assuming that the individual displacement coordinates form an orthonormal set.* This means that if q_p and q_q stand for any displacement coordinates, we write

$$q_p q_q = \delta_{pq} \qquad (9.5\text{-}4)$$

and we require that, on this basis,

$$\xi_i \xi_j = \delta_{ij} \qquad (9.5\text{-}5)$$

---

* This entire procedure is formally identical with the procedure for normalizing LCAO-MO's; cf. Section 7.1.

Thus, to normalize ξ_1 as given by Equation 9.5-1, we write

$$1 = \xi_1\xi_1 = N^2(\Delta_1 + \Delta_2 + \Delta_3)(\Delta_1 + \Delta_2 + \Delta_3)$$

where N is the constant needed to normalize $(\Delta_1 + \Delta_2 + \Delta_3)$. N is evaluated as follows:

$$\frac{1}{N^2} = \Delta_1\Delta_1 + \Delta_1\Delta_2 + \Delta_1\Delta_3 + \Delta_2\Delta_1 + \Delta_2\Delta_2 + \Delta_2\Delta_3 + \Delta_3\Delta_1 + \Delta_3\Delta_2 + \Delta_3\Delta_3$$

$$= 1 + 0 + 0 + 0 + 1 + 0 + 0 + 0 + 1$$

$$= 3$$

Hence

$$N = \frac{1}{\sqrt{3}}$$

Similarly, for ξ_2 as given by 9.5-3, we compute the normalizing constant as follows:

$$\frac{1}{N^2} = (z_1 + z_2 + z_3 - 4z_4)^2$$

$$= z_1z_1 + z_1z_2 + z_1z_3 - 4z_1z_4 + z_2z_1 + z_2z_2 + z_2z_3$$
$$- 4z_2z_4 + \cdots$$
$$= 1 + 1 + 1 + 16 = 19$$

Thus in normalized form ξ_1 in internal displacement coordinates and ξ_2 in Cartesian displacement coordinates are

$$\xi_1 = \frac{1}{\sqrt{3}}(\Delta_1 + \Delta_2 + \Delta_3)$$

$$\xi_2 = \frac{1}{\sqrt{19}}(z_1 + z_2 + z_3 - 4z_4)$$

Wave Functions of the Normal Modes

The wave functions of the normal modes can be written in the simplest possible way using the normal coordinates as the variables. As is shown in many books on elementary quantum mechanics, these wave functions, assuming that the oscillations are harmonic (potential energy a function only of the square of the displacement coordinate) have the form:

$$\psi_i(n) = N_i e^{-(\alpha_i/2)\xi_i^2} H_n(\sqrt{\alpha_i}\xi_i) \tag{9.5-6}$$

where N_i is a normalizing constant, $\alpha_i = 2\pi\nu_i/h$ (in which ν_i is the frequency of the ith normal mode) and H_n is a Hermite polynomial of order n. The number n is the vibrational quantum number; it is 0 in the ground state, 1 in the first excited state and so forth. The first few Hermite polynomials, $H_n(x)$, are

$$H_0(x) = 1 \qquad\qquad H_1(x) = 2x$$
$$H_2(x) = 4x^2 - 2 \qquad H_3(x) = 8x^3 - 12x \tag{9.5-7}$$

As shown in Section 5.1, the wave functions must form bases for irreducible representations of the symmetry group of the molecule and this of course holds for all kinds of wave functions, vibrational, rotational, electronic, and so on. Let us now see what representations are generated by the vibrational wave functions of the normal modes. Inserting $H_0(\sqrt{\alpha_i}\,\xi_i)$ into 9.5-6 we obtain

$$\psi_i(0) = N_i e^{-(\alpha_i/2)\xi_i^2}$$

In the event ξ_i represents a nondegenerate vibration, all symmetry operations change it into ± 1 times itself. Hence ξ_i^2 is unchanged by all symmetry operations. $\psi_i(0)$ is thus invariant under all symmetry operations and forms a basis for the totally symmetric representation of the group. If ξ_i is one of a set of normal coordinates belonging to a set of degenerate vibrations, any symmetry operation will change it into ± 1 times itself or into a linear combination of all members of the set (cf. Section 9.2). Let us suppose ξ_a and ξ_b are the normal coordinates of a pair of degenerate vibrations and that some symmetry operation, R, acting on ξ_a has the effect:

$$R\xi_a = \xi_a' = r_a\xi_a + r_b\xi_b$$

If ξ_a, ξ_b are normalized, r_a and r_b will be such that ξ_a' will also be normalized. We then have, by 9.5-5,

$$\xi_a^2 = 1$$
$$\xi_a'^2 = 1$$

Thus, in the degenerate case also, $\psi_i(0)$ is invariant to all symmetry operations.

We may therefore state the following important rule.

All wave functions for normal vibrations in their ground states, $\psi_i(0)$, are bases for the totally symmetric representation of the point group of the molecule.

For the excited vibrational states, $\psi_i(n)$, the wave functions are products of the same exponential as in the ground state, which we have seen is always totally symmetric, and the nth Hermite polynomial. $\psi_i(n)$, therefore, has the symmetry of the nth Hermite polynomial.

For the first excited state, we then find that the wave function, $\psi_i(1)$, has the same symmetry as ξ_i; for the second excited state, $\psi_i(2)$ has the symmetry of ξ_i^2 which means that it is totally symmetric, and so on.

Selection Rules for Fundamentals

Consider a molecule with k normal modes of vibration. At any time each of these modes will be in a certain quantum state; the wave function for the ith mode in the nth state is $\psi_i(n)$. For the total molecular vibrational wave function, ψ_v, we may use the product of the $\psi_i(n)$ since the variables in each, the ξ_i, are linearly independent. Thus we write

$$\psi_v = \psi_1(n_1) \cdot \psi_2(n_2) \cdot \psi_3(n_3) \ldots \psi_k(n_k) \tag{9.5-8}$$

When each of the n_i is equal to 0 the molecule is in its vibrational ground state. If it absorbs radiation so that the ith normal mode is excited to the state with $n_i = 1$, while the remaining $k - 1$ normal modes remain in their lowest ($n = 0$) states, the molecule is said to have undergone a *fundamental transition* in the ith normal vibration. The k different transitions of this kind are called the *fundamentals* of the molecule.

Since the fundamental transitions generally give rise to infrared absorption bands and Raman lines which are at least an order of magnitude more intense than any other kinds * of transition, they are of the greatest interest and we shall deal only with the fundamentals here. Selection rules for other types of transition can also be obtained by arguments of the type we shall use but the reader is cautioned that where degenerate modes are concerned subtle complications often arise.†

For a fundamental transition of the jth normal mode we may write

$$\prod_i \psi_i(0) \rightarrow \psi_j(1) \prod_{i \neq j} \psi_i(0)$$

Abbreviating the total molecular vibrational wave functions in the

---

* If one mode alone is doubly excited this transition is called the *first overtone* of the fundamental; if one mode alone is triply excited this is called the *second overtone*, and so on. Transitions in which two or more modes are simultaneously excited (by one or more units each) are called *combination tones*. If the molecule initially has one or more fundamentals in an excited ($n > 0$) state, *any* transitions it makes are called *hot transitions*.

† For details on the selection rules for other types of transitions, *Molecular Vibrations*, by Wilson, Decius, and Cross, should be consulted.

ground and excited states by $\psi_v{}^0$ and $\psi_v{}^j$ respectively, we can also write

$$\psi_v{}^0 \rightarrow \psi_v{}^j$$

For a fundamental transition to occur by absorption of infrared dipole radiation (cf. Section 8.6 for more detailed discussion of the analogous case for electronic transitions), it is necessary that one or more of the integrals

$$\int \psi_v{}^0 x \psi_v{}^j \, d\tau$$

$$\int \psi_v{}^0 y \psi_v{}^j \, d\tau$$

$$\int \psi_v{}^0 z \psi_v{}^j \, d\tau$$

be nonzero. The x, y, and z in these integrals refer to the orientation of the oscillating electric vector of the radiation relative to a Cartesian coordinate system fixed in the molecule.

Now, using the results of Section 5.2, it is extremely easy to determine whether such integrals vanish or not. Since $\psi_v{}^0$ belongs to the totally symmetric representation, the coordinate and $\psi_v{}^j$ must belong to the same representation in order that the representation of their direct product will contain the totally symmetric representation. Since $\psi_j(1)$ must have the same symmetry as the jth normal coordinate, ξ_j, and since all of the other wave functions, $\psi_i(0)$, are totally symmetric, $\psi_v{}^j$ belongs to the same representation as the normal mode which is undergoing its fundamental transition.

We therefore have the following very simple rule for the activity of fundamentals in infrared absorption:

A fundamental will be infrared active (that is, give rise to an absorption band) if the normal mode involved belongs to the same representation as any one or several of the Cartesian coordinates.

Of course the character tables show which representations the Cartesian coordinates belong to so that this rule can be used with the utmost ease.

For Raman scattering, it is necessary that at least one integral of the type

$$\int \psi_v{}^0 P \psi_v{}^j \, d\tau$$

be nonzero. In these integrals P is one of the quadratic functions of the Cartesian coordinates, viz., x^2, y^2, z^2, xy, yz, zx, all of which (simply or in combinations such as $x^2 - y^2$) are listed opposite the representations they generate in the character tables. These P's are components of the polarizability tensor and the requirement that the above integrals be nonzero means physically that there must be a change in polarizability of the molecule when the transition occurs. By exactly the same reasoning as used above in regard to infrared absorption, we obtain the following simple rule for Raman activity of fundamentals:

A fundamental transition will be Raman active (that is, give rise to a Raman shift) if the normal mode involved belongs to the same representation as one or more of the components of the polarizability tensor of the molecule.

We may illustrate these rules using the carbonate ion as an example. We see in the D_{3h} character table that (x, y) form a basis for the E' representation and z for the A_2'' representation. For the polarizability tensor components we see that one or more of these belong to the A_1', E', and E'' representations. Thus, for *any* molecule of D_{3h} symmetry, we have the following selection rules:

$$\begin{array}{rl} \text{Raman-active only:} & A_1', \; E'' \\ \text{Infrared-active only:} & A_2'' \\ \text{Both Raman- and infrared-active:} & E' \end{array}$$

In the particular case of the carbonate ion:

$$\begin{array}{ll} \nu_1(A_1'): & \text{Raman only} \\ \nu_2(A_2''): & \text{Infrared only} \\ \nu_3(E'), \; \nu_4(E'): & \text{Infrared and Raman} \end{array}$$

9.6 Some Important Special Effects

The Exclusion Rule

Consider a molecule which has a center of symmetry. When one of the Cartesian coordinates, x, y, or z, is inverted through this center it goes into the negative of itself. Hence all representations generated by x, y, or z or any set of these must belong to a u representation. On the other hand, a binary product of two Cartesian coordinates, say xy or z^2, does not change sign on inversion since each coordinate separately does change sign and $-1 \times -1 = 1$. It therefore follows that all such binary products, which represent components of the polarizability tensor, belong to g representations.

From these rules, which can be verified by inspection of the character tables, we conclude that in centrosymmetric molecules only fundamentals of modes belonging to g representations can be Raman-active and only fundamentals of modes belonging to u representations can be infrared-active. It is also obvious that the same must be true for other transitions besides fundamentals since the reasoning is completely general.

Another way of stating this result, the so-called *exclusion rule,* is:

In a centrosymmetric molecule no Raman-active vibration is also infrared-active and no infrared-active vibration is also Raman-active.

Fermi Resonance

From the considerations of Section 5.2 it follows that in order for there to be *any* energy of interaction between two states having wave functions ψ_1 and ψ_2 and represented by the integral

$$E_i = \int \psi_1 \mathfrak{K} \psi_2 \, d\tau$$

where $\mathfrak{K}$ is the Hamiltonian operator, ψ_1 and ψ_2 must belong to the same irreducible representation. In the event that there is an interaction, a perturbation treatment shows that the two states interact to give two mixed states whose energies E_1' and E_2' are given, approximately, by

$$E_1' = E_1 + E_i$$

$$E_2' = E_2 - E_i$$

where E_1 and E_2 represent the energies of the states ψ_1 and ψ_2 in the absence of any interaction and $E_1 > E_2$. Perturbation theory also shows that the magnitude of E_i depends inversely on $E_1 - E_2$.

The commonest manifestation of this kind of interaction, termed a resonance interaction, between vibrational states occurs when an overtone or combination tone has a frequency very close to that of another fundamental, that is, the energies of the two excited states are nearly the same. Then with the energy difference, to which the interaction is inversely proportional, being small, E_i may become quite appreciable. The result is that instead of there being only the one strong fundamental absorption band (or Raman line) there are two fairly strong bands because the upper states for the overtone and fundamental transitions are mixed together when they interact and the normally very weak overtone transition acquires some fundamental character and corresponding intensity.

This phenomenon is called *Fermi resonance* since the first example of it was recognized by Fermi in CO_2. In this molecule the three fundamental transitions have frequencies of 667, 1300, and 2350 cm^{-1}. The first overtone of the 667 cm^{-1} vibration, which is doubly degenerate, has a frequency of 1334 cm^{-1}, which is quite close to that of the 1300 cm^{-1} fundamental. Now it can be shown * that the excited state for the 1300 cm^{-1} fundamental and one component of the representation generated by the excited state corresponding to the first overtone of the 667 cm^{-1} vibration do belong to the same representation of the group $D_{\infty h}$ and hence a Fermi resonance occurs. Thus, in the Raman spectrum of CO_2, there are observed two strong bands at 1285 and 1388 cm^{-1} instead of just one at $\sim$1300 cm^{-1}.

Site Symmetries

All of our treatment here has pertained to molecules which are completely isolated from any other molecules—either of the same kind or other kinds. The vibrational states of the isolated molecule have been shown to be directly dependent on the molecular symmetry. However, in liquids and crystals, molecules are in close proximity to other molecules and the question arises whether intermolecular interactions will have a significant effect on the vibrational modes and vibrational transitions and if so whether symmetry considerations are of importance in understanding them. We shall restrict the discussion to crystals where the surroundings of a molecule have a fixed and well-defined configuration. For a more extended discussion of this subject the reader is referred to Halford's paper.†

As Halford has pointed out, while a full consideration of all the consequences of the interactions between the motions of molecules in a crystal lattice leads to a very complicated picture, practically all commonly observed effects of the molecular interactions can be satisfactorily treated by a less rigorous but far more manageable idealization. In this we do not specifically analyze the dynamic intermolecular interactions themselves, but instead we consider that the molecules surrounding any given mole-

---

* It is to be noted that for overtones of degenerate modes, the symmetries of the excited states cannot be obtained simply from the direct product representations of the first excited states. The reason for this is not difficult to understand but the argument is lengthy and the reader is referred to Wilson, Decius, and Cross, pp. 152–155, for the explanation.

† R. Halford, *J. Chem. Phys.*, **14**, 8 (1946).

cule provide an environment of fixed symmetry in which the given molecule vibrates. The form of the vibrational modes will then depend not
only on the intrinsic symmetry of the molecule itself but on the symmetry
of its environment. The effective symmetry governing the behavior of
the vibrational states of the molecule in the crystal is called the *site
symmetry*.

In general a crystal lattice has various elements of symmetry. Some
of these are of the same kind as those occurring in molecules, that is, they
generate symmetry operations which cause no translation of the center
of mass of the object to which they are applied. Thus a given point in a
crystal may be a center of inversion, it may lie on a proper or improper
axis or it may lie in a reflection plane. Of course several such symmetry
elements may intersect at one point in the crystal lattice. The collection
of all the operations made possible by the symmetry elements intersecting at such a point in the crystal constitute a point group which can be
used to specify the *site symmetry* of a molecule whose center of mass is
situated at this point. In a rigid, ordered crystal, the site symmetry can
never be such as to contain symmetry elements not belonging to the free
molecule * and in general the site symmetry is lower than the molecular
symmetry. That is, of a number of symmetry elements present in the free
molecule, only some will correspond with symmetry elements of the
lattice. Those symmetry elements of the free molecule which do not
correspond with symmetry elements inherent in its crystal environment
are not part of the site symmetry. In principle, the molecule loses those
symmetry elements when it enters the crystal, and its vibrational behavior must be treated only in terms of the site symmetry. The point
group for the site symmetry will in general then be a subgroup of the
molecular point group, though occasionally the two groups are the same
(for example, for the $[SiF_6]^{2-}$ ion in the cubic form of K_2SiF_6).

It should be noted that the degree to which the vibrational spectrum
of a molecule in a site of low symmetry will deviate *observably* from the
behavior of the free molecule depends on just how strongly the molecule
interacts with its surroundings in the crystal. Symmetry considerations
alone can of course tell us nothing about this, and it varies from one

---

* There are some apparent exceptions to this. In the ammonium halides which have
the rock salt lattice, the ammonium ions, which do not themselves have centers of
symmetry, lie at lattice points which would, were the ammonium ions not present, be
centers of inversion. Depending on the particular halide and the temperature, the
ammonium ions are either freely rotating, so that the time-average symmetry is cen-
tric or else ammonium ions at different sites have different orientations so that while
any particular site is not centrosymmetric the crystal as a whole appears to be centrosymmetric. In this brief discussion we shall consider only cases in which the crystals
are completely ordered and contain no rotating molecules.

case to another. A few examples now to be considered will give an idea of the magnitude of such effects in some typical cases.

Qualitatively, the effects of low site symmetry are of two general types: (1) changes in selection rules and (2) splitting of degeneracies. A nondegenerate vibration may be inactive in the high symmetry of the free molecule but active in the symmetry of one or more subgroups of that molecule. For example the A_1' mode of the carbonate ion (totally symmetric CO stretching, Figure 9.1) is not infrared-active under the full D_{3h} symmetry of CO_3^{2-}. $CaCO_3$ occurs in two crystallographically different forms, calcite and aragonite. In the former, the site symmetry of the CO_3^{2-} ion is D_3 and in the latter it is C_s. Reference to the character tables for these two groups shows that in D_3 the totally symmetric mode is still not infrared-active whereas in the group C_s totally symmetric vibrations are infrared-active. In agreement with these expectations, the symmetric CO stretching mode of CO_3^{2-} (known from the Raman spectrum of solutions of carbonates) is not observed in calcite but appears weakly in aragonite.

The effect of low site symmetry in splitting degeneracies is also nicely demonstrated in the two forms of $CaCO_3$. The E' representation of the group D_{3h} correlates with the E representation in D_3. Hence, in calcite, both ν_3 and ν_4 (Figure 9.1) are observed as single peaks. In the group C_s there are no representations of order greater than 1 which means that the degenerate vibrations of CO_3^{2-} must be split by the C_s site symmetry of aragonite. Actually ν_3 is still observed as a single peak, which means that the magnitude of the splitting is too small to permit resolution or that one component has very low intensity, but ν_4 is distinctly split into two peaks separated by 14 cm^{-1}.

As another example of the effect of low site symmetry in splitting degeneracy we may consider the thiocyanate ion in KNCS.* The SCN$^-$ ion is linear and in the absence of perturbing influences has as one of its normal modes a doubly degenerate bending vibration. The degeneracy exists in the isolated ion because bending of the molecule in any given plane containing the molecular axis is entirely equivalent to bending in a plane perpendicular to the first one. However, if the site symmetry of the ion in a crystal is such that these two planes are not equivalent then the frequencies of bending in the two planes need not be identical. Figure 9.10 shows the structure of KNCS and it can be seen that planes parallel to the plane of the drawing are not equivalent to planes perpendicular to the drawing. It was found that while the bending vibration gives rise to a single peak at 470 cm^{-1} in the infrared spectrum of NCS$^-$ in solution, crystalline KNCS has two absorption peaks at 470 and 484 cm^{-1}.

* L. H. Jones, *J. Chem. Phys.*, **25**, 1069 (1956).

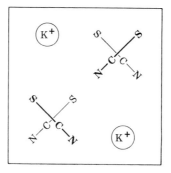

Figure 9.10   Sketch of the unit cell of KNCS.

9.7   Illustrative Examples

1. *trans*-N_2F_2. This molecule has the following planar, nonlinear structure:

It belongs to the point group C_{2h}. Since it is a nonlinear four-atomic molecule it has $3(4) - 6 = 6$ degrees of internal freedom.

The set of twelve cartesian displacement vectors for the entire molecule generates the following reducible representation:

C_{2h}	E	C_2	i	σ_h
Γ	12	0	0	4

This can be reduced in the following manner:

$$\Gamma = 4A_g + 2B_g + 2A_u + 4B_u$$

Inspection of the character table shows that the translations and rotations span the representations $A_g + 2B_g + A_u + 2B_u$. On deleting these from the total number constituting Γ we are left with the following list of the representations spanned by the genuine normal vibrations:

$$3A_g + A_u + 2B_u$$

The selection rules for the fundamentals of these modes are obtained immediately from the right columns of the character table and are:

Infrared-active: A_u, B_u
Raman-active: A_g

It will be noted that the exclusion rule operates here since this molecule has a center of symmetry.

The nature of these six vibrations may be further specified in terms of the contribution made to each of them by the various internal coordinates. We first note that A_g and B_u vibrations must involve only motions within the molecular plane since the characters of the representations A_g and B_u with respect to σ_h are positive. The A_u vibration will however involve out-of-plane deformation since the character of A_u with respect to σ_h is negative. Thus we may describe the normal mode of A_u symmetry as "the out-of-plane deformation." In order to treat the remaining five in-plane vibrations we need a set of five internal coordinates so chosen that changes in them may occur entirely within the molecular plane. A suitable set, related to the bonding in the molecule is: the two N—F distances, the two NNF angles, and the N=N distance.

It is found that the two N—F distances form the basis for the representation Γ_{NF}, the two NNF angles form the basis for the representation Γ_{NNF} and the N=N distance for Γ_{NN}, each of which is given below:

C_{2h}	E	C_2	i	σ_h
Γ_{NF}	2	0	0	2
Γ_{NNF}	2	0	0	2
Γ_{NN}	1	1	1	1

It is then easily shown that

$$\Gamma_{NF} = A_g + B_u$$

$$\Gamma_{NNF} = A_g + B_u$$

$$\Gamma_{NN} = A_g$$

It therefore follows that the three Raman-active vibrations (A_g) will be compounded of symmetric NF stretching, symmetric NNF bending, and NN stretching, the relative amounts of each involved in each normal mode depending of course on the actual values of the force constants and atomic masses. Similarly the two B_u vibrations in the infrared will involve asymmetric N—F stretching and NNF angle bending. Again the proportion of each of these in each of the true normal modes will depend on force constants and atomic masses.

2. NH_3. This molecule belongs to the point group C_{3v}. As a nonlinear, four-atomic molecule it has $3(4) - 6 = 6$ degrees of internal freedom.

The set of twelve Cartesian displacement vectors for the entire molecule forms a basis for the following reducible representation:

C_{3v}	E	$2C_3$	$3\sigma_v$
Γ	12	0	2

This can be reduced, giving

$$\Gamma = 3A_1 + A_2 + 4E$$

Eliminating those irreducible representations corresponding to translations and rotations we have, for the genuine normal modes,

$$2A_1 + 2E$$

The selection rules for the fundamentals are, from the character table,

Infrared- and Raman-active: A_1, E

That is, all the fundamentals will appear in both the infrared and Raman spectra.

The nature of the vibrations in terms of changes in internal coordinates may be found by using the three N—H bond lengths and the three HNH angles as internal coordinates. In this case no spurious or redundant results will be obtained because all of these six internal coordinates may change independently. The representations, Γ_{N-H}, given by the bond lengths, and Γ_δ, given by the bond angles, are readily found to be the following:

C_{3v}	E	$2C_3$	$3\sigma_v$
Γ_{N-H}	3	0	1
Γ_δ	3	0	1

The two representations are identical and each reduces to $A_1 + E$. Therefore it follows that each of the A_1 normal modes will involve both bond stretching and deformations of the bond angles and so also will the E modes. In Figure 9.11 are drawings of the actual normal modes for ND_3. These have been obtained from experimental values of the fundamental frequencies by a detailed calculation (cf. Wilson, Decius, and Cross, *loc. cit.*, for a description of the methods for such a calculation).

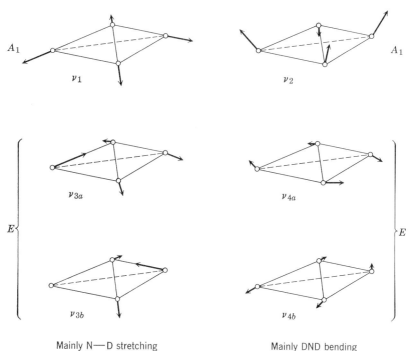

Mainly N—D stretching   Mainly DND bending

Figure 9.11   The normal vibrations of ND_3 (after Herzberg).

It will be seen that in fact one each of the A_1 and E modes involve *almost* purely bond stretching and the others *almost* purely angle bending. Such a situation is not uncommon, but it is to be emphasized that this is a consequence of the particular values of the masses and force constants and no such separation is rigorously required.

3. CH_4. This tetrahedral molecule belongs to the point group T_d. As a nonlinear, five-atomic molecule it has $3(5) - 6 = 9$ degrees of internal freedom.

The set of fifteen Cartesian displacement vectors forms a basis for the following representation:

T_d	E	$8C_3$	$3C_2$	$6S_4$	$6\sigma_d$
Γ	15	0	-1	-1	3

This reduces as follows:

$$\Gamma = A_1 + E + T_1 + 3T_2$$

The character table shows that the rotations transform as T_1 and the translations as T_2; hence the symmetry types of the genuine vibrations are

$$A_1, E, 2T_2$$

The character table also shows that the activities of these fundamentals are as follows:

Raman only: A_1 and E

Infrared and Raman: T_2

Since the molecule has no center of symmetry there can be, and in this case are, some vibrations which are both infrared- and Raman-active.

To find the contributions of the internal coordinates, C—H bond lengths and HCH angles, to these vibrational modes we first use the set of four C—H bond lengths as the basis for a representation, obtaining Γ_{C-H} shown below.

T_d	E	$8C_3$	$3C_2$	$6S_4$	$6\sigma_d$
Γ_{C-H}	4	1	0	0	2
Γ_{HCH}	6	0	2	0	2

This is easily found to reduce as follows:

$$\Gamma_{CH} = A_1 + T_2$$

Similarly, we can use the six interbond angles to generate a representation, obtaining Γ_{HCH}, which reduces thus:

$$\Gamma_{HCH} = A_1 + E + T_2$$

It will be seen that the total dimensionality of these two representations, ten, is one in excess of the correct number, and, specifically, that there is an extra A_1 representation. It is easy to determine that the spurious or redundant one is the one in Γ_{HCH}, for while it is possible for all four of the C—H distances to change independently, it is not possible for all six angles to change independently. If any five are arbitrarily altered, the alteration of the sixth one is then automatically fixed. For an A_1 vibration all six angles would have to change in the same way at the same time (that is, all increase or all decrease) and this is clearly impossible. Hence we obtain the results that the A_1 vibration of CH_4 consists purely of C—H stretching, and the E vibration consists purely of HCH angle deformations while both bond stretching and angle bending contribute to each of the normal vibrations of T_2 symmetry.

4. SF_6. This molecule belongs to the point group O_h. As a nonlinear, seven-atomic molecule it has $3(7) - 6 = 15$ degrees of internal freedom. The twenty-one Cartesian displacement vectors generate the representation Γ given in the table below.

O_h	E	$8C_3$	$6C_2$	$6C_4$	$3C_2(= C_4{}^2)$	i	$6S_4$	$8S_6$	$3\sigma_h$	$6\sigma_d$
Γ	21	0	-1	3	-3	-3	-1	0	5	3
Γ_{SF}	6	0	0	2	2	0	0	0	4	2
Γ_{FSF}	12	0	2	0	0	0	0	0	4	2

The representation Γ reduces as follows:

$$\Gamma = A_{1g} + E_g + T_{1g} + 3T_{1u} + T_{2g} + T_{2u}$$

The character table shows that the rotations and translations belong, respectively, to the T_{1g} and T_{1u} representations. After deleting these we obtain the following list of genuine normal modes, grouped according to the activities of their fundamentals:

$$\begin{aligned} \text{Infrared-active:} &\quad 2T_{1u} \\ \text{Raman-active:} &\quad A_{1g}, E_g, T_{2g} \\ \text{Inactive:} &\quad T_{2u} \end{aligned}$$

It will be noted that the exclusion rule is obeyed as it must be since the molecule has a center of symmetry. We also encounter here for the first time the occurrence of a normal vibration which is completely inactive as a fundamental. This phenomenon is not commonplace but is encountered occasionally in relatively symmetrical molecules.

In the table above we also give the representations generated by the set of six S—F bonds, Γ_{SF}, and the set of twelve FSF angles, Γ_{FSF}. These representations can be reduced as follows:

$$\Gamma_{SF} = A_{1g} + E_g + T_{1u}$$

$$\Gamma_{FSF} = A_{1g} + E_g + T_{2g} + T_{1u} + T_{2u}$$

Obviously there is some redundancy here; since the S—F coordinates are entirely independent, the redundancy must be entirely in Γ_{FSF} (see the preceding discussion of CH_4). By comparing the total of Γ_{SF} and Γ_{FSF} with the correct list of genuine internal modes we see that the A_{1g} and E_g occurring in Γ_{FSF} are the spurious ones. Thus we conclude that the two T_{1u} modes will each involve a combination of bond stretching and angle deformation, the A_{1g} and E_g modes will involve only bond stretching, while the T_{2g} and T_{2u} modes will involve only angle deformation.

Part III

Appendices

Appendix I

Some Properties of Determinants;
The Reciprocal of a Matrix

Expansion and Evaluation of Determinants

A determinant is a square array of numbers. The number of rows or columns is called the order, n, of the determinant and it contains a total of n^2 elements.

A determinant, unlike a matrix, is a scalar quantity. Its value is given by the sum of $n!$ different products each containing n elements so chosen that each row and each column is represented but once. The sum of these products is called the expansion of the determinant. That there are $n!$ such products is easily shown. To form one of them we select an element from the first row, which may be done in n ways. In choosing an element from the second row we are not permitted to choose it from the column to which the element from the first row belongs; thus for this choice we have only $n - 1$ possibilities. We can then choose an element from the third row in only $n - 2$ ways and so forth. Thus there are $n(n - 1) \times (n - 2)(n - 3) \cdots 2 \cdot 1 = n!$ different ways of composing a product. In addition, each product is given a sign, $+$ or $-$. The choice of sign is determined as follows. We write down all of the factors in such a way that the row (column) indices run serially and count the number of transpositions (exchanges of neighbors) which are required to put the column (row) indices in serial order. If this number is even the sign is $+$ and if it is odd the sign is $-$. Consider for example the following product which would be obtained from a third-order determinant:

$$a_{31}a_{23}a_{12}$$

Written with the row indices in serial order, it is

$$a_{12}a_{23}a_{31}$$

To put the column indices in serial order we must perform two successive interchanges of adjacent factors, viz.,

$$a_{12}a_{23}a_{31} \; \longrightarrow \; a_{12}a_{31}a_{23}$$

$$a_{12}a_{31}a_{23} \; \longrightarrow \; a_{31}a_{12}a_{23}$$

Hence this product is given a positive sign.

The value of a determinant, $|A|$, of order 2 is given by

$$a_{11}a_{22} \; - \; a_{12}a_{21}$$

and that of a third-order determinant by

$$a_{11}a_{22}a_{33} \; + \; a_{12}a_{23}a_{31} \; + \; a_{13}a_{21}a_{32} \; - \; a_{11}a_{23}a_{32} \; - \; a_{12}a_{21}a_{33} \; - \; a_{13}a_{22}a_{31}$$

The results for these two simple and frequently occurring cases can easily be remembered. The positive terms are products obtained by selecting elements along diagonal lines running from upper left to lower right and the negative terms are products of elements on lines running from upper right to lower left. For determinants of the fourth and higher orders the number of products (24 for $n = 4$) exceeds the number which may be enumerated in this way (8 for $n = 4$) and more labor is required to write down the complete expansion of the determinant.

Determinants of order ≥ 4 may conveniently be evaluated by the *method of cofactors*. Inspection of the list of six products whose algebraic sum is the value of a determinant of order 3 shows that we may rewrite it in the following way:

$$a_{11}(a_{22}a_{33} \; - \; a_{23}a_{32}) \; + \; a_{12}(a_{23}a_{31} \; - \; a_{21}a_{33}) \; + \; a_{13}(a_{21}a_{32} \; - \; a_{22}a_{31})$$

Each of the terms in parentheses is the expanded form of the determinant made up of those elements of the original determinant which remain after we strike from it the elements belonging to the row and column of the element in front of the parenthesis. It is given a $+$ sign if the sum of the indices of the element before it is even and a negative sign if the sum of these indices is odd. The terms in the parentheses are called the *cofactors* of the elements in front of the parentheses. Thus we see that the third-order determinant can be evaluated by finding the sum of the products of each element in the first row with its cofactor. A little reflection will show that we could just as well have arranged the six terms in the expansion so as to have a sum of the products of *any* row or *any* column with their cofactors. For instance, choosing the second column, we can write:

$$a_{12}(a_{23}a_{31} \; - \; a_{21}a_{33}) \; + \; a_{22}(a_{11}a_{33} \; - \; a_{13}a_{31}) \; + \; a_{32}(a_{13}a_{21} \; - \; a_{11}a_{23})$$

It should also not be difficult to see that a similar process can be carried out on a determinant of any order. Using A^{ij} to represent the cofactor of a_{ij}, we can thus write that

$$|A| = \sum_i a_{ij}A^{ij} = \sum_j a_{ij}A^{ij}$$
$$\text{(for any } j) \qquad \text{(for any } i)$$

One further important property of any determinant is that *if any two rows or columns are identical the value of the determinant is zero.* This is easily proved. Suppose the pth and rth rows are identical. Then for any term in the expansion, say

$$a_{l1}a_{m2}a_{n3} \ldots a_{pi}a_{rj} \ldots$$

there must be another which is identical except that it will contain a_{ri} and a_{pj}. Now suppose that the column indices are arranged serially in the term shown above, that $p > r$, and that x transpositions are required to put the row indices in serial order. Then, if exactly the same x transpositions are carried out in the term

$$a_{l1}a_{m2}a_{n3} \ldots a_{ri}a_{pj} \ldots$$

it will still be necessary to make an additional $2(p - r - 1) + 1$ transpositions to put a_{ri} and a_{pj} in their proper places, making $x + 2(p - r - 1) + 1$ transpositions in all. Thus if x is even, $x + 2(p - r - 1) + 1$ must be odd and vice versa. It therefore follows that all the terms in the expansion will cancel out in a pairwise fashion. Obviously a similar argument could be made if we assume two columns to be identical.

The Adjoint Matrix

Before defining the adjoint matrix we must define the transpose of a matrix. This is a matrix of which the columns are the rows, and vice versa, of the original matrix. Symbolically, the transpose of the matrix $[a_{ij}]$ is $[a_{ji}]$. Now, the adjoint matrix of a matrix $[a_{ij}]$ is defined as follows:

$$\text{Adjoint of } [a_{ij}] = [A^{ji}]$$

That is, we treat the array of elements constituting $[a_{ij}]$ as a determinant, write the cofactor, A^{ij}, of each element in place of the element giving the matrix $[A^{ij}]$, and then make the transpose of $[A^{ij}]$. The matrix adjoint to $\mathfrak{a}$ will be symbolized $\hat{\mathfrak{a}}$.

The Inverse of a Matrix

The inverse α^{-1} of a matrix α is, by definition, such that

$$\alpha\alpha^{-1} = \alpha^{-1}\alpha = \varepsilon$$

Let us now look at the product $\alpha\hat{\alpha}$ for a square matrix of order 3. It is

$$\alpha\hat{\alpha} = \begin{bmatrix} a_{11} & a_{12} & a_{13} \\ a_{21} & a_{22} & a_{23} \\ a_{31} & a_{32} & a_{33} \end{bmatrix} \begin{bmatrix} A^{11} & A^{21} & A^{31} \\ A^{12} & A^{22} & A^{32} \\ A^{13} & A^{23} & A^{33} \end{bmatrix}$$

$$= \begin{bmatrix} a_{11}A^{11}+a_{12}A^{12}+a_{13}A^{13} & a_{11}A^{21}+a_{12}A^{22}+a_{13}A^{23} & a_{11}A^{31}+a_{12}A^{32}+a_{13}A^{33} \\ a_{21}A^{11}+a_{22}A^{12}+a_{23}A^{13} & a_{21}A^{21}+a_{22}A^{22}+a_{23}A^{23} & a_{21}A^{31}+a_{22}A^{32}+a_{23}A^{33} \\ a_{31}A^{11}+a_{32}A^{12}+a_{33}A^{13} & a_{31}A^{21}+a_{32}A^{22}+a_{33}A^{23} & a_{31}A^{31}+a_{32}A^{32}+a_{33}A^{33} \end{bmatrix}$$

We see that each diagonal element is the expansion of the determinant $|A|$ in terms of a row and its cofactors. On the other hand each off-diagonal element is the sum of products of the elements of a certain row, say the ith, with the cofactors of the elements of some other row, say the jth. Such a sum is, in fact, the expansion in the elements of the ith row with their cofactors of a determinant in which the ith and jth rows are identical. Since we have already seen that the value of such a determinant must be zero, all off-diagonal elements of the product $\alpha\hat{\alpha}$ are zero. It is also easy to see that $\alpha\hat{\alpha} = \hat{\alpha}\alpha$. Thus we have the result

$$\alpha\hat{\alpha} = \hat{\alpha}\alpha = \begin{bmatrix} |A| & 0 & 0 & 0 & \cdots & 0 \\ 0 & |A| & 0 & 0 & \cdots & 0 \\ \vdots & & & & & \vdots \\ 0 & \cdots & & & & |A| \end{bmatrix}$$

$$= |A| \begin{bmatrix} 1 & 0 & 0 & 0 & \cdots & 0 \\ 0 & 1 & 0 & 0 & \cdots & 0 \\ \vdots & & & & & \vdots \\ 0 & \cdots & & & & 1 \end{bmatrix}$$

$$= |A|\varepsilon$$

Now, referring back to the definition of α^{-1}, we see that

$$\alpha^{-1} = \frac{\hat{\alpha}}{|A|}$$

That is, each element of α^{-1} is the element of $\hat{\alpha}$ divided by $|A|$. Since division by zero is not defined, only matrices for which the corresponding determinants are nonzero can have inverses. A matrix α such that $|A| = 0$ is said to be *singular* (no inverse), whereas matrices of which the corresponding determinants are nonzero are said to be *nonsingular*. Only nonsingular matrices can occur in representations of a group.

It is suggested that the working of a few examples, which the reader can make up *ad libitum*, would be helpful in developing a practical grasp of these results.

Appendix II[*]

B. Correlation Table for the Group O_h

This table shows how the representations of group O_h are changed or decomposed into those of its subgroups when the symmetry is altered or lowered. This table covers only those of use in dealing with the more common symmetries of complexes. A rather complete collection of correlation tables will be found as Table X-14 in *Molecular Vibrations* by E. B. Wilson, Jr., J. C. Decius, and P. C. Cross, McGraw-Hill, New York, 1955.

* Appendix IIA is in the pocket in the back cover of this book.

O_h	O	T_d	D_{4h}	D_{2d}	C_{4v}	C_{2v}	D_{3d}	D_3	C_{2h}
A_{1g}	A_1	A_1	A_{1g}	A_1	A_1	A_1	A_{1g}	A_1	A_g
A_{2g}	A_2	A_2	B_{1g}	B_1	B_1	A_2	A_{2g}	A_2	B_g
E_g	E	E	$A_{1g}+B_{1g}$	A_1+B_1	A_1+B_1	A_1+A_2	E_g	E	A_g+B_g
T_{1g}	T_1	T_1	$A_{2g}+E_g$	A_2+E	A_2+E	$A_2+B_1+B_2$	$A_{2g}+E_g$	A_2+E	A_g+2B_g
T_{2g}	T_2	T_2	$B_{2g}+E_g$	B_2+E	B_2+E	$A_1+B_1+B_2$	$A_{1g}+E_g$	A_1+E	$2A_g+B_g$
A_{1u}	A_1	A_2	A_{1u}	B_1	A_2	A_2	A_{1u}	A_1	A_u
A_{2u}	A_2	A_1	B_{1u}	A_1	B_2	A_1	A_{2u}	A_2	B_u
E_u	E	E	$A_{1u}+B_{1u}$	A_1+B_1	A_2+B_2	A_1+A_2	E_u	E	A_u+B_u
T_{1u}	T_1	T_2	$A_{2u}+E_u$	B_2+E	A_1+E	$A_1+B_1+B_2$	$A_{2u}+E_u$	A_2+E	A_u+2B_u
T_{2u}	T_2	T_1	$B_{2u}+E_u$	A_2+E	B_1+E	$A_2+B_1+B_2$	$A_{1u}+E_u$	A_1+E	$2A_u+B_u$

Appendix III

Character Tables for Some Double Groups

D_4'		E	R	$\begin{matrix}C_4\\C_4{}^3R\end{matrix}$	$\begin{matrix}C_4{}^3\\C_4R\end{matrix}$	$\begin{matrix}C_2\\C_2R\end{matrix}$	$\begin{matrix}2C_2'\\2C_2'R\end{matrix}$	$\begin{matrix}2C_2''\\2C_2''R\end{matrix}$
Γ_1	A_1'	1	1	1	1	1	1	1
Γ_2	A_2'	1	1	1	1	1	-1	-1
Γ_3	B_1'	1	1	-1	-1	1	1	-1
Γ_4	B_2'	1	1	-1	-1	1	-1	1
Γ_5	E_1'	2	2	0	0	-2	0	0
Γ_6	E_2'	2	-2	$\sqrt{2}$	$-\sqrt{2}$	0	0	0
Γ_7	E_3'	2	-2	$-\sqrt{2}$	$\sqrt{2}$	0	0	0

O'		E	R	$\begin{matrix}4C_3\\4C_3{}^2R\end{matrix}$	$\begin{matrix}4C_3{}^2\\4C_3R\end{matrix}$	$\begin{matrix}3C_2\\3C_2R\end{matrix}$	$\begin{matrix}3C_4\\3C_4{}^3R\end{matrix}$	$\begin{matrix}3C_4{}^3\\3C_4R\end{matrix}$	$\begin{matrix}6C_2'\\6C_2'R\end{matrix}$
Γ_1	A_1'	1	1	1	1	1	1	1	1
Γ_2	A_2'	1	1	1	1	1	-1	-1	-1
Γ_3	E_1'	2	2	-1	-1	2	0	0	0
Γ_4	T_1'	3	3	0	0	-1	1	1	-1
Γ_5	T_2'	3	3	0	0	-1	-1	-1	1
Γ_6	E_2'	2	-2	1	-1	0	$\sqrt{2}$	$-\sqrt{2}$	0
Γ_7	E_3'	2	-2	1	-1	0	$-\sqrt{2}$	$\sqrt{2}$	0
Γ_8	G'	4	-4	-1	1	0	0	0	0

Appendix IV

A Caveat Concerning the Resonance Integral

On pages 129–131 we have described a seemingly straightforward and obvious method for evaluating the integral β. This involved equating the so-called experimental or empirical resonance energy of benzene, defined as the energy difference between "real" benzene and Kekulé benzene, to a multiple of β. This procedure is widely used and is of at least empirical validity as shown by the fact that it gives essentially the same value to β in various molecules. Some results illustrative of this point are given in the following table.

Table of Experimental Resonance Energies and the Derived Value of β

COMPOUND	OBS. RESONANCE ENERGY, KCAL/MOLE	THEOR. RES. ENERGY, HÜCKEL APPROX.	$-\beta$
Benzene	36	2β	18
Diphenyl	70–80	4.38β	$\sim$17
Naphthalene	75–80	3.68β	$\sim$21
Anthracene	105–116	5.32β	$\sim$20
Phenanthrene	110–125	5.45β	$\sim$21

Vertical Resonance Energy

In the process just described we are not actually considering only the energy of delocalization but also the energy required to stretch and compress the carbon-carbon bonds in Kekulé benzene from the lengths 1.54

and 1.34 A to the common length 1.39 A found in real benzene. Thus the experimental resonance energy, $R_{\exp}$, is related to the true delocalization energy, or vertical * resonance energy, R_v, and to the combined energies of bond stretching, bond compression, and other changes (as for instance in repulsive forces between nonbonded atoms) collectively denoted by E_C, by the following equation:

$$R_{\exp} = R_v + E_C$$

Now it can be argued that the MO calculation actually applies to R_v and that in order to evaluate β we should equate the multiple of β given by theory to R_v and not $R_{\exp}$. In order to do this, E_C must be calculated. For benzene † E_C has been estimated to be -37 Kcal/mole. From this we estimate that $R_v = 36 + 37 = 73$ Kcal/mole and hence β must be about 37 Kcal/mole, or about twice the value used in the calculations of experimental resonance energies. Thus, for estimating the actual separations of energy levels in the real molecule, this larger value of β should be more nearly correct.

The Spectroscopic β

On page 121 it was noted briefly that the Hückel assumption of negligible overlap between neighboring $p\pi$ orbitals seems physically unlikely since just such overlap would be required to allow formation of multicenter molecular orbitals. This point has been considered in more detail by Mulliken, Rieke, and Brown,‡ and we summarize here their discussion.

Without the assumption that all $S_{ij} = \delta_{ij}$ our secular equations will take the form (a) rather than form (b) which has been used in the Hückel approximation:

$$(a) \quad \begin{vmatrix} H_{11} - E & H_{12} - ES_{12} \\ H_{21} - ES_{21} & H_{22} - E \end{vmatrix} = 0$$

$$(b) \quad \begin{vmatrix} H_{11} - E & H_{12} \\ H_{21} & H_{22} - E \end{vmatrix} = 0$$

Thus the true value of β is not $H_{12} = H_{21}$ but $H_{12} - ES_{12} = H_{21} - ES_{21}$. It can be shown that the value of E (referred to the true zero of

---

* The term vertical is used with respect to a diagram in which we plot energy on the ordinate against internuclear distances on the abscissa. Thus, if the internuclear distances are held the same in the hypothetical, nonresonating and the real, resonating molecule, the change in energy is a purely vertical change on the plot.

† See R. S. Mulliken and R. G. Parr, *J. Chem. Phys.*, **19**, 1271 (1951).

‡ R. S. Mulliken, C. A. Rieke, and W. G. Brown, *J. Am. Chem. Soc.*, **63**, 41 (1941).

energy which is the energy of an electron when completely separated from the molecule) is about 50 electron volts (1 ev. = 23.06 Kcal/mole). Moreover, S_{12} must have a value between 0.2 and 0.3 so that ES_{12} must be between 10 and 15 ev. Mulliken et al. note that the integral H_{12} should also be of about this magnitude, which is consistent with the fact that β turns out to be only 1–2 ev., that is, a small difference between two larger numbers.

It is therefore rather surprising that β remains substantially constant from one molecule to another since relatively small variations in H_{12} or ES_{12} could cause relatively large variations in β. Empirically, however, this approximate constancy is observed.

On the other hand, we should perhaps not be too surprised if values of β derived from different kinds of measurements do not agree exactly, and indeed this is the case. We have seen above that β obtained from the vertical resonance energy of benzene is about 37 Kcal/mole, whereas Platt * first showed that the best overall fit to the spectra of benzene and other unsaturated hydrocarbons was obtained in the framework of the Hückel approximation by taking β to be 55–60 Kcal/mole. This high value has subsequently been widely adopted to estimate actual differences in energies between MO's and is generally known as the spectroscopic value of β.

* J. R. Platt, *J. Chem. Phys.*, **15**, 419 (1947).

Index